l t ture

soho

STORIES ✦ ESSAYS ✦ POEMS ✦ PICTURES

Edited by Isabel Fonseca

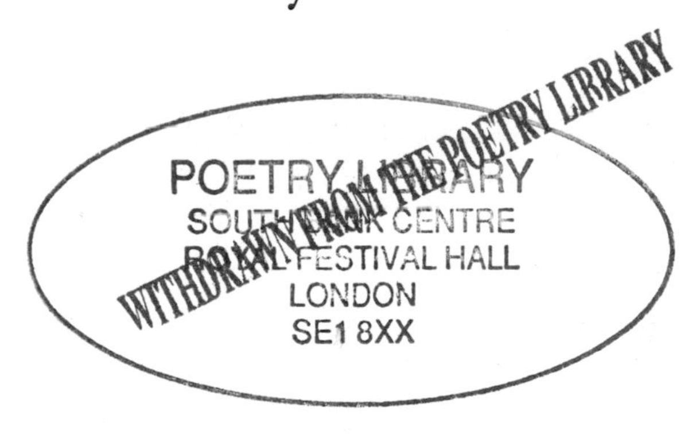

BLOOMSBURY

First published 1988
Reprinted November 1988

Bloomsbury Publishing Ltd, 2 Soho Square, London WIV 5DE

British Library Cataloguing in Publication Data

Soho Square.
1. English literature. 1945—Anthologies
I. Fonseca, Isabel
820.8'00914

ISBN 0-7475-0231-5

Acknowledgements

Versions of the following contributions have appeared elsewhere:
Murray Bail's 'Killing an Elephant' (*Sydney Morning Herald*);
Alexander Cockburn's 'The Great Tzotzil Dictionary' (in his
Corruptions of Empire, Life Studies and the Reagan Era, Verso, 1987);
and Tobias Wolff's 'Smorgasbord' (*Esquire*).
'A Place As Good As Any' by Joseph Brodsky is reprinted
by permission of Farrar, Straus and Giroux, Inc.
The editor would like to thank everyone at Bloomsbury
for their help and support,
especially Sarah-Jane Forder and Liz Calder.
Thanks go also to Chris Jones, the designer,
and to the artists who donated
their drawings and photographs.

Designed by Chris Jones
Jacket illustration by Jeff Fisher
Photoset in Linotron 202 Sabon by
Rowland Phototypesetting Ltd
Bury St Edmunds, Suffolk
Printed in Great Britain by
Butler and Tanner Ltd, Frome, Somerset

CONTENTS

CONTENTS

Poems

Drawings and photographs

As a child I often went to play in the big house of an elderly neighbour. Thick with incongruous treasures, each room had the fascination of an attic. An American weathervane mediated between two medieval minoras from Toledo; a foot-high Mayan head guarded over a collection of miniature tea-sets; portraits of pinch-faced Early Americans were offset by erotic Japanese drawings; huge Han jars flanked some Cubist configuration; an old couch, springs exposed, shared a side-table with an austere Bauhaus high-chair; a Sixties macramé wall-hanging touched fringes with a Persian rug; early plastic mingled with ancient ivories; the television buzzed sociably under shards of pre-Colombian pottery. And it was, improbably, the most harmonious place.

The first anthology from a new publishing house – with its atmosphere of 'pure possibility', as a character in Tobias Wolff's story says, clutching a crisp new hundred-dollar bill – was the ideal place to apply this approach to literature. Partly by accident, but mostly by design, a collection developed whose strength derives neither from a common theme, nor from one predominant style, but from the inherent virtues of each contribution. As in that dark house, one may meet in *Soho Square* with something shadowy and menacing alongside other pieces that are cosily familiar, plainly funny or simply (at first) baffling. (In spite of what we thought was our vigilance, certain themes did emerge: obsession with the past and the idea of home; apocalyptic visions of the future – usually some sort of post-nuclear desolation; madness; marriage; and rather a lot of cynicism about the healing power of love.) In a miscellany, where writers of different genres, genders, nationalities and generations meet in a bazaar of literary offerings, attention is encouraged to stray.

Julio Cortázar offers a seductive description of the process of reading at its most intense. The reader should come away 'as if from an act of love, exhausted and oblivious to the surrounding world, to which he returns little by little with a surprised look of slow recognition, many times of relief and other times of resignation'. Some of the pieces here may have this power to mesmerize, while others seek only to amuse or to nudge gently. Patricia Highsmith's almost slapstick story, or Mark Ford's whimsical poem, might find a closer parallel in the art of flirting.

Soho Square aims, then, to give a little of each of the different kinds of pleasure to be had from books. The reader who naturally makes a beeline for poetry may be quietly derailed one evening into a bracing encounter with the directly political self, such as that considered, or reconsidered, in Hans Magnus Enzensberger's 'Second Thoughts on Consistency'. The reader who favours a free ride on the investigative tails of Hitchens and Cockburn, as they plumb the depths of the Forbidden City and a lost Mayan language respectively, may also read Paul Muldoon and discover that 'Home' too can be a pretty exotic place. Those who open straight to Brodsky (here musing on travel and nostalgia), because they know they can expect excellence, might also pause for Kurt Tidmore who is published here for the first time. Those who know themselves to be enriched by fictions – including, perhaps, the thirteen new stories in *Soho Square* – might also be interested in the real lives shared here: Philip Roth's (literal) trial as a

Jewish writer, Nan Green's extraordinary experience of the Spanish Civil War. (Truth *is* stranger than fiction.)

Ours is an age characterized by specialization, whether of scholarship or of practical skills. This is borne out in communal life as well. So many peripheral public facilities describe themselves as 'central' – the Electronics Centre, the Pets' Accessories Centre, the Leisure Centre, even the *Mecca* Leisure Centre – that our world seems literally inside-out. We are 'experts', developing one function of the psyche at the expense of all the others. From the age of sixteen British schoolchildren must choose between a life in the sciences and a life in the arts. It is unlikely in these days that a modern American president would spend his free time, as Jefferson did, translating Homer or designing buildings; and improbable that a world record will ever again be held by an athlete with a full-time job.

And yet it is clear that not everyone can do everything. We would have no virologists, we would have no concert pianists, no master chefs, no one to mend the car. Quite apart from the obvious difficulties of implementation, Marx's vision of a world in which we would all be a poet in the morning and an angler in the afternoon, however picturesque, would spawn its own insidious homogeneity; a population of inept dilettantes or, as the late John Hewitt said of the 1947 Education Act, a society in which a lot of perfectly good bricklayers would recklessly be encouraged to become bad poets.

Limitation, as most of us have probably discovered, enforces depth. Not just in scientific research, but in poetry (the tyranny of metre and rhyme is a secret liberator) and in love, which is presumably the idea behind marriage. But – and it is unclear whether for lack of time or for lack of imagination – even in leisure we are specialists. This is cause for alarm.

While positively unlike any of the anthologies among which it is likely to be lodged – including, say, collections of gay fiction, ghost stories, travel writing, new American, African or British fiction, new work by young poets, old work by old poets, stories of the unemployed or of the under-thirties – *Soho Square* has, in its anarchic approach, no hidden agenda to reverse the de-humanizing trend towards specialization. But it does hope to encourage adventurous reading. The miscellanies of another era, which supplied inspiration for *Soho Square*, were known as bedside books; perhaps because, both in their eclecticism and in their power to deliver us, for a while, from our daily drudgery, their contents resembled nothing so much as dreams.

But it is perhaps beside the point, and in any case off-putting, to speculate on the redemptive or replenishing power of literature, let alone embark on an interpretation of dreams. A much happier project would simply be to read as children do; without regard for fashion or self-improvement, but simply for pleasure; as Auden said, 'Pleasure is by no means an infallible critical guide, but it is the least fallible.'

Isabel Fonseca
London 1988

EPITHALAMION

Cart-tracks, drove-roads,
coast-paths and bridle-ways,
lanes banked high with campion and rose:

along the dotted lines of England
we signed away one summer
mile after mile after mile.

BLAKE MORRISON

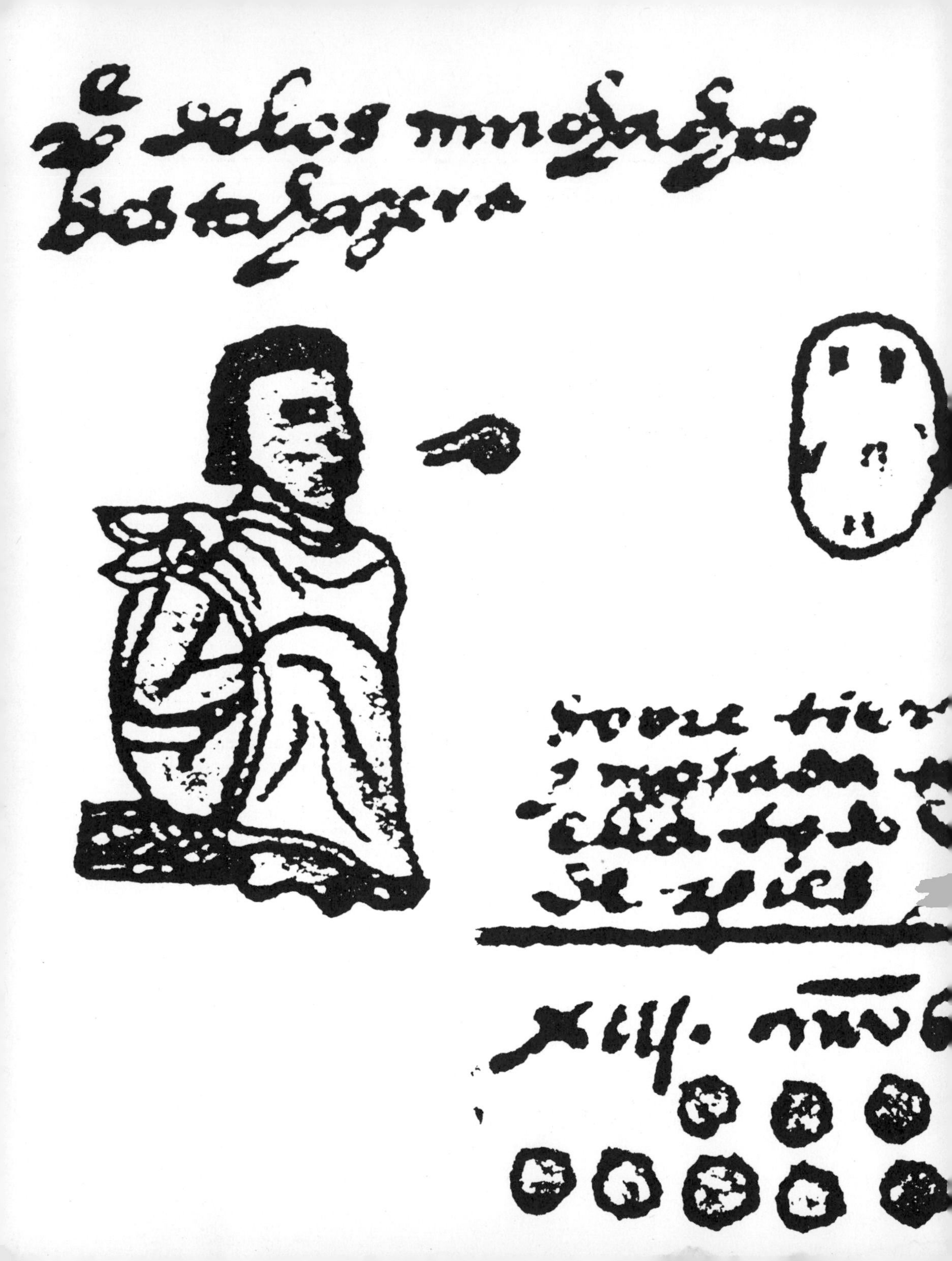

The Great Tzotzil Dictionary

ALEXANDER COCKBURN

The days turned into months, and the months into years. He started as a poet and ended up as a lexicographer. Now he sits in the Natural History Museum in Washington DC, flushed with a triumph he says is absurd. He has compiled the largest dictionary of a native language ever assembled in the Western hemisphere. He thinks often of poor Praharaj, the great Indian lexicographer who lived to witness his mammoth quadrilingual dictionary, the fruit of twenty-five years of labour, carted off in wheelbarrows to be sold by the pound as scrap paper.

But at least he finished it, and in January 1976 he approached the chief magistrate of Zinacantan in southern Mexico, sank to his knees and held up the book which had lost him fourteen years of his life. Falteringly he started to chant in Mayan couplets: 'k'usi yepal li yo kee / li yo hti'e / kahval' ('This is the sum of my humble mouth, my humble lips, My Lord'). He muffed some of the words and the magistrate tried to cut him short. 'Then,' as he later said, 'I heard a person who was watching me say that I must be a shaman. The couplets just came tumbling out.'

Robert Laughlin first visited the Tzotzil, otherwise known as the 'People of the Bat', back in 1961. These Indians, about 120,000 of them, live in the province of Chiapas and speak one of the thirty Mayan languages still in common usage. They are depressed and drink a large amount of cane liquor. They grow corn but are themselves under intensive cultivation. The capital town of Zinacantan is an entrepôt for scores of American anthropologists saturating the province of Chiapas.

Among these academics was young Laughlin. In the early 1960s he started to record Tzotzil dreams and found they were mostly nightmares. The madness, slowly at first, started to engulf him and he recorded some Tzotzil words and their English equivalents in a small black notebook. In 1963 he wrote to Washington that an extensive dictionary of the Tzotzil language had not been compiled since the eighteenth century. He proposed to amend this lack. 'It is hoped that this material will be ready for publication in a year's time.'

The *Great Tzotzil Dictionary* of San Lorenzo Zinacantan was finally published in December of 1975. Now Laughlin sits in his Washington office. The day I saw him he was studying a map of the world. Marked on it with large dots were the institutions to which the dictionary had been sent. There was an extra large blob over Novosibirsk. That's where Professor Kaladnikov lives. Not that Kaladnikov cares about Tzotzil. It's just that all anthropological publications from the Smithsonian Institution – which is what pays Laughlin his salary – go to Kaladnikov.

Laughlin, very thin and sad, with bare feet in Tzotzil sandals, stops thinking about the mysterious Kaladnikov.

'At what point did you realize that your little dictionary was going to take fourteen years?'

'I suppose it was in the first fourteen weeks, when I realized there were so many words I didn't know existed.'

'Were you always compulsive about collecting information?'

'I suppose so, yes. And compulsive about detail. I remember criticism of my work when I was at boarding school. Too much concentration on detail. My father is an expert on American pewter, which I suppose influenced me because if you do something you do it as completely as you can. He spent years and years studying American pewter.'

'Had you had much training before you started?'

'None, no. I didn't know how to do it. I just did it. When I started I adopted a method where you just go automatically through AA, AAB and so on.'

'But that could lead to infinity.'

'I know. I had *bak*, so I knew there could be a suffix *bak-um*. Then is there a word *bakumtasvan*? Is there a word *bakumtasvanan*? Sometimes the Tzotzil helping me would get so they couldn't remember if words they told me really existed. They sounded like good words. I worked mainly with two men. One of them is an alcoholic now. I don't know that I can say I am responsible. They became more sensitive to language. And there was one woman whose grammar seemed much more sophisticated. Like lacework. I don't know why. She was a very smart woman, very aggressive and outgoing.'

'Were you living alone?'

'In the beginning, then I got married. One of my sons was drowned there. He fell into a swimming pool. I have two others.'

'What were the effects of working on a dictionary for fourteen years?'

'Well, a dictionary is like stone soup. It fed us, my family and me, for years. It prevented my wife from doing creative writing because she thought she oughtn't to be doing it while I was immersed in the dictionary. Which I didn't realize and she didn't realize till the dictionary was finished.'

'Why?'

'Well, she thought it would be difficult for me if she was writing away and there I was enmired in the words.'

'Did she hate the dictionary?'

'I don't think she liked it.'

'Did you find yourself getting very monomaniacal?'

'Yes. But I thought I should exhaust all the possibilities.'

'What do you feel the whole function of the enterprise was?'

'That's the problem. Because it is an obvious absurdity. Here's a dictionary published in letters that are so esoteric that no one can read them, in an Indian language that almost no one can read, translated into English, which is not the language of Mexico.'

Laughlin's voice was getting rather high and thin. He has long, graceful fingers which were shaking a little. 'It's totally absurd. I was going to do it into Spanish, but I got tired.'

'Did you think it was necessarily a bad thing that it was all absurd?'

'What? No, I don't. Oh, I think it's amusing. I had the kind of feeling too that if I'm going to be an academic, then by God I'm going to be an academic and I'm going to do it to the point of absurdity.'

'Did you want to be an academic?'

'No, not really. In a way I want to be, in a way no. I want to be a freer person.'

'Did you want to be something else; a writer, an aviator . . . ?'

'No, not an aviator. Yes, I had wanted to be a writer, but I could never think what I had to say. I thought of this dictionary as being similar in a way to someone playing chess with himself as the city crumbles.'

'Do you still feel depressed that this 595-page dictionary doesn't matter much?'

'Yes, sometimes. Sometimes not. Then I say, "Ha ha, I've done it and who cares?" Also I'm consoled by the thought Lévi-Strauss defined in his first book, *Tristes Tropiques*. How do you define civilization and what are its ultimate goals? There are people like the Nambikwara, who no one knows about but whose style of living is perhaps as great as great civilizations. I was thinking of this creation of mine as truly having no utilitarian value. So I was influenced by *Tristes Tropiques*.'

'Well, what are your claims for the *Great Tzotzil Dictionary*?'

'It's the largest dictionary of any native language of this hemisphere. It gives more of a context to the words than others do. It has more accurate scientific information than any other dictionary. It may be bigger than any other dictionary of a native language in the world. I don't know what else to say. Hopefully it will help in translating Mayan glyphs.'

'How many people could review it properly?'

'Well, I've had the thought at times, wouldn't it be fun if this dictionary was a complete hoax. Really, there's hardly anyone in the world who would know, apart from a Zinacantan. And he wouldn't know the English. In fact no one knows these 30,000 words. You can take the logical extensions of the language and create a word which may or may not exist. A linguist could tell if there were errors, but he couldn't tell if I had padded it greatly or not.'

We worked out the implications of the hoax on a paper napkin in the Smithsonian canteen: $238,000 total salary over fourteen years, plus $50,000 publication cost plus $70,000 in extra grants. Total: $358,000.

'Was there a time when you thought you were really going mad?'

'I thought I'd throw myself off the cathedral of Notre-Dame at one point. I happened to be there. The dictionary was in the computer and nothing was getting out. There seemed to be no way of getting at it. There was this feeling of total helplessness. One operator resigned because she didn't want to print the word "shit". She kept putting in "unprintable word". The people at the Smithsonian, when it was nearly finished and I only needed $15,000 more, stopped giving me money. They called it the Great Tzotzil Disaster. My chairman here was doing everything he could to stop it. Internal politics. He is properly memorialized in the dictionary, if you know where to look.'

'What is the genius of Tzotzil?'

'I realized how much the Mayan languages concentrate on shape and movement, and sound. All that is totally foreign to us. And there are no words for Question, Plan, Family, Peace, Liberty or Faith. There's a word for the noise a pig makes when it is chomping peach pips. It's a very puritan, repressed culture. The word for to talk to a girl means to have an affair with her. The girls are watched all the time.'

'How did you feel when you finished?'

'At first I felt nothing. Then I began to feel liberated. I went to Seville to look for the Spanish original of a Tzotzil translation. It wasn't there. I got back here and found it right here in the Library of Congress. My wife and I would like to write, but we don't come from very self-confident families.'

It's all finished now, even though no one can actually obtain the *Great Tzotzil Dictionary* from government bookshops, because one of the reference numbers was omitted from the final copies. Laughlin is toying with all the many, many Tzotzil words describing what people do and feel when they are drunk. Fiddling with some index cards he went back to the day in January when he presented the *Great Tzotzil Dictionary* to the magistrates in Zinacantan.

'I wanted to do it on the Fiesta of San Sebastian. It's the biggest fiesta of the year. And there's one account of its background that tells how once there was a book of knowledge that St Sebastian had and that it was lost. And the Indians say that is how the Ladinos, the non-Indians, are rich today because they had the book of knowledge and we lost ours. So I said to the magistrate, "If any Ladino comes and says you are stupid, asinine Indians, please show him this book, show him the 30,000 words of your knowledge, of your reasoning." '

Home

PAUL MULDOON

The hedges on either side of the lane
were so overgrown

it was less a lane than a tunnel,
its bed a runnel

in mid-August.
The shale-encrusted Lucozade

and Milk of Magnesia bottles.
The lop-sided, rain-filled kettle.

The bellows
ignorant of the stir

they once created among the stars.
The plough

ploughing itself under.

Someone had nailed an oil-drum
from door-jamb

to door-jamb. Through a cicatrice
in the piece of ice

of the left-hand window
I saw a yellow gas-cylinder

and a tatty cardigan;
my mother's mother

was cleaning goose-eggs
with a salty rag,

bending to her task
as though to a narwhal's fluted tusk.

It might have been that, after a canful
of stout,

she would again lash out
at my mother, my aunt or uncle,

then retire to the dunghill
and commune with thc guinea-fowl;

men must endure

that toil of growing up
even as their coming hither . . .

Something in this sounded a false note
and I turned round. Surely not

the bellows-wheel
struggling to reinvent the wheel?

The mare and stallion
in some Aristotelian

judder of fear and pity?
I twisted the cap off my duty-free.

A dandle of ether
fled my grandmother's cup.

The window was now no more than a smear
on the back garden –

a flaming whin-bush
and a ewe, an old one, swinging her cosh.

The Ink Imp

R. M. LAMMING

That morning it rained in Skelpton, solid, businesslike rain, the kind that quickly saturates your collar, and, worse, it was full of dirt, which I suppose is the price we pay for building a town of factories. In Skelpton everything is contaminated: the brickwork is black, all black; the shop windows are glazed with a grey deposit; parlour curtains hang limp and pale, their colours muted by the overlay of grime, while every railing and ledge has its black coat of velvet turning to inky liquid in the rain and ruining your clothes when you brush against it. The very townsfolk are affected: even the youngsters have strangely discoloured faces that appear to possess the consistency of tired rubber, with lines around the mouth and eyes that are too well defined, as if they had been sketched in with a black pencil.

Skelpton, you will appreciate, is nowhere out of an idyll. It is not where most of us would choose to launch a literary career. In fact I can think of no one who would choose such a place besides my brother, but then, squalor has always attracted him. The hovels of poverty, the filth of modern industry with its furnaces and engines, they hold some diabolical fascination for him; and I remember that even when we were children, while I played by the trout stream, Marcus always had to be grubbing about in rubbish-tips left behind by the gypsies.

'More interesting,' he would say. 'More fun.'

Fun! I cannot pretend that we have ever understood each other or felt for each other any great affection; after his break with the family, I had not expected to hear from him, and if anyone had suggested that he might desire me to visit him, I would have answered in a word: impossible.

Yet this same impossibility had brought me all the way from Hertfordshire.

Inside the cab, while it rumbled and splashed through the Skelpton streets, I took his card from my overcoat pocket as I had done many times on the journey, and studied it again. A more enigmatic and disturbing communication I had never received from anyone.

In the top right-hand corner on one side, Marcus had given his address:

36 Water Tower Street
c/o Mrs Brideson

and this was written clearly enough in the hand I recognized – large, assertive letters, all sloping forwards at a nicely calculated angle – but then followed the heart of the thing in writing which I could scarcely credit was by the same man. It looked more like a child's, stiff and upright, the letters pinched together:

Come and see me, for God's sake.

Even more distorted was the signature, the 'M' squeezed in upon itself to convey an impression of fingers barely able to move, the 'a' so wide open that it resembled a crude cup, the 'r' non-existent, and the rest – a line, a kind of skid down the card.

I simply did not know what to make of it. The erratic nature of the scrawl and the urgency of the words filled me with misgivings. Indeed, since Marcus and I are not fond of each other, his appeal seemed nothing short of desperate. That my brother should turn to *me*, someone he considered an insipid nonentity!

It had left me no choice but to cancel my business arrangements, and come.

Presently the cab turned into an ugly road of terraced houses that I guessed was a fairly recent addition to Skelpton, since the red of its brickwork still held out against the grime, and the spear-heads that topped its railings looked barbarously sharp and modern. I returned the card to my pocket, and, as we drove along, amused myself by peering in through the rain-splashed windows, trying to guess what kind of person lived there. These houses were obviously not the homes of factory workers – they were much too grand, with tasselled curtains and potted plants; but railway officials and bank clerks, I thought, with a schoolmaster or two, would fit in nicely, the respectable folk of Skelpton; and this led me to expect a turn into some yet uglier street, a labourers' quarter, where Marcus would have taken up lodging to sit and sneer at the local gentry – a mistaken notion, for the cab rattled to a sudden halt, and the driver called, 'Water Tower Street, didn't yer say? Number thirty-six?'

Feeling I had arrived much too soon, I clambered out with my bag and paid the fellow, whose cap, I couldn't help noticing, channelled rainwater down across his eyes in a great spout, but this inconvenience seemed not to bother him. He looked as though very little bothered him: his broad face seemed quite bloated with lethargy, and his eyes, when he reached down for the money, resembled those nodules of lead I had used to weight a fishing line as a boy.

He took the fare and my generous tip without comment, snarled at his nag, then splashed away down the road, abandoning me.

And now my immediate desire was to be out of the rain. I lost no time in giving a strong pull at the bell, and I heard it jangle in the house. Soon a shape rose behind the door's opaque glass panel, and in the next moment I was looking at a lean, sharp-faced woman to whom I took an instant dislike. She appeared to move in sudden jerks, and her slightly protuberant eyes gave the strange impression of being many. I would hazard a guess that she was about fifty years of age. She wore her hair, which might have been auburn once, scraped back in a tight knot. Her voice was thin and unpleasant.

'Yes?'

She peered at me round the edge of the door. Smells of luncheon – I could detect onions and watery kale – came wafting down the passageway behind her.

Despite the fact that she kept me out in the wet, I determined to be polite, and I paid her the courtesy of implying that Mrs Brideson might employ a lady-companion or housekeeper, someone other than herself to answer the bell. Had I the honour of addressing Mrs Brideson in person?

Her knuckles tightened on the door.

'What do you want?' she said. 'If you're another of them doctors, I've nothing more to say. You hear?'

'Madam – ' this time I spoke with greater firmness, since the rain was pelting on my back ' – I've come to see my brother, Mr Davies. Mr Marcus Davies. He lodges here, I believe?'

She had become very still: only her eyes moved, scrutinizing my face, my attire, and finally coming to rest, I thought with some significance, on the bag I held. To hide my unease, I asked, 'Is my brother in?'

The eyes came back to my face.

'His brother, are you? Well, you're too late. He's gone. Taken.' And she emphasized her last words with peculiar satisfaction.

Gone. I stood there, urgently summoned, the downpour soaking my coat, confronted by this female who clung to the side of the door like a human spider, and I could do nothing but echo: 'Gone?'

Then with one hand she opened the door just sufficiently to admit me, at the same time with her other hand drawing her grey shawl tighter round her shoulders.

'You'd best come in. He's gone, and he owed me. There's a week's rent, and things I bought. Then there's the mess upstairs. I'll have to insist on compensation . . . '

I followed her into the front parlour, closing the house door very softly behind me, although why I took such pains to make no noise would be difficult to say. It was as if I feared to disturb someone who lay upstairs.

The parlour was ice-cold and as grey as the rest of Skelpton, depressing in the way of all unused rooms, smelling of dust and damp. Its soft-backed chairs had a mildewed look so that I felt sure they would be spongy to the touch, while its other furniture was dark and coffin-like, seemingly set apart from the ordinary business of life. Nevertheless, from a cheap bureau Mrs Brideson drew out a notebook that clearly was business of some sort. She started to flick through its pages.

'Mrs Brideson, where exactly *is* my brother?'

'Eleven shillings – that's rent and board . . . Two shillings and sixpence – that's for pens and ink . . . Then the walls will need papering . . . '

She broke off, as if my question had taken time to penetrate these calculations, and regarded me with an expression of barely restrained hostility. Then, turning from me, she crossed the room and seated herself.

'In the madhouse. They took him yesterday.'

She watched me as a spider might watch a fly.

'I beg your pardon?' I said.

But I had heard clearly enough. I sat down on the nearest thing to hand, which was a stiff-backed prayer stool by the door, and my mind became what I can best describe as granulated, forming fragments of questions, the beginnings of emotions, and completing none of them. The woman must have guessed I had heard, because she made no reply, and at last I think I asked, 'Here? In Skelpton?'

'Just outside. It used to be the workhouse. Now it's the madhouse.'

She pursed her lips in a self-congratulatory manner, and waited. Rain crawled in wrinkled shapes down the windows. I could think of nothing to say. In the end perceiving this, and perhaps forming the opinion that I wasn't the hysterical sort, Mrs Brideson became more communicative.

'He had to go,' she said flatly. 'Your brother was sick, Mr Davies – ' and then, in case I had missed her meaning ' – sick in the head.' Her shoulders moved; a slight shrinking of her frame beneath the shawl. 'Sounds up there, all hours, day and night. Not coming down for meals . . . Sending me out for ink and that, like an errand boy . . . I should have seen before that it wasn't natural . . . but yesterday . . . '

Once more she clamped her lips together, hesitating, but after a few moments she spoke rapidly.

'We was breakfasting in the kitchen, my daughter and me, when all of a sudden there's this crashing overhead – like chairs going over. Then there's a roar – a loud, mad roar, and Mary goes as white as chalk. "What was that?" she says. "Nothing," I was going to say; the word was on the tip of my tongue, when we heard him come out on to the landing and start bawling. So I says, "You stay here and keep quiet!" Then I came out . . . I went halfway up the stairs, and there he was . . . '

She broke off again; and by now, I think, she was relishing her narrative. She sat with her dark dress spread around her and that notebook of expenses resting in her lap like – it occurred to me – some malign accomplice.

'There he was . . . ' I prompted her.

'He was just stood there, sobbing like a babe, his face in his hands. I called up to him, and he shouted, "Fetch help! A doctor!" Then he ran back into his room and locked the door.'

Mrs Brideson nodded soberly. 'I fetched help right enough,' she said. 'I sent Mary for the constable. He and another police lad broke in. They took him away. There was no fuss, bar some scuffling on the pavement . . . but I wish they hadn't broke the lock,' she added. 'It was a good one. Being as you're a gentleman, Mr Davies, I dare say you'll remember that in the compensation . . . '

'I'm afraid I don't understand.'

She clutched the notebook and stood up.

'The mess. Wait till you see it. You'll be wanting to see it, I suppose?'

'Oh, certainly . . . '

And so, for a second time, I followed, leaving my bag by the prayer stool and traipsing after her, dazed, I would even say in a state of shock; for I may not much love my brother, but I have never wished him any ill more terrible than a taste of poverty, just enough to teach him the merits of family life. Nor had I ever suspected Marcus of any fatal weakness of mind. His eccentricities I remembered as perfectly consistent

poetry international

Friday 28 October - Sunday 6 November 1994

Britain's biggest poetry festival: ten days of readings, workshops, discussions and performance poetry from some of the finest poets in the world. Events include:

Young Berliners : two poets from Berlin's thriving, happening poetry scene

Wednesday 2 November, Voice Box, 7.30pm
DURS GRUNBEIN AND LIOBA HAPPEL
with readings in English by Glyn Maxwell

Durs Grünbein is the most talked about German poet of his generation. Following in the line of John Donne, Lowell and Brodsky, he is a tough, intellectual poet, metaphysical as well as passionate.

Lioba Happel has won a number of awards for her ironic, witty and melancholic work, which includes five poetry collections and a novel.

Tickets £3.50 (£2 concs)

Full details and tickets
0171 928 8800

Poetry International

Friday 28 October

PR 7.30pm
Tony Harrison

Saturday 29 October

Daniel Weissbort, Ciaran Carson and Fleur Adcock
Translation as Recreation (Workshop)

Kit Wright
Poetry for Children (7-11 years)

VB 2pm
Jackie Kay and Matthew Sweeney
Poetry for Children (8-13 years)

Sorley MacLean, Paul Muldoon, E J Scovell and Marin Sorescu

Sunday 30 October

Michael Hofmann & Jo Shapcott
A Poem in Two Versions
(Translation Workshop)

CR 2pm
Christina Rossetti:
A Centenary Celebration
Jan Marsh, John Heath-Stubbs, and Michèle Roberts

PR 7.30pm
Ciaran Carson, Elizabeth Jennings, and Yunna Morits
English translations read by
Daniel Weissbort

Monday 31 October

Paul Beatty, Merle Collins, Jayne Cortez and Joolz

Tuesday 1 November

Chinese Poets in Exile
Yang Lian with readings in English by **Brian Holton. John Cayley** reads the poetry of **Gu Cheng** and **Xie Ye**

Wednesday 2 November

Durs Grünbein & Lioba Happel

Thursday 3 November

John Ashbery, Les Murray, and Zsuzsa Rakovszky
English translations read by
George Szirtes

Friday 4 November

Eavan Boland, Kamala Das, U A Fanthorpe and Liz Lochhead

Saturday 5 November

Lavinia Greenlaw (Poetry Workshop)

Eavan Boland
The Poetry Book Society's Ronald Duncan Lecture
Gods Make Their Own Importance:
The Authority of the Poet in our Time

Poetry and Film
Film Premiere and Discussion resulting from national education project

Kamau Brathwaite, Jorie Graham, Michael Longley and Nancy Morejón

Sunday 6 November

Matthew Sweeney (Poetry Workshop)

PR 7.30pm
After Ovid
Fleur Adcock, Eavan Boland, Vicki Feaver, Jorie Graham, Michael Hofmann, Ted Hughes, James Lasdun, Michael Longley, Derek Mahon, Jamie McKendrick, Les Murray, Robin Robertson & Jo Shapcott

Events take place in **The Purcell Room** PR **Voice Box** VB **Chelsfield Room** CR **Waterloo Bar** WB

ALL AT THE SOUTH BANK CENTRE LONDON SE1 8X ⊖ **WATERLOO OR EMBANKMET**

BOX OFFICE: 0171 928 8800

with his outlook; however bizarre his behaviour, he had always been able to justify it according to his beliefs, and they themselves were not so odd that no one else has voiced them. Marcus in a madhouse! I was still struggling to give some credence to this news when we came back into the hall.

There, a pale, sickly-looking girl of perhaps twelve or thirteen was standing by a door which I knew must lead to the kitchen, as the smell of kale had grown stronger with its opening. This child gaped up at me with large, frightened eyes.

'Get back to your dinner, Mary,' said Mrs Brideson, sparing no more than a glance at her, 'there's fruit on the sideboard.' Then she led the way upstairs.

We climbed, and I fancied the house grew darker, more oppressive, as we left the hall below us. The impression still clung to me that someone lay resting in one of the bedrooms, and this person, whoever it might be, was more than ready to resent my intrusion. An invalid husband, perhaps? An ageing parent?

'And your husband, ma'am?' I asked nervously. 'What does he make of this – unfortunate business?'

'Mr Brideson has passed on. There's just me and the girl.' She looked back sharply across her shoulder. 'That's why I'd be obliged for the compensation. It's hard on your own.'

'Ah, quite . . . '

No one upstairs. The revelation affected me strangely. In an instant, my legs became weak and heavy, while my hand on the stair rail grew hot, sticking to the rail as if my palm had been coated with grease. All at once it seemed plain to me that the presence I felt in the house came from past events, from whatever had befallen my brother, lingering there although Marcus himself had gone.

This idea was so distressing that I began to be short of breath, and, indeed, I must have been panting quite audibly when, to my relief as much as to my consternation, the woman stopped. We had reached the second landing. Before us stood a door. She nudged it, and it moved slightly. Its brown paintwork, I observed, was badly scratched where at least one heavy boot had kicked against it. Splinters of wood blossomed out of the doorframe in the vicinity of the lock, unmistakable tokens of violence – and, oddly enough, these changed my mood for the better. Whatever lay beyond that door, I resolved that I would face it like the man I had always been taken for – practical, and unimaginative.

Mrs Brideson stood aside, twisting her mouth to express God knows what inner conflict. Scathingly she said, 'Go on in, Mr Davies. See for yourself. I've touched nothing since they took him.'

I met her challenge. I entered.

The curtains were drawn together, so that at first gloom obscured everything and I was chiefly conscious of the stench – stale, sweaty bed-linen – but very soon I perceived the disorder, the bed things all tumbled, a chair upturned on the floor, a desk littered with papers. Then – far worse. I saw, and I think I gave some exclamation. Hurrying over to the window, I tore the curtains back, hoping to dispel what I had seen as an illusion; but instead the bleak Skelpton day confirmed it as the reality.

Ink. The walls were spattered with it. Blues, black, vivid purples – bursts of ink everywhere! And not only on the walls, but also on the curtains, the carpet, the papers cluttering the desk, as if whole bottles of the liquid had literally been thrown against whatever surface was nearest.

There were splashes shaped like large chrysanthemums, and others that were smudged, as though something – a board or a book – had been brought down on them and scraped along. Even more mysterious, here and there the walls presented a pocked, or pitted appearance, as though inky points had been driven through the paper, an effect that I also noticed on the leather top of the desk and the wooden back of the blotter – countless small holes, all of them dark with ink.

Then the books. Some two dozen of them lay scattered about on the floor, their pages ripped or bent back, the covers ink-stained. I could only conclude that Marcus had removed them from the bookcase in a fit of anger, emptied penloads of ink on to each, then thrown them around the room.

Other disturbing features: beside the desk, a tall wicker waste-paper basket had fallen over on to its side, spilling a heap of empty ink bottles out across the carpet; and on the desk itself, an assortment of nibs and pens, all bent and twisted, lay strewn about in the rest of the litter.

Signs of derangement? I confess, despite my resolution to accept calmly what I found, I had not expected such strong evidence. For want of other means to express my dismay, I turned over some of the papers, reading lines, phrases, searching for the old, articulate Marcus. The content, so far as I could tell, was fiction – uncouth monologues, which I took for an exercise in the local dialect; and this illustration of my brother's struggle to work according to his principles touched me deeply. However, it also added greatly to my dismay. Page after page, I came upon nothing but fragments; and even on the clearest pages there were never more than five or six lines before the writing changed: always the letters deteriorated, either sloping down the page, as if some unseen pressure had been applied to the pen, or closing up tight and desperate, as if the writer had been forced to push against some obstacle. I thought of the writing on the card in my pocket, and saw that it found its home amongst this wreckage.

Laudanum? Alcohol? What destructive agent had been at work here? While I was taxing my brain with this riddle, Mrs Brideson came stealthily into the room behind me. I started when her hand – the skin as transparent as gelatine – stretched out at my side to pick up papers from the desk. She peered at one or two suspiciously.

'A clever man, was he? Your brother?'

As though he were dead.

'In his way.'

Disliking her proximity, I began to edge round the desk, my apparent desire being to examine the handsome wooden inkstand. It was amply coated with ink, and that part of it in which the inkwell was set looked velvety black from its many soakings.

I remarked, 'He's always been in too much of a hurry. Always spilling things' – an observation which, considering the state of the room, verged on the ludicrous. In my embarrassment, I lifted the inkwell's pewter lid, and let it fall again with a dull clank. This moment of fidget left a black smudge on my finger.

The woman grunted.

'You see what a mess it is – and have you looked at this? The linen ruined.'

She crossed to the bed and lifted one of the sheets by a corner so that I could examine the ink stains as well as other, rust-coloured marks which I had not noticed before.

'Blood?'

'He was no pretty sight when they took him – I'll say no more than that. Have you seen enough?'

'Yes.'

Blood . . . and yet, at the time, my mind refused the word. I already had enough to worry about. Trivial though it may seem, I was becoming extremely concerned about the matter of compensation: it was a point of honour.

We went down again to the parlour, where I took five pounds from my wallet, and laid them in the woman's hand.

'I trust that will pay for everything?'

'I imagine.'

Without a word of thanks, she locked the money in her bureau, pulled out the key and pocketed it. Then she said, 'You'll be going to see him, I suppose, now that you've come. You can stop here for tonight, and pack his things.'

These were instructions, not questions; and I dare say I looked in need of directing as I stood there, awkward in my overcoat. I hesitated. I did not warm to the idea of Mrs Brideson's hospitality, and yet I could think of no sounder plan. It made sense to sleep a night beneath her roof, for of course she was right. I would have to sort my brother's things, just as though he were truly dead.

'I'll only charge you for your breakfast.'

'Well, if it's . . . '

'No trouble.' She jerked her head with something like triumph. Doubtless she had not relished the prospect of clearing my brother's rubbish herself. 'There's another room, quite comfortable.'

'Thank you. And this establishment . . . '

'You mean the madhouse?'

Her thin voice gloried in the word. Even with the compensation settled – and such considerable compensation – she was manifestly resentful. But I suppose I should not blame her for it. To find that one's lodger, so seemingly quiet and learned, is in fact a lunatic might well give anyone a deep sense of injury. It was unpleasant, but I could understand: the relatives of madmen are not easily forgiven.

'Walk out to it,' she advised, with small, pleased nods. 'That's what I'd do. Unless you want your name in the local paper . . . Gentleman from the South, visiting the madhouse . . . Two miles out on the Mill Road. It won't take long.' Then she pulled her shawl tighter around her, as if to remind me how wet and vile the day was.

So I walked; and why expound on the miseries of that walk? I have written enough about the charms of Skelpton. Suffice it to say that the black rain continued to fall in torrents until the gutters overflowed, and I was soaked to the bone. Yet this physical discomfort was far surpassed by the wretchedness of my mental condition. While terraced streets gave way to alleys, and houses to factory walls, I walked in a stupor of revulsion and despair. My own brother in a madhouse. Myself, setting out to visit such a place! Think it monstrous if you will, but so overwhelmed was I by the horror of these circumstances, that even then, with the first shock abated, I scarcely spared for Marcus one moment of anxiety that was untrammelled by other considerations. I was much too occupied. I laboured at going forwards, afflicted by a most vigorous desire to abandon my brother, forfeit my belongings at Water Tower Street, and hasten back to the railway station to catch the first train south.

Believe me, this was a sore temptation; and it reached its height at my first glimpse of the asylum.

On both sides of the road I followed, the factory yards abruptly gave up their companionship to expose me to the open hillside: derelict land, strewn with garbage and patched with mud, looking out across which I saw, slightly distorted by the rain, a vast grey edifice. Tall and box-like, it rose beside the road a good distance yet ahead of me, and I was terrified. Why, I cannot explain. It is, perhaps, wiser not to try, since experts assure us that the thoughts by which we endeavour to account for our feelings are rarely our true thoughts. However that may be, at my first glimpse of the asylum, I felt cold with fear, and this much I will say: that building put me in mind of a certain reverend gentleman well known to me in my boyhood, a stern, immensely virtuous person who had taught me my Aristotle, and who had always dressed in black and smelled of soap. Ah, but he was of all things the most horrible! Whenever my memory had played me false in the recitation of a passage, or my reason had failed to grasp some paradox, he had let fall from his upper jaw a plate of dentures – long, yellow teeth – and this had been the terror of my early days. It had brought together in my blood all the ingredients of shock, disgust, fright and fascination; and never since had I experienced such a union of these emotions until I saw the asylum.

To encourage myself to go on, I pulled out the card from my pocket.

Come and see me, for God's sake. Marcus.

I stared at those words until they were blurred by the rain and the ink ran down in pale streaks on to my hand.

Mercifully, Skelpton Mental Asylum is at least no more terrible on the inside – not where the visitor walks – than it is without. My frantic holloaing at the gate brought forth a perfectly amicable porter, skipping across the yard with an apron pulled over his head to protect him against the weather. Through a grille in the gate I watched him advance. Did he look mad? Was this some trustee from among the inmates? I waited tensely while he drew the bolts and poked out a red-veined face at me. He looked too hearty to be a Skelpton man.

'Sorry t'keep yer waitin', sir,' he said, grinning. 'My, but yer wet! Though, beggin' yer pardon, sir, but yer should ha' pulled t'bell.'

I had been in too great a fright to see it, the heavy brass ring set in the wall.

'Business, sir?'

'I wish to see . . . I wish to enquire about a relative. A cousin. He was brought here yesterday.'

'Better come an' see t'guvnor.'

The gate thudded shut at my back. Bolts closed off the world. To my right and left and ahead, there were walls with barred windows, row upon row of windows. I followed my jovial guide across the yard, and I shall not easily forget the patter of rain on the flagstones, nor the chuckling sound it made in the gutters. That walk seemed endless. The yard gleamed silver-grey, and looking up at the square of sky that fitted over the walls like a lid, I found it difficult to believe that I had not fallen into some deep pit – an impression no doubt exaggerated by the state of my nerves.

Looking up was, in any case, a mistake, because I saw, peering through the bars of one of the windows, a face, very thin and white, and, although it was too high up for me to distinguish its features, this face brought me to a halt; it held me, as a snake is said to mesmerize its victims.

The porter came scuttling back to my side.

'Come along, sir . . . No point gettin' wetter than we have ter . . . '

He took the liberty of plucking at my sleeve, and that, together with his reasonable tone, broke the spell: I was free to move again.

Long, cold corridors, morbidly silent, and yet, I thought, strangely crowded with muffled noises; the brickwork all painted a pale green that glistened at the corridor junctions, where gas lamps hung from the ceiling; ranks of closed doors, each bearing a number; flights of stone steps; long, wooden benches.

'You wait here, sir,' said the porter at last, 'an' I'll tell 'em yer come. What name was it, sir?'

'My name is Davies . . . And the patient's name is Marcus Davies.'

Then, panicked by the thought that this fellow might abandon me without a word to anyone, I offered him a shilling. He took it with a wink.

'Thankin' you, sir. Don't yer worry . . . '

He vanished round a corner.

I sat down. I opened my coat and shook off as much of the rain as had not already soaked into the fabric. I longed to wring the water from my trouser legs as well, and even thought of pulling off a boot to examine the state of my foot – but, of course, that was out of the question: anyone might come, and, if they did, why, even more than in the interests of decorum, I wished to be fully clothed so that I might leap up and run at a moment's notice.

Indeed, I almost did run when, round the corner from the direction the porter had taken, appeared a great bear of a man – I heard him coming before I saw him: heavy footsteps, and a jangling that in my fright I took for the music of severed chains, but which, in fact, testified to the many keys he wore at his belt. A truncheon also hung at his belt. I suppose he was a warden, although he looked to me very like a jailer, his face black with stubble, his shirtsleeves rolled up to display strong arms criss-crossed with scars.

Stopping a few paces from my bench, this individual ignored the feeble smile I offered, and appraised me sternly.

'Bin attendered ter, are yer?'

I assured him that I was, and he shambled on.

But I began to despair of my porter. Slowly, the minutes circumnavigated my watch, second by second. Four, five minutes passed; and, finally, to dispel my alarm – just to prove how much at ease I felt in the place – I coughed. For this bravado I repented at leisure: my cough prowled up and down the corridor like a spectre, lingering on the very edge of my senses for an unnatural length of time. I began to shiver; I was bathed in a cold perspiration – when, suddenly, more footsteps. This time they were brisk, they were even cheerful, and round the corner came a young man with a pink face and a civilized smile. His moustache was beautifully curled.

'Mr Davies?' He had a bright, pleasing voice. 'I'm Dr Forster's assistant. He will see you now. Would you be so good . . . ?'

I was already on my feet, and with the utmost politeness he conducted me down the corridor.

II

AUGUST 18th

This place will do. The woman cooks abominably and is about as interesting as a block of wood. I've given orders for meals to be left outside my door on a tray so that I'll not be tied to her routine and will be spared her company. Besides the widow there is only her daughter, a mouse of a thing, about thirteen, who runs away whenever we meet on the stairs.

No more family censure! Freedom. I feel I shall write great things here. From my window I look out on to factory chimneys and black roofs. I've turned the desk round so that, when I'm at work, this view will inspire me.

Objective: a novel without hypocrisy. No picturesque setting. No heroine, all honey-sweetness. No terrific hero. To show that the misery of life lies in its dullness – how unsensational everything is, even the so-called scandalous or horrific elements. To convey this by using 'shocking' material in such a way that it fails to shock.

AUGUST 26th

I've made a start. It's going well. The words come tumbling out. I brew coffee to a thick syrup on the gas ring by my bed and drink it when my brain flags. It tastes unspeakably vile – but how it makes the ideas dance!

Mostly I'm working at night, beginning around five in the evening and carrying on till dawn. Then I sleep until midday. The Brideson woman leaves a breakfast tray of bread and butter at my door before she goes to bed, so this system works pretty well. I eat breakfast before I sleep, and wake up to lunch.

Sometimes in the afternoon I stroll through the alleys and factory yards, listening to the workers cursing, and I try to penetrate their faces, those hard, ungiving faces. Or I walk out along the Mill Road to look at the mess – the unchronicled, haphazard ruin of an English hillside. And sometimes I explore the hovels of the very poor, who have no occupation and who live on their wits like curs.

A number of prostitutes congregate at one of Skelpton's beer halls, some of them quite attractive in a predatory way, but I'll not meddle! Talk with them, certainly, to hear how jaded and bored they are – but lie with them, never.

I must let nothing distract me. Besides, I already know the lessons which these women teach, and now I have to learn the other sort of deprivation: suppression of appetite.

Excess *and* its opposite: I must have experienced both, if I'm to write this book convincingly.

AUGUST 28th

The devil take my family, with their precious education! I'm writing about a drunkard, a wife-beater. I'm describing his thoughts as he staggers home one night full of drink – and how does it come out? Ridiculous! Great rolling Latin phrases, beautifully sustained periods, choice reflections! Like a carnival float squeezing down a backstreet.

This so-called culture, this gift that brother Robert used to say we should thank God and His saints for, will end by suffocating me! It's like a skin that needs flaying off. It taints every part of my life that it touches.

Witness, for God's sake, my last entry. Those prostitutes: 'a number . . . congregate at one of Skelpton's beer halls, some of them quite attractive in a predatory way, but I'll not meddle . . . ' What a pious lecher I sound! But how to avoid it? How shall I not sound like a hypocrite when I've been taught the language of hypocrisy, with all its euphemisms and deceptions?

I see I have my work cut out, undoing this 'education'.

Another problem: the coffee I drink. It stimulates ideas, but it also mars my sleep, so that I feel tired and am easily disheartened. Still, I'd not willingly be without it. There are times in the night after a cup of that poison when I think so clearly, see things with such perspicacity, that I'm brimming over with happiness. I don't even care that there's no one with whom I can share my thoughts. At such moments I become astonishingly patient. Ah, let them wait, I tell myself, time will bear me out. They will read this one day, and see . . .

I'm working a steady twelve hours a day.

SEPTEMBER 1st

The re-write of Chapter 2 is good. Or, at least, it's better. I'm improving. My sentences are shorter, colder; my words, blunter. I'm becoming so absorbed in the creation of my characters that going out now seems a chore; I've stocked up with ink and nibs. Mrs Brideson delivers food to my door like clockwork, and I'm settling into the toil of writing without any distractions. There are no external events to record.

Correction: there is one. The girl, Mary, seems to have lost her fear of me. Now I think she's fascinated, as she would be by some pet ogre.

Last evening, as I came from the bathroom, I found her on the landing dressed only in a cotton nightshirt, her feet bare, and her hair loose on her shoulders. The sight quite startled me. Why? Well, I couldn't say she's pretty – she's too much of a ghost for that – but her body is more developed than those little-girl clothes would have one believe. Then again, when she saw me I thought she'd scamper off as usual, but, on the contrary, she stood where she was – in my way, as it happened, so that I was obliged to step round her – simpering, and rubbing her hands on the sides of her shirt.

SEPTEMBER 3rd

It's going well. Difficult to bring myself to stop, even for a pretence of sleep. My dreams, when I do sleep, are full of memories of childhood: Robert, chubbily virtuous, the darling of visiting aunts; myself being punished – shut in dark cupboards for using my bible as a makeshift hammer, or whipped and sent to bed for inking fangs on to one of the portraits in the hall. There are other dreams as well, of voluptuous women with heavy breasts and creased, blue-veined thighs. Awake, I think of these creatures as revolting, but in my dreams they come to me like goddesses, promising all manner of delight.

How savagely the flesh fights back! Restrained all day in this sedentary occupation, given half a chance it would tyrannize me. 'Lie down for a while,' it whispers, 'and give pleasure to yourself, since you're too fastidious for the Skelpton whores.' Then it adds in a vicious undertone, 'Hypocrite!'

I drink coffee and write. I channel this energy into work. For the book's sake, haven't I said I must learn what they're like, these deprivations?

I've finished Chapter 3. I'm amazed by my pace, terrified that suddenly there'll be nothing left to say, and the pen will falter. To stave off this fear, I play a game.

There's a shallow inkwell set in an ornamental stand on the desk; and every night I fill it from the ink bottle, saying to myself, 'No sleep, until this is empty.'

Then I set to work.

A childish ritual – but effective.

SEPTEMBER 6th

Chapter 4. The son of my drunkard has left for the city to become a swell. I keep putting dry, sarcastic speeches into his mouth, but it's too soon. He wouldn't have the detachment yet, nor the style. Will have to re-write this.

SEPTEMBER 8th

Stuck on Chapter 4. Went for a walk yesterday, but it didn't help. Came back – *et ecce veritas: masturbatus*

Afterwards, a black, cloying sleep. Failure.

SEPTEMBER 9th

An extraordinary symptom of overwork!

Last night, Chapter 4 began to move, creakily, but with hopes of gaining momentum, so, to help it along, I drank a good six inches of distilled coffee, and by one o'clock this morning my pen was fairly skating across the paper. I grew hot, and had stopped for a moment when a curious thing happened, a ridiculous thing. I'll describe it exactly as it was – complete nonsense, the quirk of a tired brain.

The lid of the inkwell stood open, as it usually does when I'm writing; and I found myself staring at it, thinking of the next words to be written; and, as I stared, the lid trembled slightly – indeed, so slightly that I thought nothing of it, yet neither did I carry on working. I peered more closely. The pool of black ink also seemed to be trembling, coagulating –

Suddenly, something flimsy and long-limbed started to separate itself from the liquid and clamber up the inkwell's side. At first I thought it must be an insect, a fly or spider that had fallen into the ink and was making a valiant attempt to save itself. Yet, more honestly, I believe I never really thought that. I knew it was something quite different, with particular significance to myself.

The thing was bluish-black, moved in flickers, and was as tall as my middle finger. It was naked, and, so far as I could see, perfectly formed with all the parts of a man, only so lean and tenuous that it seemed no more substantial than a stick figure drawn with a thick nib.

With something of an effort, this creature heaved itself on to the edge of the inkwell and balanced there. Then it looked at me.

In its dark face, red eyes; and, when it smiled, the tip of a red tongue. The smile I couldn't interpret, although in retrospect I'd compare it to a street urchin's – cheerful enough, but capable of hiding malice. Maybe a thief's smile.

I felt no fear. Neither did I rush out of the room, crying for Mrs Brideson to fetch a doctor. Instead, stretching out my pen, I endeavoured to poke the manikin very gently, to discover whether it had substance; but he moved too quickly for me. He slid along the shaft of my pen like a child sliding down banisters, until he reached my fingers. Then, springing nimbly to his feet, he ran back up the shaft to the rim of the inkwell, and from there he put out his tongue at me before slipping down once more into the ink.

Madness! And madness to ignore the warning. I must sleep more.

But what to make of it? I mean, its significance? Why spawn such an image? Compare with the angels stirring the pool at Bethesda in the New Testament, the sick and crippled waiting for a cure. Could that be the genesis of my imp?

SEPTEMBER 10th

No imps today! I took a brisk walk down the Mill Road, well past the lunatic asylum. On the way back, I stopped to talk to the girls at the beer hall. One of them, Essie, might take my fancy if it weren't for the book. But I won't give in again.

Worked tonight without one sip of coffee.

SEPTEMBER 12th

Have abandoned Chapter 4, and shall go back to it later. Intend to brew coffee again tonight. It's no use. The ideas won't come without it.

SEPTEMBER 13th

The imp is back. He came out last night to sit cross-legged on the desk like a tailor.

I didn't see him arrive. One moment – just a blank sheet of scrap paper by my elbow: the next, he was there, sitting in the middle of it, grinning away with that red tongue he so likes to exhibit. Knowing he's an hallucination, I did my best to ignore him, and he gave me no trouble. He sat very still. Whenever I looked at him, he grinned; otherwise, nothing. I think he means to be friends. He disappeared again without my noticing.

Oddly enough, Chapter 5 is going well – a description of the woman's life: a drunkard for her husband; a drab, hopeless existence, punctuated by moments of violence. It has needed careful treatment – there must be no facile pathos – and I think I'm succeeding. Her sufferings are tedious in the extreme; they are full of grey practicality.

The irony, though. To write this chapter on the dullness of life with so much ease, while I have this bizarre adventure in my head! But I must guard against glamorizing the matter. The ink imp, too, is nothing. Nothing at all.

SEPTEMBER 15th

Couldn't sleep. Can't write. Ventured downstairs to ask Mrs Brideson for more bread, and found the girl alone in the kitchen. She was stirring a mess of flour in a bowl, and became afflicted with giggles when she saw me. More bread? Certainly. She cut me a thick slice from the loaf, and I meant to chuck her under the chin for the service, but coyly she slid aside, so that my hand brushed against her breast.

I came away with the absurd idea that she wouldn't have protested if my hand had stayed there.

Obviously, I'm overtired. Must try to relax more.

SEPTEMBER 16th

He came out while I was reading, the fiend! It took no brew to conjure him up this time. I knew he was present before I looked. I forced myself to read to the end of the section before turning my head, and – *voilà!* – perched on the pile of my manuscript, sticking that red tongue out. The impudence! When he saw me look, he waved happily, got to his feet, and started prancing about over my carefully written last page. It was provocation – amicable, but provocation none the less.

'Damn you,' I said, 'I'll prove you don't exist!' and, flinging down the book, I went over to the desk to make a grab at him. I thought: if I can only touch him and feel it's air I'm touching, that'll put an end to the matter . . .

But he evaded me, capering from inkstand to blotter, then smartly back to the manuscript, while my hand came down – slam, slam – just an inch behind him; I was like a fussy clerk trying to swat a fly, and, all the time, though I could hear nothing, I could see that he was laughing, his bluish face creased up merrily. He's a great acrobat. There were somersaults and herculean leaps for my entertainment. Oh, it was rare fun! Down fell the manuscript, scattering on the carpet; the blotter rocked like a cradle. Round and round the desk we went, until it became quite evident that I couldn't catch him, not without his connivance, so finally I shrugged, retreated a couple of paces, and said: 'Imp, you win! I only wanted to touch you, to prove you're real.'

He leaned against the inkstand, panting. I could see his meagre black chest heaving in and out. His red eyes blazed at me. Then, all at once, he stretched out a hand; it was long, with excessively pointed fingers, and out of proportion with the rest of his body. He seemed to beckon me.

'Is this an invitation?'

He nodded. I reached forward. The imp remained backed up against the inkstand, watching.

'May I touch you?'

My voice was full of mockery. I'm not so ill but I found it comic, asking permission of an hallucination.

Again he nodded. Slowly I put out a finger and brushed it lightly against his chest. I expected to feel only the wood of the inkstand, but in this I was mistaken. He was as cold and wet as ink itself. I rubbed my finger along his side, and felt his ribs. I stroked his lean thighs and felt him tense at the sensation. All the while, he never took his eyes from my face, and he smiled, his lips apart to show scarlet gums. My imp, it seems, is a creature of sensual pleasure; he submitted to my exploration with every sign of enjoyment.

Well, I thought, this isn't the way to prove I imagine him. And I withdrew my finger.

What to do?

He waited, then made an agitated gesture. More! He wanted more!

So he has great appetites in that thread-like body. The answer, then, must be to ignore him.

Deliberately I went back to my book. I became rigid with the effort not to glance at him, but once or twice my willpower failed me and, whenever I did look, I found him sitting on the very edge of the desk, his knees drawn up to his chin, watching me with an expression of intense annoyance.

I pretended to read.

What to do? Should I visit a doctor? But any treatment a doctor prescribed would be sure to involve breaking off the novel. I might be packed off on a rest-cure, there would be copious sleeping draughts. No. If my work isn't to be interrupted, I shall have to fight this demon myself.

At last, dawn showed at the window, and my eyes grew heavy. I longed to go to bed, but this presented a difficulty. When I laid down the book and stood up, what if he was still there, watching? Go to bed in any case, I resolved.

Mercifully, he had gone.

So I came and lay down, exhausted; but I haven't slept. Despite myself, I'm alert, waiting for him to appear again, and so I've written all this to try to calm myself. As luck would have it, I'd left my journal on the bed and, rather than risk a return to the desk, I've used this stub of a pencil, which I keep beneath my pillow with a pad for jottings when I wake up suddenly.

I must simply ignore him. If I do, very likely he'll soon fade back where he came from – into my brain –

SEPTEMBER 18th

Last night the imp made a late appearance. I was so absorbed in my work, I had almost forgotten him. Chapter 5 is completed, and now, in Chapter 6, I've flung my drunkard out of his job; he's reaching new depths of despair and degradation. I think it will do. My language has coarsened wonderfully. I drag the fellow through every kind of squalor without any of it reading in the least strange or exotic, and that's exactly what I intended. If only I can keep this up!

True to my resolve, I ignored the imp – treatment which didn't please him. He pattered about on the scrap paper and, when that failed to distract me, he sprang across to the page on which I wrote and executed cartwheels, a swift, skilful line of them down the margin. Even then, I pretended not to see; and even when he stood at last, panting; but from a glance I knew that his grin had given way to a scowl. Damned mischief-maker! He meant to have attention! I went on writing, and sweated. How to rid myself of this phantom? I can't express how I longed to concentrate on my chapter – and, in fact, I might have succeeded had it not been for one thing: a sound – the first I've heard from the imp's lips – a sharp, thin squeak, something like a baby rat's. It took me so much by surprise that I stopped writing and stared round at him. He was standing, black arms akimbo, by my left wrist, those red eyes of his very fiery, his face distorted with anger.

'What is it?' I asked.

He squeaked again, and made a beckoning gesture.

'You want me to stroke you, is that it?'

Grins and nods. He lay down obligingly, full-length.

But I said, 'I've work to do,' and started to write again – although understandably the sentence I put down was rubbish. Suddenly, another squeak; and then – a most amazing thing: my pen skidded down the page in a wild zig-zag. The wretch! He had leapt across in front of my eyes, caught hold of the pen, and now he swung on it, his spindly legs moving together, backwards and forwards . . .

I slammed the pen down hard, hoping to trap him beneath it – no luck. He slithered aside with the fluidity of ink, and gave me a look of fury. Then he cast his eyes about for an instrument, a weapon . . .

By this time, of course, my concentration had quite gone, so I gave up the struggle to write, and watched him. He climbed on to the inkstand, and up to its ridge, where I keep a penknife, pins and clips, spare nibs and so forth: and, nimbly clambering about amongst this ironmongery, he appeared to be making a selection.

So it was my turn to grin.

'Don't be a fool!' I mocked him. 'A sprat like you could never lift anything that size!' He was struggling with a good stout nib, the one I use for italics. My scorn was torture to him. There were more squeaks, and he broke off his labours to shake a fist at me.

'Bravo!' I applauded. 'Bravo!'

That did it. Frantic with rage, he grabbed hold of a pin, clutched it like a spear and, thus armed, came slipping and bounding down on to the sheet of paper which I had just covered with writing.

It's hugely comic, I dare say, but never has a pin seemed so terrible to me. He raised it, a pygmy on a hunt, aiming it soberly at a point between my eyes, while I sat frozen. I hadn't thought there could be the strength in him to raise any object. Such careful, deadly aim he took, his tongue wetting his lips, his limbs tensed . . . Then, abruptly, with a shriek he flung the pin point-downwards into the sheet of paper, and dragged at it until the paper ripped, my bright new sentences splitting in two, separating in opposite directions.

My God, if he does that again!

I let out a roar and brought down my fist with a thud – but he dodged me. Stab! Stab! went the pin into my fingers, like wasp stings. I was too astonished to pull my hand back. I registered pain, and sat like an idiot. But finally I cried out, 'Pax! Very well!' – and the stabbing ceased. I nursed my hand: it throbbed; it was flecked with ink. I surveyed the desk. Where was he? Why, there, the dark victor, lying full-length on the wooden back of the blotter, his face stretched in a grin like a half-moon. He beckoned me, and I stroked him, along his ribs, across his abdomen and testicles, while he grinned and grinned.

Some five minutes passed, after which he rose and gave me an ironic bow, before submerging himself in the inkwell.

I closed the lid and placed a paperweight on top of it. Then I fell asleep in the chair.

Today, Mrs Brideson knocked on my door to enquire whether I'd slept well. Hadn't I had bad dreams? Yes, yes, I said. Her stretched, querulous voice is loathsome to me. Why can't she say what she means? Her cold eyes imply that a hard day's work in one of the local factories would cure me of dreams.

I keep staring at the puncture marks on my hand. Did I inflict them on myself? If so, I'm well and truly mad. And yet the cause is simple – isolation, that's all it is – so could the remedy not be just as simple? A few hours in the company of someone practical and unimaginative, a champion of mediocrity – and all this effervescence of my mind might evaporate. Summon brother Robert. Maybe it's worth a try.

SEPTEMBER 22nd

He has me like a eunuch, the fiend! Somehow he keeps pushing off the paperweight that holds the lid down. (No. I won't believe that I lift it off myself.) He comes out, and demands his pleasure. I stroke him till he wearies of it. If I refuse, he waits till I begin to write, then leans up against the pen nib so that I can barely push the words out, or else he pulls on the shaft to make the whole illegible. Another game: he sits on the inkwell's rim, and flicks ink down on to the page from his fingers.

So I humour him, and, afterwards, for a while he'll sit quietly, until he grows bored. Then he explores the desk, or climbs on to my sleeve and scales my arm to crawl about on my neck. His sharp fingernails dig into my skin; he flattens his body against my cheek, wet and cold. It's revolting. I daren't go out in case he's hiding on me when I go. I'd lose whatever's left of my reason if somewhere in the street I felt him, clambering out of my collar, perhaps . . . Never mind that other eyes might fail to see him. To be mad in public is a confirmation that one is lost, whereas to be mad in private – that's no more than we all are sometimes.

He consumes ink at an incredible rate. I no longer fill the inkwell, but he thieves it out of the bottles. Maybe he drinks it. Maybe he's made of it, and has to renew himself daily. A good deal of it he wastes in spills over my papers when I annoy him. I'm obliged to keep my manuscript locked in the bedside cabinet.

Much against my inky friend's will, I've written to Robert. But how to post my card, since I daren't go out?

A card was best, I thought. Damnably penned – through no fault of mine – I've kept my appeal brief and mysterious, dramatic. That might jolt Robert into coming. Nothing else would.

SEPTEMBER 23rd

We've had a fight! Tonight I lost patience and refused to stroke him, so he retaliated, ripping every page the instant I set pen to it. I retreated to the sofa. I took my pencil, rested a sheet of paper on a book, and tried to forget him. But, confound him, he'd stolen a ride in my pocket! No sooner was I settled than he leapt out, opened his mouth, and spewed ink, thick black ink, on to the book – a precious copy of Engels. I'd tried to escape, and, oh, he was enormously angry. He pranced up and down on the back of Engels in the slimy puddle he'd made, squeaking magnificently. I'm sure he's gaining voice. His squeaks grow louder by the day. Spoilt little princeling! I laid down Engels very gently, and, reaching behind me to the bookcase, brought out a good, solid Macaulay. Slam! Down with it, into the inky mess! But I missed. Always, always I miss. I saw him, the fiend, scampering away across the carpet, and I took leave of my senses: book after book I flung at him, while he dodged and weaved his way about, now stopping to pull a mocking face at me, now tearing a page from one book – catching hold of a corner and dragging it after him as he ran – now spitting ink across the spine of another; and still, stupidly, I threw them, book after book. The more of them he ruined, the more I hurled, until, tiring of this sport, he ran (with such speed!) to the wall, and started to scale it, swinging across the curtains and on to the next wall, all the time spewing ink in great blotches.

I had to do something. I snatched my pen from the desk and gave chase, endeavouring to spike him to the wall with one thrust of the nib – but still he defeated me. He would freeze until I'd crept up close, and then, one twitch, and he was a yard or so away. It was horrible. Like a tailless lizard, flattened there, clinging with his nails – or maybe he can stick to a surface, I don't know. I only know he uses those nails on *me*.

In the end, I flung aside the pen and tried to swat him with a sheaf of papers. No use. He's much too quick. I gave up; and now here I sit on the bed, wretchedly pencilling notes. For the moment he's disappeared, my tormentor. He could be anywhere.

I must trap him somehow. I have to be rid of him.

One spot of brightness today: when I heard the lunch tray being set down, I opened the door, and it was the girl, Mary. I begged her to post the card. At first she backed away. She appeared confused, as though it were not quite proper that I should know she brings my meals up. Or else, perhaps, she saw something strange in me.

I spoke softly: 'You're not scared of me, surely, are you?'

She stood against the stair rail, a mouse about to scamper, while I smiled so desperately that it hurt. The card had to be posted. At last, I suppose, my smile won. Creeping forward, she took the card in her warm, damp fingers, and, as she did so, overwhelmed with relief I kissed her head, just where her hair parts in a white line. She ran off down the stairs. I felt exhilarated. I believe it was then that the resolution formed in me to resist the imp tonight.

I only just had the presence of mind to call after Mary that I need more ink, and if she or her mother would fetch it, I'd settle for that and the rent at the same time. Since noon yesterday, he has consumed two whole bottles.

SEPTEMBER 25th

I have him! At last I have him! He's stretched out on the wooden back of the blotter, *pinned* down. Oh, barbaric of me, no doubt, but there seems no other way and, after all, it's not as though he were flesh and blood, for all his squeaks and squeals. And if I'd merely trapped him under a cup, say, he might have slithered out beneath the rim, he has so many of the properties of ink. No. Pinning it had to be. I have him spiked through both shoulders, another in the left leg, and one in the right arm, at the elbow. By this unorthodox arrangement, I hope to avoid any absurd analogies with crucifixion. I mean, I have him like this, staked out in this haphazard fashion, to remind myself that, let him squeal as much as he likes, there can be nothing here that's tragic or metaphysical. I'm simply ridding my mind of an obsession.

Perhaps in time I shall have to add another pin – through the right leg – in case by tossing about he works loose, but, so far, he lies quite feeble, squeaking, his red eyes rolling in what he'd have me take for agony, and his mouth opened so wide that I can examine at leisure not only his scarlet gums and tongue, but also a set of black, pointed teeth that form a circle round the entrance to his throat. Fascinating.

Naturally, pinning him down is only a temporary measure. He must be finished with. I've thought of burning blotter and him together, but the weather continues so mild that I have no fire in my room, and to carry the thing down to the kitchen stove seems another of those confirmations of madness.

Yet how else to be rid of a creature that can live even submerged in ink? I have in mind an experiment. I'll fade him out. Cover him with blotting paper, and hope that it's absorptive powers, combined with ink starvation, will make an end of him.

Oh, it's so good to sit at this desk again, dipping the pen and writing without his despicable interference!

Squeak on, you wretch! Kick your one free leg at me! My God, the look of venom on his face! Why, it's nothing, nothing, my fine fellow. Soon you'll not exist even to this extent – which is not at all. Not by one twitch of your miserable body.

In the end, catching him proved simple. When he came out and threw himself against the nib to attract my attention, I smiled, I laid aside the pen and said, 'Peace. I'm in no mood for another fight. Can't you see, I haven't found the strength yet to clear up after our last one? Why shouldn't we be friends, and entertain each other? What would you like?'

Like? To be stroked and caressed, of course! Down he lay invitingly on the back of the blotter, and I flattered him with my most patient attention, until his tongue moved across his lips in his ecstasy, and his eyes almost closed. Never had I been so obliging.

'Do you like that?' I asked. 'You like that?'

He grinned up at me, with eyes no more than slits. I continued to stroke . . . and his eyes closed.

In went the pins, one simultaneously into each shoulder. I had one concealed at the ready in my left hand, and another was pressed between thumb and index finger of my right; such is his greed, the imp had failed to notice that, against all precedent, I used my middle finger for my slavish stroking of him.

No sooner had the pins penetrated than his eyes opened like poppies, full of pained amazement. He began to howl, and struggled to rise, but I was already at work on his elbow, squeezing my pin home into the soft wood.

Clamping down the left leg took some time longer, for he kicked at first, and so hard that tiny white spots appeared in the wood where he scuffed it.

Now I have him! I'll lay the blotting paper over him, and sleep well tonight.

Tomorrow or the day after will bring brother Robert, all solicitous from the bosom of the family; and I'll laugh and say, 'Wrong? Nothing wrong, old chap. Just a way of getting you here. Time we had a drink together.'

That will outrage him completely.

'To bring me all this way for nothing!' I can almost hear him sputtering as I write!

III

'You would be distressed,' said Dr Forster mildly, 'were you to see your brother. Allow me to suggest, sir, that for the present you do not. Leave him to our care, our expert care . . . Later, when his injuries have healed, perhaps . . . ' He paused, and there was about him a little brightening, a modest optimism.

'Injuries?'

I remembered the woman holding up a blood-stained sheet, but only at this instant, in the quiet, primrose room of Dr Forster, did I fully realize that Marcus was hurt. To the consternation of the doctor's assistant, although not, I think, to his own, I rose at once from my chair, crying, 'But of course I must see him! Of course!'

'Pray, calm yourself, sir,' said the younger man, moving with alacrity to stand between me and the door.

Dr Forster smiled.

'To what end?' he asked. 'We have given him a sleeping draught. The wretched man was in the last straits of exhaustion. So, even if you would speak with him, he cannot speak with you.'

'But at least I must see . . . '

'The bandages? Mr Davies, please sit down.'

Dumbly I obeyed. Dr Forster regarded me sympathetically. He said, 'I see your brother's landlady has spared you the details.' Then he studied his wonderfully manicured hands, as if to express the delicacy with which he proceeded.

I found I was shivering. If only I had come sooner, I thought, might not all this have been avoided?

'The truth is,' continued the doctor, speaking as gently as any priest, 'that even if Marcus – I may call him Marcus? – regains his mental faculties, his personal appearance will never be . . . quite what it was. He has lost one eye completely, you understand. The other is damaged, but may do. We have hopes.' He sighed into my appalled silence. 'There are, besides, deep incisions in his cheeks and lips, which will certainly leave scars. The instrument he used was not one to cut with a clean edge.'

'An *eye*? The *instrument*?' I repeated his words like a primitive struggling to comprehend some strange catechism.

'A pen nib. In his demented state, your brother used a pen nib on himself.'

'But . . . why?'

At the foolishness of this question, Dr Forster spread his white hands to the heavens in a gesture that begged for enlightenment. His eager assistant, however, broke in with a rapid speech.

'He has delusions, sir. When they brought him in, he was all the time shouting out that the Fiend had broken loose while he slept, and taken revenge on him.'

'The Fiend?' This sounded so unlike Marcus that I protested, 'Impossible. My brother's not that sort . . . he's not a religious man!'

'He's not a sane man, sir,' said Dr Forster, and without warning he rose stiffly, apparently wearied of the interview. He looked towards the door. 'Are you still of a mind to see your brother? There are besides documents to sign . . . '

See him? I rose, swayed, sickish and undecided. To see Marcus, now it came to it, to peer into a musty cell, and see, curled up on a mattress, my once arrogant brother, maybe to have him wake up and shriek nonsensical things at me – I shrank from the prospect. Who would not? And yet, just to walk away . . .

Mercifully, observing my confusion, Dr Forster's young assistant came to the rescue and, laying an angelic hand on my sleeve, he suggested, 'Would it not be wiser, sir, to come back tomorrow? When you've had time to – reflect a little?'

Oh, infinitely!

I allowed this deliverer to lead me out, barely gasping, 'Good afternoon!' to Dr Forster before I found myself once more in the corridor.

'I'll take you down to the gate,' said the assistant, and so we walked together, the greater part of the way in silence; and, in my shocked condition, as we went I involuntarily noticed strange things, quite select things. There was one corridor, for instance, which hugged the outer wall of the building, a corridor of windows along one side but with the usual row of doors ranged along its inner side, and I noted how the stone flags on this inner side were much less worn than the others – an observation which forced me to conclude that anyone who walked there kept as close as possible to the windows, and as far as possible from the doors; then I saw how many of these doors had not one, but two keyholes.

And through the windows came my promise of a grim walk back to Skelpton: it appeared that the rain had turned to mist, evil mist.

At last we came into the courtyard, and we had started across when Dr Forster's assistant suddenly began to disburden himself of thoughts and facts which I sensed his superior either did not consider important or knew nothing about.

'Your brother's case,' he said, glowing with enthusiasm, 'is really extremely interesting! Not at all like most religious mania . . . I went round to the house last night, you know.'

'You? Ah, yes.'

Dimly I recalled Mrs Brideson's reference to a doctor's visit.

'I hoped to see his room, perhaps find some writing.'

'Well,' I said, 'no doubt you found plenty of that. He came here to write a novel.'

'Oh, I mean a different sort entirely. Diaries, journals, jottings . . . Something of a personal nature. Formal writing would have little value.' And there, in the middle of the courtyard, he stopped, and turned to gaze earnestly at me through what we had discovered to be not so much a mist as a thick drizzle. 'If you find anything like that,' he appealed, 'will you let me have it? It could help your brother enormously. That woman wouldn't let me look . . . She kept going on about compensation. If I hadn't come about that, what did I think I was doing there? When I tried to get past her up the stairs, she threatened to call the police!'

He laughed delightedly at his recollection of the incident, and I took to him, this enthusiast with raindrops shining on his moustache. I thought I detected in him a wholesome enjoyment of life, and a practical mind. Surely, I thought, this is the man to help Marcus.

If I found any writing of interest, I promised to deliver it when I returned the next day.

To my sorrow, I found nothing. Only the soiled heaps of half-written pages, and, in the bedside cabinet, my brother's literary effort – the novel, so coarse and so sordid in concept that I could not stomach it. Indeed, for me this was the final bitter proof of his madness, and, even allowing for that, I was ashamed that Marcus could have written such gutter-filth. I took the whole bundle down to the kitchen stove and consigned it to oblivion. Dr Forster's assistant had said, after all, that the novel would not greatly interest him, and I had no desire to expose the family name to more ridicule than could be helped.

So I burned every page – a sad, dismal business. To this day, the sound of paper burning – the crackling, then the gasp as the flames flare up – fills me with nausea, particularly in the evening, if mingled with the sound is the faint hiss of a gas light, for there was a gas light in that kitchen, hissing and flickering with a kind of sour indolence while I attended to my task.

And, to make matters worse, the woman was present. She sat in a rocking chair close to the door, and that chair creaking backwards and forwards, backwards and forwards, made her appear to be nodding all the time with satisfaction. Then there was the girl, seated at the table, making a pretence of studying whatever she had in her tattered notebook – but in reality watching my every movement. It was deeply unnerving; when I turned from the stove to smile at her, she would immediately lower her eyes to her notes, as if what she read there was of absorbing interest, and, when I turned away again to thrust more papers down into the flames, she would look up: I could feel her eyes on me.

I was glad when it was done, the entire manuscript reduced to ash, and I could escape back upstairs to pack away the rest of my brother's possessions; but even then I worked as speedily as possible, because I hated his room. It still plagued me with the hint of another presence, and no sooner had I made an end of my chore than I retreated to the bedroom which Mrs Brideson had assigned to me, and locked myself in. I went to bed desperate for a good night's sleep after such a day of calamity.

Vain hope! For hours I lay awake, my face to the ceiling, tangled in a web of images: Marcus, the woman in her shawl, the madhouse, that squalid novel, Dr Forster with his elegant hands, his perky assistant . . . dark skeins of meaningless writing.

Finally, a little before dawn, I dozed off, but only to wake again an hour or so later feeling weak and sick, quite incapable of a second visit to the asylum; and when I got up my nerves issued an ultimatum. I had crossed to the mirror with my hairbrush, where the sight of my reflection gave me such a scare that I lost any sort of strength and let the brush fall to the floor with a thud. Yet it was only my own face staring, wide-eyed and pale, back at me.

What did I do? Blame me, whoever will: as soon as I could extricate myself from 36 Water Tower Street, I took a train for home. I wrote to Dr Forster from the safe distance of Hertfordshire, complimenting him on his sound advice that I should not see Marcus in his present condition, and I desired him to mail any necessary documents . . . If, later, a visit from me could be beneficial to my brother, would Dr Forster kindly let me know?

For this dreadful summons, after four years I am still waiting.

To the eager assistant I addressed not a word. What was there to say? I had found no journal, no diary to offer him: I could be of no service. Besides, what I had read in my brother's novel had filled me with such disgust for the workings of crazed minds that – I confess – this had tainted my estimation of the assistant. So he thought he might rescue Marcus, did he? Very well, let him try. I, for one, knew the limits of my strength, and could not relish wrestling with demons.

Indeed, I wondered at the time, and have often wondered since, whether a man may not have to be a little mad himself to set up as champion for the depraved.

...[illegible]ed
...er confront
...s made authors
...romising political
...not read Chesterton
...ds War remains in

...parodying the Inter-
...amed for the regime's
...e the State Budget, a[illegible]
...ry, however, never [illegible]
...ependent evidence emerg-
...rt of it was collected under
...tent to which corruption had
...regime was the discovery that
...n going to resolve the genuine
...pockets on the mainland by
...spontaneity, so heralded by [illegible]
...deceptive. Some local managers
...ked to contribute products to the
...eft in no doubt that their operations
...f they didn't comply.
...ost visible expression of Argentina's
...nds conflict were mass rallies in the
...[illegible] patriotism proved deceptive; the
...anifestations for its own political ends
...omacy, more important even than logistics
...were conveyed as the irreversible statement
...all the conviction of ultimate victory. And
...participants or simply observers; the rallies
...the release of national emotionalism elicited by the
...Third Reich and Mussolini's Ordine Nuovo. They
...vindication of Argentina's rights to the islands than the
...of a political malaise. Before the Falklands War, the
...1978 World Cup celebrations, and before that the dem-
...ns organised in support of Perón and Evita. The events

POSADA

POLITICA

Lo que se ve y lo que no se ve.

The Past

EAVAN BOLAND

I can imagine, if
I came back again,
Looking through windows at
Broken mirrors, pictures,
And, in the cracked upstairs,
The beds where it all began.

The suburb in the rain
This October morning,
Full of food and animals
And children will be –
When I come back again –
Gone to rack and ruin.

I will be its ghost,
Its revenant discovering
Again in one place,
The history of my pain,
My ordeal, my grace –
Unable to resist

Seeing what is past,
Judging what has ended
And whether, first to last,
From then to now and even
Here, ruined, this
Is what love intended –

Finding even the yellow
Jasmine in the dusk,
The smell of early dinners,
The voices of our children,
Taking turns and quarrelling –
Burned on the distance –

Gone. And the small square
Where under cropped lime
And poplar, on bicycles
And skates in the summer,
They played until dark,
Propitiating time.

And even the two whitebeams
Outside the house gone,
With the next-door neighbour
Who used to say in April,
When one was slow to bloom,
They were a man and woman.

Braids

DAVID LEAVITT

When I got the invitation to Diana's wedding – elegantly embossed, archaically formal (the ceremony, it stated, would take place at 'twelve-thirty o'clock') – the first thing I did was the *TV Guide* crossword puzzle. After that I pondered. I was not so much surprised by Diana getting married as I was by her inviting me. What, I wondered, would motivate a person like Diana to ask her former lover, a woman she had lived with for a year and a month and whose heart she had suddenly and callously broken, to a celebration of her union with a man? It seems to me that that is asking for trouble.

I decided to call Leonore, who had been a close friend of Diana's and mine during the days when we were together, and who always seemed to have answers. 'Leonore, Diana's getting married,' I said when she picked up the phone.

'If you ask me,' Leonore said, 'she's wanted a man since day one. Remember that gay guy she tried to make it with? He said he wanted to change, have kids and all? It's not him, is it?'

I looked at the invitation. 'Mark Charles Cadwallader,' I said.

'Well, for his sake,' Leonore said, 'I only hope he knows what he's getting into. As for Miss Diana, her doings are of no interest to me.'

'But Leonore,' I said, 'the question is: should I go to the wedding?' imagining myself, suddenly, in my red T-shirt which said 'Baby Butch' (a present from Diana), re-introducing myself to her thin, severe, long-necked mother, Marjorie Winters.

'I think that would depend on the food,' Leonore said. You could always count on Leonore for an answer like that. Her advice always meant the same thing. It meant: be an adult and make up your own mind.

After I hung up, I poured myself some coffee and propped the invitation in front of me to look at. For the first few seconds it hadn't even clicked who was getting married. I had read: 'Mr and Mrs Humphrey Winters cordially invite you to celebrate the wedding of their daughter, Diana Helaine', and thought: who is Diana Helaine? Then it hit me, because for years, in fact, the whole year and a month, Diana had refused to tell me what her middle initial stood for – positively refused, she said, out of embarrassment, while I tried to imagine what horrors could lie behind that 'H' – Hildegarde? Hester? Hulga? She was coyly, irritatingly insistent about not letting the secret out, like certain girls who would have nothing to do with me in eighth grade. Now she was making public to the world what she insisted on hiding from me, and it made perfect sense. Diana Helaine, not a different person, is getting married, I thought, and it was true, the fact in and of itself didn't surprise me. During the year and a month, combing the ghost of her once knee-length hair, I couldn't count how many times she'd said, very off-the-cuff, 'You know, Ellen, sometimes I think this lesbian life is for the birds. Maybe I should just give it up, get married and have two point four babies.' I'd smile and say, 'If you do that, Diana, you can count on my coming to the wedding with a shotgun and shooting myself there in front of everybody.' To which, still strumming her hair like a guitar and staring into the mirror, she would respond only with a faint smile, as if she could think of nothing in the world she would enjoy more.

First things first: we were lovers, and I don't mean schoolgirls touching each other in exploratory ways in dormitories after dark. I mean, we lived together, shared tampons and toothpaste, had one bed to sleep in, and for all the world (and ourselves) to see. Diana was in law school in San Francisco, and I had a job at Milpitas State Hospital (I still do). Each day I'd drive an hour and a half there and an hour and a half back, and when I got home Diana would be waiting for me in bed, a fat textbook propped on her lap. We had couple friends, Leonore and Callie, for instance, and were always invited to things together, and, when she left me, we were even thinking about getting power-of-attorney over one another. I was Diana's first woman lover, though she had had plenty of boyfriends. I had never slept with a boy, but had been making love with girls since early in high school. Which meant that, for me, being a lesbian was just how things were. But for Diana – well, from day one it was adventure, event and episode. For a while we just had long blushing talks over pizza during which she confessed she was 'curious'. It's ridiculous how many supposedly straight girls come on to you that way – plopping themselves down on your lap and fully expecting you to go through all the hard work of initiating them into Sapphic love out of sheer lust for recruitment. No way, I said. The last thing I need is to play guinea pig, testing ground, only to be left when the fun's over and a new boyfriend shows up on the horizon. But no, Diana said. I mean, yes. I think I *do*. I mean, I think I *am*. At which point she would always have just missed the last bus home and would have to spend the night in my bed, where it was only a matter of time before I had no more defences.

After we became lovers, Diana cut her hair off, and bought me the 'Baby Butch' T-shirt. She joined all sorts of groups and organizations, dragged me to unsavoury bars, insisted, fiercely, on telling her parents everything. (They did not respond well.) Only in private did she muse over her other options. I think she thought she was rich enough not to have to take any vow or promise all that seriously. Rich people are like that, I have noticed. They think a love affair is like a shared real estate venture they can just buy out of when they get tired of it.

Diana had always said the one reason she definitely wanted to get married was for the presents, so the day before the wedding I took my credit card and went to Nordstrom's, where indeed I found her name in the bridal registry, and was handed a computer printout with her china pattern, silver, stainless and other assorted requirements. I was already over my spending limit, so I bought her the ultimate – a Cuisinart – which I had wrapped to carry in white crêpe paper with a huge yellow bow. Next came the equally important matter of buying myself a dress for the wedding. It had been maybe five, six years since I'd owned a dress. But buying clothes is like riding a bicycle – it comes back – and soon, remembering age-old advice from my mother on hems and necklines, I had picked out a pretty yellow sundress with a smattering of daisies, and a big, wide-brimmed hat. It was easy.

The invitation had been addressed to Miss Ellen Britchkey and guest, and afterwards, in the parking lot, that made me think about my life – how there was no one in it. And then, as I was driving home from Nordstrom's, for the first time in years I had a seizure of accident panic. I couldn't believe I was travelling at sixty miles an hour, part of a herd of speeding cars which passed and raced each other, coming within five or six inches of collision and death every ten seconds. It astonished me to realize that I drove every day of my life, that every day of my life I risked ending my life, that all I had to do was swerve the wrong way, or look only in the front and not the side mirror, and I might hit another car, or hit a child on the way to a wedding, and have to live the rest of my life with the guilt, or die. Horrified, I headed right, into the slow lane. The slow lane was full of scared women, crawling home alone. It was no surprise to me. I was one with the scared women crawling home alone. After Diana left me, I moved down the peninsula to a miniature house – that is the only way to describe it – two rooms with a roof, and shingles, and big pretty windows. It was my solitude house, my self-indulgence house, my remorse and secret-pleasure house. There I ate take-out Chinese food, read and re-read *Little House on the Prairie*, stayed up late watching re-runs of *Star Trek* and *The Honeymooners*. I lived by my wits, by survival measures. The television was one of those tiny ones, the screen smaller than a human face.

Diana – I only have one picture of her, and it is not a good likeness. In it she wears glasses and has long, long hair, sweeping below the white fringe of the picture, to her knees. She cut all her hair off as an offering to me the day after the first night we made love, and presented it that evening in a box – two neat braids, clipped easily as toenail parings, offered like a dozen roses. I stared at them, the hair still braided, still fresh with the smell of shampoo, and joked that I had bought her a comb, like in *The Gift of the Magi*. She didn't get it. 'Don't you see?' she said. 'I did it for you – I changed myself for you, as an act of love.' I looked at her, her new boyish bangs, her face suddenly so thin-seeming without its frame of yellow hair. She was used to big gestures, to gifts which made an impact.

'Diana,' I lied (for I had loved her long hair), 'it's the most generous thing anyone's ever done for me.' To say she'd done it for me – well, it was a little bit like a mean trick my sister pulled on me one Christmas when we were kids. She had this thing about getting a little tiny tree to put on top of the piano. And I, of course, wanted a great big one, like the Wagner family down the block. And then, about ten days before

Christmas, she said, 'Ellen, I have an early Christmas present for you,' and she handed me a box, inside which were about a hundred miniature Christmas tree ornaments.

I can recognize a present with its own motive.

If I've learned one thing from Diana, it's that there's more to a gift than just giving.

The next day was the day of the wedding, and somehow, without hitting any children, I drove to the hotel in Hillsborough where the ceremony and reception were taking place. A doorman escorted me to a private drawing-room where, nervous about being recognized, I kept the Cuisinart in front of my face as long as I could, until finally an older woman with a carnation over her breast, apparently an aunt or something, said, 'May I take that, dear?' and I had to surrender the Cuisinart to a tableful of presents, some of which were hugely and awkwardly wrapped and looked like human heads. I thanked her, suddenly naked in my shame, and sturdied myself to brave the drawing-room where the guests milled. I recognized two or three faces from college, all part of Diana's set – rich, straight, preppy, not the sort I had hung around with at all. And in the distance I saw her very prepared parents, her mother thin and severe-looking as ever in a sleeveless black dress, her streaked hair cut short, like Diana's, her neck and throat nakedly displaying a brilliant jade necklace, while her father, in his tuxedo, talked with some other men and puffed at a cigar. Turning to avoid them, I almost walked right into Walter Bevins, who was Diana's gay best friend, or 'hag fag', in college, and we were so relieved to see each other we grabbed a couple of whisky sours and headed to as secluded a corner as we could find. 'Boy, am I glad to see a familiar face,' Walter said. 'Can you believe this? Though I must say, I never doubted Diana would get married in anything less than splendour.'

'Me neither,' I admitted. 'I was just a little surprised that Diana was getting married at all.'

'Weren't we all!' Walter said. 'But he seems like a nice guy. A lawyer, of course. *Very* cute, a real shame that he's heterosexual, if you ask me. But apparently she loves him and he loves her and that's just fine. Look, there he is.'

Walter pointed to a tall, dark man with a moustache and beard who stood in the middle of the drawing-room crowd, shaking hands and laughing with a circle of elderly women. To my horror, his eye caught ours, and he disentangled himself from the old women and walked over to where we were sitting. 'Walter,' he said. Then he looked at me and said, 'Ellen?'

I nodded and smiled.

'Ellen, Ellen,' he said, and reached out a hand which, when I took it, lifted me from the safety of my sofa on to my feet. 'It is such a pleasure to meet you,' he said. 'Come with me for a second, I've wanted a chance to talk with you for so long, and once the wedding takes place – who knows?'

I smiled nervously at Walter, who raised a hand in comradeship, and was led by the groom through a door to an ante-chamber, empty except for a card table piled high with bridesmaids' bouquets. 'I just want you to know,' he said, 'how happy Diana and

I are that you could make it. She speaks so warmly of you. And I also want you to know, just so there's no tension, Diana's told me everything, and I'm fully accepting of her past.'

'Thank you, Mark,' I said, horrified that at my age I could already be part of someone's 'past'. It sounded fake to me, as if lesbianism were just a stage Diana had passed through, and I was some sort of perpetual adolescent, never seeing the adult light of heterosexuality.

'Charlie,' Mark said. 'I'm called Charlie.'

He opened the door and, as we were heading back out into the drawing-room, he said, 'Oh, by the way, we've seated you next to the schizophrenic girl. Your being a social worker and all, we figured you wouldn't mind.'

'Me?' I said. 'Mind? Not at all.'

'Thanks. Boy, is Diana going to be thrilled to see you.'

Then he was gone into the crowd.

Once back in the drawing-room I searched for Walter, but couldn't seem to find him. I was surrounded on all sides by elderly women with elaborate, peroxided hairdos. Their purses fascinated me. Some were hard as shells and shaped like kidneys, others made out of punctured leather which reminded me of birth control pill dispensers. Suddenly I found myself face to nose with Marjorie Winters, whose eyes visibly bulged upon recognizing me. We had met once, when Diana had brought me home for a weekend, but that was before she had told her mother the nature of our relationship. After Diana came out – well, I believe the exact words were, 'I never want that woman in my house again.'

'Ellen,' Marjorie said now, just as I had imagined she might. 'What a surprise.' She smiled, whether with contempt or triumph I couldn't tell.

'Well, you know I wouldn't miss Diana's wedding, Mrs Winters,' I said. 'And this certainly is a lovely hotel.'

She smiled. 'Yes, isn't it? Red, look who's here,' she said, and motioned over her husband, who for no particular reason except that his name was Humphrey was called Red. He was an amiable, absent-minded man, and he stared at me in earnest, trying to figure out who I was.

'You remember Diana's friend Ellen, from college, don't you?'

'Oh yes,' he said. 'Of course.' Clearly he knew nothing. I believe his wife liked to keep him in a perpetual dark like that, so that he wouldn't be distracted from earning money.

'Ellen's a social worker,' Marjorie said, 'at the State Hospital at Milpitas. So Diana and I thought it would be a good idea to seat her next to the schizophrenic girl, don't you think?'

I winced in punishment.

'Oh yes,' Red said. 'Definitely. I imagine they'll have a lot of things to talk about.'

A little tinkling bell rang, and Marjorie said, 'Oh goodness, that's my cue. Be a dear, and do take care of Natalie,' squeezing my hand. Then she was gone. She had won, and she was glorying in her victory. And not for the first time that day, I wondered: why is it that the people who always win always win?

The guests were beginning to move outdoors, to the garden, where the ceremony was taking place. Lost in the crowd, I spied and manoeuvred my way next to Walter. 'How's it going, little one?' he said.

'I feel like a piece of shit,' I said. I wasn't in the mood to make small talk.

'Well,' he said, 'that's what weddings are for.' We headed through a pair of French doors, then, into a small, beautiful garden, full of blooming roses and wreaths and huge baskets of wisteria and lilies. Handsome, uniformed men – mostly brothers of the groom, I presumed – were helping everyone to their seats. Thinking we were a couple, one of them escorted Walter and me to one of the back rows, along with several other young couples who had brought their babies, and might have to run out to change a diaper or something in the middle of the ceremony.

As soon as everyone was seated the string quartet in the corner began to play something sweet and Chopin-like, and then the procession started – first Diana's sister, who was matron of honour; then the bridesmaids, each arm-in-arm with an usher, each dressed in a different pastel dress which was co-ordinated perfectly with her bouquet; and then, finally, Diana herself, looking resplendent in her white dress. Everyone gave out little oohs and aahs as she entered, locked tight between her parents. It had been two years since we'd seen each other and, looking at her, I thought I'd cry, I felt like such a piece of nothing, such a worthless piece of garbage without her – she was really that beautiful. Her hair was growing back, which was the worst thing. She had it braided and piled on her head and woven with wild flowers. Her skin was flawless, smooth – skin I'd touched hundreds, thousands of times – and there was an astonishing brightness about her eyes, as if she could see right through everything to its very heart. From the altar, the groom looked on, grinning like an idiot, a proud professor who seemed to be saying, with his teary grin, see, look what I've got, look what chose me. And Diana too, approaching him at the altar, was all bright smiles, all eagerness, no doubt, no regret or hesitation registering in her face, and I wondered what she was thinking now: if she was thinking about her other life, her long committed days and nights as a lesbian.

The music stopped. They stood, backs to us, the audience, before the reverent reverend. He began to lecture them solemnly. And then I saw it. It would be like the final episode of *Dynasty.* I saw myself stand up, run to the front of the garden while noises of confusion rose up from the guests, and, before anyone could say anything, do anything, pull out the gun and consummate, right there, all over the grass, my own splendid marriage to vengeance.

But of course I didn't do anything like that. Instead I just sat there with Walter and listened as Diana, love of my life, my lover, my life, repeated the marriage vows, her voice a little trembly, as if to suggest she was just barely holding in her tears. They said their 'I do's. They exchanged rings. They kissed, and everyone cheered.

At my table in the dining-room were seated Walter, the Winters' maid, Juanita, her son, the schizophrenic girl and the schizophrenic girl's mother. It was in the darkest, most invisible corner of the room, and I could see it was no accident that Marjorie Winters had gathered us all here – all the misfits and minorities, the kooks and oddities of the wedding. For a minute, sitting down and gazing out at the other tables, which were full of beautiful women and men in tuxedos, I was so mad at Diana I wanted to run back to the present table and reclaim my Cuisinart, which I really couldn't afford to be giving her anyway, and which she certainly didn't deserve. But then I realized that people would probably think I was a thief and call the hotel detective or the police, and I decided not to.

The food, Leonore would have been pleased to know, appeared mediocre. Next to me, the schizophrenic girl stabbed with her knife at a pathetic-looking little bowl of melon balls and greenish strawberries, while her mother looked out exhaustedly, impatiently, at the expanse of the hotel dining-room. Seeing that the schizophrenic girl had started, Juanita's son, who must have been seven feet tall, began eating as well, but she slapped his hand. Not wanting to embarrass him by staring, I looked at the schizophrenic girl. I knew she was the schizophrenic girl by her glasses – big, ugly red ones from the Seventies, the kind where the temples start at the bottom of the frames – and her bowl-shaped hair cut. Also, I recognized the way she slumped over her fruit salad, as if she was afraid someone might steal it.

'Hello,' I said to her.

She didn't say anything. Her mother, dragged back into focus, looked down at her and said, 'Oh now, Natalie.'

'Hello,' Natalie said.

The mother smiled. 'Are you with the bride or the groom?' she asked.

'The bride.'

'Relation?'

'Friend from college.'

'How nice,' the mother said. 'We're with the groom. Old neighbours. Natalie and Charlie were born the same day in the same hospital, isn't that right, Nat?'

'Yes,' Natalie said.

'She's very shy,' the mother said to me, and winked.

Across the table Walter was asking Juanita's son if he played basketball. Shyly, in a Jamaican accent, he admitted that he did. His face was as arch and stern as that of his mother, a fat brown woman with the eyes of a prison guard. She smelled very clean, almost antiseptic. I remembered that Diana had once told me how Juanita was her mother's greatest confidante, her best friend, and lying in bed that night, in giggles, we had speculated on whether they might not be lovers – both secretly aroused, I suppose now, by the thought of Diana's mother sleeping with Juanita, aroused by that earthy ammonia smell, the thought of all that moist dark skin. But it was too late for such games. Across the room, the bride was having her chair pulled out for her by the groom.

'Natalie, are you in school?' I asked.

She continued to stab at her fruit, not really eating it as much as trying to decimate the pieces of melon.

'Tell the lady, Natalie,' said her mother.

'Yes.'

'Natalie's in a very special school,' the mother said.

'I'm a social worker,' I said. 'I understand about Natalie.'

'Oh really, you are?' the mother said, and relief flushed her face. 'I'm so glad. It's so painful, having to explain – you know – '

Across the table Walter was trying to get Juanita to reveal the secret location of the honeymoon. 'I'm not saying,' Juanita said. 'Not one word.'

'Come on,' said Walter. 'I won't tell a soul, I swear.'

'I'm on TV,' Natalie said.

'Oh now,' said her mother.

'I am. I'm on *The Facts of Life*. I'm Tootie.'

'Now, Natalie, you know you're not.'

'And I'm also on *All My Children* during the day. It's a tough life, but I manage.'

'Natalie, you know you're not to tell these stories.'

'Did someone mention *All My Children*?' asked Juanita's son. Walter too looked interested.

'My lips are forever sealed,' Juanita said to no one in particular. 'There's no chance no way no one's going to get me to say one word.'

Diana and Ellen. Ellen and Diana. When we were together, everything about us seethed. We lived from seizure to seizure. Our fights were glorious, manic, our need to fight like an allergy, something which reddens and irritates the edges of everything and demands release. Once Diana broke the air-conditioner and I wouldn't forgive her. 'Leave me alone,' I screamed.

'No,' she said. 'I want to talk about it. Now.'

'Well, I don't.'

'Why are you punishing me?' Diana said. 'It's not my fault.'

'I'm not punishing you.'

'You are. You're shutting me up when I have something I want to say.'

'Damn it, won't you just leave me alone? Can't you leave anything alone?'

'Let me say what I have to say, damn it!'

'What?'

'I didn't break it on purpose! I broke it by accident!'

'Damn it, Diana, leave me the fuck alone! Why don't you just go away?'

'You are so hard!' Diana said, tears in her eyes, and slammed out the door into the bedroom.

After we fought, consumed, crazed, we made love like animals, then crawled about the house for days, cats in a cage, lost in a torpor of lazy carnality. It helped that the air-conditioner was broken. It kept us slick. There was always, between us, heat and itch.

Once, in those most desperate, most remorse-filled days after Diana left, before I moved down the peninsula to my escape-hatch dream house, I made a list which was titled 'Reasons I love her'.

1) Her hair.
2) Her eyes.
3) Her skin. (Actually, most of her body except maybe her elbows.)
4) The way she talks for the plants when she waters them, saying things like, 'Boy was I thirsty, thanks for the drink.' (This one was a lie. That habit actually infuriated me.)
5) Her advantages: smart and nice.
6) Her devotion to me, to us as a couple.
7) How much she loved me.
8) Her love for me.
9) How she loves me.

There was less to that list than met the eye. When Diana left me – and it must be stated, here and now, she did so cruelly, callously and suddenly – she said that the one thing she wanted me to know was that she still considered herself a lesbian. It was only me she was leaving. 'Don't think I'm just another straight girl who used you,' she insisted, as she gathered all her things into monogrammed suitcases. 'I just don't feel we're right for each other. You're a social worker. I'm not good enough for you. Our lives, our ideas about the world – they're just never going to mesh.'

Outside, I knew, her mother's station wagon waited in ambush. Still I pleaded. 'Diana,' I said, 'you got me into this thing. You lured me in, pulled me in against my will. You can't leave just like that.'

But she was already at the door. 'I want you to know,' she said, 'because of you, I'll be able to say, loud and clear, for the rest of my life, I am a lesbian,' and kissed me on the cheek.

In tears I stared at her, astonished that this late in the game she still thought my misery at her departure might be quelled by abstract gestures to sisterhood. Also that she could think me that stupid. I saw through her quaking, frightened face, her little-boy locks.

'You're a liar,' I said, and, grateful for the anger, she crumpled up her face, screamed, 'Damn you, Ellen,' and ran out the door.

As I said, our fights were glorious.

All she left behind were her braids.

Across the dining-room, Diana stood with her new husband, holding a big knife over the wedding cake. Everyone was cheering. The knife sank into the soft white flesh of the cake, came out again thick with silken frosting and crumbs. Diana cut two pieces. Like snakes, their arms intertwined, she and Charlie fed each other.

Then they danced. A high-hipped young woman in sequins got up on the bandstand and sang, 'Graduation's almost here my love, teach me tonight.'

After the bride and groom had been given their five minutes of single glory on the dance floor, and the parents and grandparents had joined them, I felt a tap on my shoulder. 'Care to tango avec moi, my dear?' Walter said.

'Walter,' I said, 'I'd be delighted.'

We got up from the table and moved out on to the floor. I was extremely nervous, sweating through my dress. I hadn't actually spoken to Diana yet, doubted she'd even seen me. Now, not three feet away, she stood, dancing and laughing, Mrs Mark Charles Cadwallader.

I kept my eyes on Walter's lapel. The song continued, ended. The couples broke up. And then, there she was, approaching me, all smiles, all bright eyes. 'Ellen,' she said, embracing me, and her mother shot us a wrathful glance. 'Ellen. Let me look at you.'

She looked at me. I looked at her. Close-up, she looked slightly unravelled, her make-up smeared, her eyes red and a little tense. 'Come with me to the ladies' room,' she said. 'My contacts are killing me.'

She took my hand and swept me out of the ballroom into the main hotel lobby. Everyone in the lobby stared at us frankly, presuming, I suppose, that she was a runaway bride, and I her maid. But we were only running away to the ladies' room.

'These contacts!' she said once we got there, and opening one eye wide peeled off a small sheath of plastic. 'I'm glad you came,' she said, placing the lens on the end of her tongue and licking it. 'I was worried that you wouldn't. I've felt so bad about you, Ellen, worried about you so much, since – well, since things ended between us. I was hoping this wedding could be a reconciliation for us. That now we could start again. As friends.'

She turned away from the lamplit mirror and flashed me a big smile. I just looked up at her.

'Yes,' I said. 'I'd like that.'

Diana removed the other lens and licked it. It seemed to me a highly unorthodox method of cleaning. Then, nervously, she replaced the lens and looked at herself in the mirror. She had let down her guard. Her face looked haggard, and red blusher was streaming off her cheeks.

'I didn't invite Leonore for a reason,' she said. 'I knew she'd do something to embarrass me, come all dyked out or something. I'm not trying to deny my past, you know. Charlie knows everything. Have you met him?'

'Yes,' I said.

'And isn't he a wonderful guy?'

'Yes.'

'I have nothing against Leonore. I just believe in subtlety these days. You, I knew I could count on you for some subtlety, some class. Leonore definitely lacks class.'

It astonished me, all that wasn't being said. I wanted to mention it all – her promise on the doorstep, the gun, the schizophrenic girl. But there was so much. Too much. Nowhere to begin.

Finished with her ablutions, we sat down in parallel toilets. 'It is nearly impossible to pee in this damned dress,' she said to me through the divider. 'I can't wait to get out of it.'

'I can imagine,' I said.

Then there was a loud spilling noise, and Diana gave out a little sigh of relief. 'I've got a terrible bladder infection,' she said. 'Remember in college how it was such a big status symbol to have a bladder infection because it meant you were having sex? Girls used to come into the dining-hall clutching big jars of cranberry juice and moaning, and the rest of us would look at them a little jealously.' She faltered. 'Or some of us did,' she added. 'I guess not you, huh, Ellen?'

'No, I was a lesbian,' I said, 'and still am, and will be until the day I die.' I don't know why I said that, but it shut her up.

For about thirty seconds there was not a sound from the other side of the divider, and then I heard Diana sniffling. I didn't know what to say.

'Christ,' Diana said, after a few seconds, and blew her nose. 'Christ. Why'd I get married?'

I hesitated. 'I'm not sure I'm the person to ask,' I said. 'Did your mother have anything to do with it?'

'Oh, Ellen,' Diana said, 'please!' I heard her spinning the toilet paper roll. 'Look,' she said, 'you probably resent me incredibly. You probably think I'm a sell-out and a fool and that I was a royal bitch to you. You probably think when Charlie does it to me I lie there and pretend I'm feeling something when I'm not. Well, it's not true. Not in the least.' She paused. 'I was just not prepared to go through my life as a social freak, Ellen,' she said. 'I want a normal life, just like everybody. I want to go to parties and not have to die inside trying to explain who it is I'm with. Charlie's very good for me in that way, he's very understanding and generous.' She blew her nose again. 'I'm not denying you were part of my life, that our relationship was a big thing for me,' she said. 'I'm just saying it's finished. That part's finished.'

Defiantly she flushed.

We stood up, pulled up our underpants and stepped out of the toilet booths to face each other. I looked Diana right in the eye, and I noticed her weaken. I saw it. I could have kissed her or something, I knew, and made her even more miserable. But I didn't really see the point.

Afterwards, we walked together out of the ladies' room, back into the ballroom, where we were accosted by huge crowds of elderly women with purses which looked to me like the shellacked sushi in certain Japanese restaurant windows.

'Was it okay?' Walter asked me, taking my arm and leading me back to our table for cake.

'Yes,' I said. 'Okay.' But he could see from my face how utterly miserable I was.

'Don't even try,' Juanita said, giggling hysterically to herself as we got back to the table. 'You're not getting a word out of me, so don't even begin to ask me questions.'

Once I knew a schizophrenic girl. Her name was Holly Reardon and she was my best friend from age five to eight. We played house a lot, and sometimes we played spaceship, crawling together into a cubby-hole behind my parents' sofa bed, then turning off the lights and pretending the living-room was some fantastic planet. We did well with our limited resources. But then money started disappearing, and my mother sat me down one day and asked me if I had noticed the money always disappeared when Holly came to visit. I shook my head vigorously no, refusing to believe her. And then one day my favourite stuffed animal, a dog called Rufus, disappeared, and I didn't tell my mother, and didn't tell my mother, until one day she said to me, 'Ellen, what happened to Rufus?' and I started to cry. We never found Rufus. Holly had done something with him. And it wasn't because of me that she went away, my parents assured me, it wasn't because of me that her parents closed up the house and had to move into an apartment. Holly was not well. Years later, when I went to work at the State Hospital, I think somewhere, secretly, I hoped Holly might be there, a patient there, that we might play house and spaceship in the linen closets. But of course she wasn't. Who knows where she is now?

After the wedding I felt so depressed I had ice-cream for dinner. I did several acrostic puzzles. I watched *The Honeymooners* and I watched *Star Trek*. I watched Sally Jesse Raphael. I watched *The Twilight Zone*. Fortunately it was not one of the boring Western ones, but an episode I liked particularly, about a little girl with a doll which says things like, 'My name is Talking Tina and I'm going to kill you.' I wished I'd had a doll like that when I was growing up. Next was *Night Gallery*. I almost never watch *Night Gallery*, but when I do it seems I always see the same episode, the one about two people who meet on a road and are filled with a mysterious sense of *déjà vu*, of having met before. It turns out they live in the mind of a writer who has been re-writing the same scene a thousand times. Near the end they rail at their creator to stop tormenting them by summoning them into existence over and over, to suffer over and over. At the risk of mysticism, it seems to me significant that every time I have tuned into *Night Gallery* in my life it is this episode I have seen.

Then there was nothing more good to watch.

I got up, paced around the house, tried not to think about any of it: Holly Reardon, or Natalie, or Diana, or those poor people living in the mind of a writer and getting re-written over and over again. I tried not to think about all the Chinese dinners I wasn't going to be able to have because I'd spent so much money on that Cuisinart for Diana, who probably could afford to buy herself a hundred Cuisinarts if she wanted. I tried not to think about their honeymoon, about what secret, glorious place they were bound for. It was too late for it still to make me mad that the whole world, fired up to stop me and Diana, was in a conspiracy to protect the privacy of the angelic married couple she had leapt into to save herself, to make sure their perfect honeymoon wasn't invaded by crazy lesbian ex-lovers with shotguns and a whole lot of unfinished business on their minds. Unfortunately, any anger I felt, which might have saved me, was counteracted by how incredibly sorry I felt for Diana, how sad she had seemed, weeping in the ladies' room on her wedding day.

I went to the closet and took out Diana's braids. God knows, I hadn't opened the box for years. But now I took it carefully from the shelf and opened it. There were the braids, only a little faded, a little tangled, and of course no longer smelling of shampoo. I lifted one up. I was surprised at how silky the hair felt, even this old. Carefully, to protect myself, I rubbed just a little of it at first against my face. I shuddered. It could have been her.

I went to the bed, carrying the braids with me. I laid them along my chest. I have never had long hair. Now I tried to imagine what it felt like, tried to imagine I was Diana imagining me, a woman she had loved, a woman she had given her hair, a woman who now lay on a bed somewhere, crying, using all the strength she could muster just not to force the braids down her throat. But I knew Diana was on a plane somewhere in the sky, or in a car, or, more likely than that, lying in a heart-shaped bed while a man hovered over her, his hands running through her new hair, and that probably all she was thinking was how much better off she was than me, how much richer, and how lucky to have escaped before she was sucked so far in that like me it would be too late ever to get out. Was I so pathetic? Possibly. And possibly Diana was going to be happier for the choice she had made. But I think more likely, lying on that mysterious bed, she was contemplating a whole life of mistakes spinning out from one act of compromise, and realizing she preferred a life of easy mistakes to one which was harder but better. Who was I to criticize? Diana had her tricks, and so did Juanita, and so, for that matter, did that schizophrenic girl stabbing at her melon balls. We all had our little tricks.

I took the braids off myself. I stood up. A few hairs broke loose from the gathered ropes, fell lightly to the floor. They didn't even look like anything; they might have been pieces of straw.

Continued On Map No. 13

A Place As Good As Any

JOSEPH BRODSKY

The more one travels, the more complex one's sense of nostalgia becomes. In a dream, depending on one's mania or supper or both, one is either pursued or pursues somebody through a crumpled maze of streets, lanes and alleyways belonging to several places at once; one is in a city that does not exist on the map. A panicky flight originating as a rule in one's home town is likely to land one helpless under the poorly lit archway in the town of one's last year sojourn or the year before. It is so much so that eventually your traveller finds himself unwittingly sizing up every locale he encounters for its potential value as a backdrop for the nightmare.

The best way to keep your subconscious from getting overburdened is to take pictures: your camera is, as it were, your lightning-rod. Developed and printed, unfamiliar façades and perspectives lose their potent three-dimensionality and their air of being an alternative to one's life. Yet one can't click non-stop, one can't constantly put things in focus – what with clutching the luggage, the shopping bags, the spouse's elbow. And with a particular vengeance the unfamiliar three-dimensional invades the senses of unsuspecting innocents at railway stations, airports, bus stations, in a taxi, on a leisurely evening stroll to or from a restaurant.

Of these, railway stations are the most insidious. Edifices of arrival for you and those of departure for the locals, they insinuate travellers, tense with excitement and apprehension, straight into the thick of things, into the heart of an alien existence, pretending to be precisely the opposite by flashing their gigantic CINZANO, MARTINI, COCA-COLA signs – the fiery writing that evokes familiar walls. Ah, those squares before railway stations! With their fountains and statues of the Leader, with their feverish bustle of traffic and cinema billboards, with their whores, hypodermic youths, beggars, winos, migrant workers; with taxi cabs and stocky cab-drivers soliciting in loud snatches of unfathomable tongues! The deep-seated anxiety of every traveller makes him register the location of the taxistand in this square with greater precision than the order of appearance of the great master's works in the local museum – because the latter won't constitute a way of retreat.

The more one travels, the richer one's memory gets with exact locations of taxistands, ticket offices, short-cuts to platforms, phone booths and urinals. If not often revisited, these stations and their immediate vicinities merge and superimpose on each other in one's mind, like everything that's stored for too long, resulting in a gigantic brick-cum-cast-iron, chlorine-smelling octopal ogre, submerged in one's memory, to which every new destination adds a tentacle.

There are apparent exceptions: the great mother, Victoria Station in London; Nerva's masterpiece in Rome or the garish monumental monstrosity in Milan; Amsterdam's Central with one of its fronton's dials showing the direction and speed of the wind; Paris's Gare du Nord or Gare de Lyon with the latter's mind-boggling restaurant, where, consuming superb *canard* under frescoes à la Denis, you watch through the huge glass wall trains departing down below with a faint sense of metabolic connection; the Hauptbanhof near Frankfurt's red-light district; Moscow's Three-Railroad-Stations Square – the ideal place to ladle despair and indirection even for those whose native alphabet is Cyrillic. These exceptions, however, do not so much confirm the rule as form the core or kernel for subsequent accretions. Their Piranesean vaults and staircases echo, perhaps even enlarge, the seat of the subconscious; at any rate, they remain there – in the brain – for good, waiting for addition.

II

And the more legendary your destination, the more readily this gigantic octopus comes to the surface, feeding equally well on airports, bus terminals, harbours. Its real dainty, though, is the place itself. What constitutes the legend – artifice or edifice, a tower or a cathedral, a breath-taking ancient ruin or a unique library – goes first. Our monster salivates over these nuggets, and so do travel agencies' posters, jumbling Westminster Abbey, the Eiffel Tower, St Basil, the Taj Mahal, the Acropolis and some pagodas in an eye-catching, mind-skipping collage. We know these vertical things before we've seen them. What's more, after having seen them, we retain not their three-dimensional image but their printed version.

Strictly speaking, we remember not a place but our postcard of it. Say 'London', and your mind most likely will flash the view of the National Gallery or Tower Bridge with the Union Jack logo discreetly printed in a corner or on the opposite side. Say 'Paris', and . . . There is perhaps nothing wrong with this sort of reduction or swapping, for had a human mind indeed been able to cohere and retain the reality of this world, the life of its owner would become a non-stop nightmare of logic and justice. At least its laws imply as much. Unable or unwilling to be held accountable, man decides to move first and loses either count or track of what he experiences, especially for the umpteenth time. The result is not so much a hodgepodge or a jumble as a composite vision: of a green tree if you are a painter, of a mistress if you are a Don Giovanni, of a victim if you are a tyrant, of a city if you are a traveller.

Whatever one travels for – to modify one's territorial imperative, to get an eyeful of creation, to escape reality (awful tautology though this is), the net result of course is feeding that octopus constantly hungry for new details for its nightly show. The composite city of your subconscious sojourn – nay! return – will therefore permanently sport a golden cupola; several bell towers; an opera house à La Fenice in Venice; a park with gloom-laden chestnuts and poplars, incomprehensible in their post-Romantic swaying grandeur, as in Graz; a wide, melancholy river spanned by a minimum of six well-wrought bridges; a skyscraper or two. After all, a city as such has only so many options. And, as though semi-conscious of that, your memory will throw in a granite embankment with its vast colonnades from Russia's former capital; Parisian pearl-grey façades with the black lace of their balconies' grillwork; a few boulevards petering out into the lilac sunset of one's adolescence; a gothic needle or that of an obelisk shooting its heroin into a cloudy muscle; and, in winter, a well-tanned Roman terracotta; a marble fountain; poorly lit, cave-like café life at street corners.

Your memory will accord this place with a history whose particulars you probably won't recall but whose main fruit will most likely be a democracy. The same source will endow it with a temperate climate adhering to the four-seasons principle and relegating palm trees to railway stations' grillrooms. It will also give your city Rejkavik-on-Sunday-type traffic; people will be few if any; beggars and children, however, will speak the foreign tongue fluently. The currency will carry images of Renaissance scholars, the coins feminine profiles of the Republic, but the numbers will still be recognizable, and your main problem – not of paying, but of tipping – can, in the end, be solved. In other words, regardless of what it says on your ticket, of whether you'll be staying in the Savoy or the Danieli, the moment you open your shutters, you'll see at once Notre-Dame, St James's, San Giorgio and Hagia Sophia.

For the aforesaid submerged monster digests legends as eagerly as reality. Add to that the latter's aspiration for the glory of the former (or the former's claim to enjoying, at least once upon a time, the status of the latter). Small wonder, then, that your city should, as though it's been painted by Claude or Corot, have some water: a harbour, a lake, a lagoon. Smaller wonder still that the medieval ramparts or molars of its Roman wall should look like an intended background for some steel-cum-glass-cum-concrete structures: a university, say, or more likely an insurance company headquarters. These are usually erected on the site of some monastery or ghetto bombed out of existence in the course of the last war. Small wonder, too, that a traveller reveres ancient ruins many times over the modern ones left in the centre of your city by its fathers for didactic purposes: a traveller, by definition, is a product of hierarchic thinking.

In the final analysis, however, there is no hierarchy between the legendary and the real, in the context of your city at least, since the present engenders the past far more energetically than the other way around. Every car passing through an intersection makes its equestrian monument more obsolete, more ancient, telescoping its great local eighteenth-century military or civic genius into some skin-clad William Tell or other. With all four hooves firmly on the plinth (which, in the parlance of sculpture, means that the rider has died not on the battlefield, but in his own presumably four-poster bed), this monument's horse would stand in your city more as an homage to an extinct means of transportation than to anyone's particular valour. The birds' kaka on the bronze tricorn is all the more deserved, for history long since exited your city, yielding the stage to the more elementary forces of geography and commerce.

Therefore, your city will have not only a cross between a bazaar in Istanbul and a Macy's; no, a traveller in this city, should he turn right, is bound to hit the silks, furs, and leather of via Condotti and, if he turns left, to find himself buying either fresh or canned pheasant at Fauchon (and the canned one is preferable).

For buy you must. As the philosopher would have put it, I purchase therefore I am. And who knows that better than a man in passage? In fact, every well-mapped trip is in the end a shopping expedition: indeed, one's whole passage through the world is. In fact, next to taking pictures, shopping comes in second at sparing one's subconscious an alien reality. In fact, that's what we call a bargain, and with a credit card you can go on infinitely. In fact, why don't you simply call your whole city – it surely ought to have a name – American Express? This will make it as legal as being included in the atlas: no one will dare to challenge your description. On the contrary, many would claim they've been there, too, a year or so ago. To prove this, they'll produce a bunch of snapshots, or, if you are staying for a meal, even a slide show. Some of them have known Karl Malden, that city's dapper old mayor, personally for years and years.

III

It is an early evening in the town of your memory; you are sitting in a sidewalk café under drooping chestnuts. A streetlight idly flashes its red-amber-green eye above the empty intersection; higher up, swallows criss-cross a platinum, cloudless sky. The way your coffee or your white wine tastes tells you that you are neither in Italy nor in Germany; the bill tells you that you are not in Switzerland, either. All the same, you are in Common Market territory.

On the left, there is the Concert Hall, and on the right there is the Parliament. Or it is the other way around: with architecture like this, it's hard to tell the difference. Chopin came through this town, so did Liszt, and so did Paganini. As for Wagner, the book says he went through this place three times. So did, it seems, the Pied Piper. Or maybe it's just Sunday, vacation time, midsummer. 'In summer,' the poet said, 'capitals grow empty.' An ideal season for a *coup d'état*, then, for introducing tanks into these narrow cobblestone streets – almost no traffic whatsoever. Of course, if this place is indeed a capital . . .

You have a couple of phone numbers here, but you've tried them already twice. As for the goal of your pilgrimage, the National Museum, justly famous for its Italian Masters, you went there straight from the train, and it closes at five. And anyhow, what's wrong with great art – with Italian Masters in particular – is that it makes you resent reality. If, of course, this is a reality . . .

So you open the local *Time Out* and consider theatre. It's Ibsen and Chekhov all over the place, the usual continental fare. Luckily, you don't know the language. The National Ballet appears to be touring Japan, and you won't sit through *Madam Butterfly* for the sixth time even if the set was designed by Hockney. That leaves movies and pop groups, yet the small print of these pages, not to mention the bands' names, makes you briefly nauseous. On the horizon looms further expansion of your waistline in some Lutèce or Golden Horseshoe. It is actually your widening diameter that narrows your options.

The more one travels, though, the better one knows that curling up in the hotel room with Flaubert won't do either. The sounder solution is a stroll in an amusement park, half an hour in a shooting gallery, or a video game – something that boosts the ego and doesn't require knowledge of the local tongue. Or else take a taxi to the top of the hill that dominates the view and offers a terrific panorama of your composite city and its environs: the Taj Mahal, the Eiffel Tower, Westminster Abbey, St Basil – the whole thing. This is yet another non-verbal experience; a 'wow' will suffice. That's, of course, if there is a hill, or if there is a taxi . . .

Return to your hotel on foot: it's downhill all the way. Admire shrubs and hedges shielding the stylish mansions; admire the rustling acacias and sombre monoliths of the business centre. Linger by well-lit shop windows, especially those selling watches. Such a variety, almost like in Switzerland! It's not that you need a new watch; it's just a nice way of killing time – looking at the watches. Admire toys and admire lingerie: these appeal to the family man in you. Admire the clean-swept pavement and perfect infinity of avenues: you always had a soft spot for geometry, which, as you know, means 'no people'.

So if you find somebody in the hotel bar, it's most likely a man like yourself, a fellow traveller. 'Hey,' he'll say, turning his face towards you. 'Why is this place so empty? Neutron bomb or something?'

'Sunday,' you'll reply. 'It's just Sunday, midsummer, vacation time. Everyone's gone to the beaches.' Yet you know you'll be lying. Because it is neither Sunday nor the Pied Piper, nor neutron bomb nor beaches that makes your composite city empty. It is empty because it is easier for an imagination to conjure architecture than human beings.

Truth, Beauty and Goodness: A Report

MARY FLANAGAN

Early in the autumn of 1962 Frances Marion Hodgkins's name was changed to Cal. This pleased her because she never had liked Frances and because Cal was a shortened form of Calypso, implying an allure she had not thought she possessed.

A group of her fellow students often gathered in the lounge of Marigold Quadrangle to play Botticelli or Exquisite Corpse, and when the weather was good they went outside for Capture the Flag. They also invented a diversion of their own which they called Casting the Classics. Zelda Turpin became Dido, Mark Lasky Aeneas. Ralphie Sabovic, clever, dissolute and cynical, found no contenders for Ulysses, and Nancy Phoner, the best-natured girl in the Sophomore Class, was Penelope. No one had suggested a role for Frances until Harlan Getz proposed her for Calypso. Assent was unanimous, and so as Cal she went on, much improved.

Harlan previously had discussed her suitability for the character with his roommate Jay. They agreed about her. They sensed the secret glamour behind her small-town exterior. The corduroy shirtwaists and round-collared blouses hid something dark and flexuous, an unconscious greed that wanted to hold on to everyone, binding and clinging without being aware of what it did. They had glimpsed the seductress. She just needed someone to tell her who she was.

Cal admired Harlan, and she loved Jay. But she hardly dared speak to them because they lived in an apartment off campus. Here they entertained friends who wrote poetry and involved themselves in radical politics. They contributed to the university paper and the *Bruckner Review*, went on peace marches to Washington, and were members of SANE and SNCC. Professors of English, Psychology and Economics were regular dinner guests. Cal felt intimidated.

'She just wants to watch people and play,' Ralphie Sabovic told Jay.

'Uh-huh, Ralphie. She's a woman of mystery.' Jay nodded towards Cal across his living-room which was crowded with students, all very drunk. It was the first time Cal had come to one of his parties. Later that night the police answered a neighbour's complaint and dispersed the company. Jay hid Cal in his room where they talked until morning and fell asleep on the only bed in the apartment with sheets.

Cal spent more time in the house on Flood Street. She came to know all Jay's friends, but was herself known for nothing in particular apart from her consistent appearance on the Dean's List and a prettiness which she now exposed with black jeans and sweaters. She liked the anarchy of the cold dirty apartment and returned with reluctance to the pink cinder-block walls of her dormitory and to her melancholic room-mate Stephanie, regularly asleep under the soft plastic helmet of her hair-dryer. When Stephanie was thus occupied, it was impossible to talk to her about Jay. So Cal lay on her bed in Fenwick Hall in Marigold Quad, in the middle of Bruckner University – small, academically exclusive, and politically febrile, crowning the highest hill in the Boston area and overlooking the dismal town of Waterville – and thought about her lover.

Jay and Harlan shared their chaotic apartment with Joel Cheevers. The three of them were ardent friends, and Cal loved to sit on their collapsing sofa, holding herself in her own arms, while the others listened to Shostakovich and Charlie Mingus and argued about Behaviourism and Zen and Marcuse. She understood little of all this. She listened and hardly spoke. They were better-read, worldly-wise, city-raised, and she wanted to learn. An intense curiosity about everything in life kept her quiet until invited or compelled to talk about herself. She was amazed they wanted her there, aside from the fact that she was Jay's lover.

Early in the autumn of 1962 the four of them were nineteen and had known each other throughout their Freshman year. Harlan and Joel were without girlfriends, and so attached themselves to the couple.

Joel adopted a light, lofty view and enjoyed relating literature to life. It was he who first compared himself and his two friends to the Platonic virtues. Harlan was Truth, Joel himself Beauty, and Jay was Goodness. The personification was lightly made, as if Casting the Classics. But to Cal it was serious and real, and she saw her friends as the tangible manifestations of ideal qualities. Truth, Beauty and Goodness: from then on she called them by those names.

Beauty and Cal had won scholarships. Truth's father, a police inspector, managed, just, to pay outright for his son's education. But Goodness's family was well off. Only he had a car, and so he drove the others, and numerous friends besides, to Cambridge and the movies and 'Hayes Bickford's'. He lent money to Truth and Beauty and paid the rent when they fell behind, ignoring his parents' complaints of extravagance. Cal had given her virginity to Goodness. He wrote her poems, dutifully used prophylactics and read sex manuals to increase her pleasure. He felt bound to her. He changed the sheets once a week and kept the heater in his room on High. Cal loved him, but not because of his kindness to her. Not at all. He was an image she had picked out right away, watching him from a distance, imagining him her own, drawing him nearer by her passivity, feeling him yield and watch her, then finally touching him, sure of his attraction to something in her she could not name.

He was big and fair and ruddy and well made. She liked his little nose and blue eyes, his dry-cleaned Levi's and open tweed sports coat and bare feet in penny loafers; the kind of obvious things, she later realized, that appealed to inexperienced girls from small towns. He was not exciting, but she wanted him because he seemed the kind of boy she ought to want – she could not say why, except that no one who had known her before she became Cal would have expected her to get a boy as good as him.

TRUTH, BEAUTY AND GOODNESS: A REPORT

Truth, Beauty and Goodness were all in love with Cal, and their love made her glamorous. More and more they let themselves be held by her secret greed which they had discovered and defined. They continued to discuss at length their favourite topics: literature, politics, the Bomb. They gave parties which were terminated by the arrival of the police. They talked about their futures, and about what they might do with their lives, as an alternative to remaining exactly where they were – in a cold bare apartment on Flood Street, lying on naked mattresses, smoking grass, bathed in the presence of Cal. She never questioned why they loved her. Her expectations had been low. She was surprised, pleased. She let them continue.

When they asked her if she loved them too she sometimes said yes, sometimes no; sometimes she just got in a bad mood. She stayed with Goodness and let herself be seen as his, but in the autumn of her Sophomore year she was restless, wanting to tell others about herself. She had poured as much of herself as she could into Goodness, but he proved an inadequate vessel. He could not contain all she told him, and it spilled over and flooded around their feet. She needed new listeners.

Goodness was not anxious about the feelings of the other two. It seemed natural to him that everyone should love Cal (except Ralphie Sabovic who maintained that she was nothing special). She possessed an unconscious grace, she was innocently provocative, she had the right to be selfish. But he did like being alone with her in his own room, with clean sheets and his grandmother's dresser and the heater turned up, either in bed or trying to study.

Goodness studied hard. He had entered university with commendable grades and was devoted to learning, holding it high against the backdrop of his father's supermarket chain. He and Beauty and Cal were enrolled in English 221a. They read Wyatt and Sidney and Spenser aloud to each other and gossiped about the professor. The men complained that he showed favouritism to Cal, who always managed better grades than they. Cal conceded that their work was more original.

Truth and Beauty seldom studied or attended classes. They ignored their reading lists and immersed themselves in current fiction, politics, critical theory and drugs. All their term papers were late. Goodness rose at seven to make an eight o'clock Physics class, devoured his reading lists, received B's and C's for his pains. Cal lived in procrastination, preferring Flood Street to the library where a stack of books was on hold for her. She began her term papers the day before they were due and handed them in untyped. During finals and mid-terms she would go forty-eight hours without sleep, living on black coffee and No-Doze, cramming her brain with the facts, quotes and ideas she should have been absorbing over the previous weeks. She would retain everything just long enough to pour it, during the course of three hours, into the pale blue ruled notebooks provided for the purpose. Then she would collapse, fall ill, get straight A's. The professor of English 221a stopped her outside the classroom and kissed her hand, congratulating her as she blinked at him. Beauty teased her without malice. Truth accused her of telling the authorities what they wanted to hear. But Goodness was wounded. There were tears in his eyes as he protested over what he had begun to regard as the pervasive and adamant injustice of this world. Beauty laughed at his indignation.

Cal needed new listeners. Goodness was neither suspicious nor jealous. When his grandmother suffered a stroke he drove alone to Albany, sacrificing Ralphie Sabovic's party and leaving Beauty to accompany Cal. In the crush, they stayed close to each other all evening, finding at last some space on a sofa where they selfishly kept a bottle of wine to themselves. Beside them Ophelia and Agamemnon were necking casually. Cal felt relaxed and accepted and very close to Beauty. She looked into his face. When he ascribed Beauty to himself, he had not been referring to his looks. (Goodness was much more vain. It was one of his few little failings.) He had meant rather that beauty was his first love; that he valued art more highly than being virtuous or objective; that he worshipped Apollo and the Muses. Still, he was the most charming of the three, with his fresh smooth skin, his cherub curls, his round grey eyes and lips so ready to smile and his light short body which he carried with ease. She held up his hand, hardly bigger than hers, and pressed her own against it, fingers splayed.

'We're so alike,' said Cal.

He quoted her something from a Donne sonnet as she passed him the bottle. He returned it and recited some e. e. cummings. They slid downwards until they nestled against Agamemnon's back, then did as their illustrious companions. Truth watched them through the open doorway, but they didn't notice him. They were perfectly happy and saw nothing but each other as the room went round and round.

At three a.m. they woke up in the municipal playground. They thought they had gone home. There was no more wine. They supported each other unsteadily past the swings and seesaws, found the gate, and turned into Flood Street, talking about their childhoods as the moon cast shadows through the maple leaves. It shone purple-white into the window of Beauty's room, lighting the walls which bore reproductions of Goya's *Maja* and Vermeer's *Head of a Girl*. The books lined up along the wainscoting were mainly poetry. Cal saw the titles on the spines appear and vanish as she and Beauty changed positions on the mattress. She wasn't thinking of Goodness at all when Beauty smiled at her and said, 'Guess what, I'm a virgin.'

She thought, I hope this isn't the beginning of a trend.

She sensed that he intended to make sex with her into an exercise in romanticism; now she would be the Experienced Woman. She put her barely experienced arms around him and stroked his curls and let him imagine whatever he pleased.

In the morning he threw open the window and leaned out and called, 'Hello Waterville, you ugly city!'

Cal giggled, then she moaned and turned to the wall. Truth did not come back for two days, and they regretted his absence because all of Saturday they were very sick.

Goodness returned on Sunday night with two dozen of his grandmother's frozen blueberry blintzes. The three of them sat at the kitchen table under a bare light bulb and devoured them in contentment. There was no hot water for baths.

Cal met Beauty whenever she could – at the furthest end of the cafeteria, with cups of black coffee and packets of Oreos, until they were joined by Truth or Goodness at whom they would smile in perfect innocence; between classes, leaning against a high stone wall, dangling their green book bags; in the woods behind the chapels on a golden floor of leaves; or, when it was cold, in a borrowed room in one of the boys' dorms.

They knew they were special, as though a god or goddess had declared them sacred offspring. They repeated to each other how alike they were because their hands were the same size and they loved the same poets and believed that art was all and nothing was higher than art. They could afford to be careless.

Beauty was very prolific. He kept journals, wrote one-act plays and essays on aesthetics – in short he did everything but hand in his term papers and pass his exams. His parents lamented; Dean Bags admonished him. He also wrote letters, mainly to Cal. He took great pains and derived great pleasure in describing her to herself: her shiny brown hair and hazel eyes that sometimes went yellow like a wicked little she-goat's; her long white legs and the place where they joined. He was reading Byron and Henry Miller and both crept occasionally into his one-sided correspondence. He left the letters at her dormitory or recklessly slipped them into her biology textbook. She read them once through and put them away in her brown accordion file. On nights when she stayed in her own room, she would take them out and look at them while Stephanie snored under the hair-dryer.

At Flood Street Beauty and Cal behaved as if nothing had happened – until Truth forced Beauty to tell Goodness the truth. Candour appealed to Beauty almost more than deception had. When Goodness begged her to discuss the matter with him, Cal lay on the bed and refused to speak. She lay there for two days until Goodness returned to normal. She wasn't being cruel, and he understood this; she simply didn't know what to say. Her responsibility was diminished; she was blameless. And he could not hate Beauty for following his nature.

Cal loved being with Truth. She would sit beside him as he argued about politics, besting the other students with his conviction and his integrity, making them appear pale dilettantes. One of them reasoned that nuclear arms prevent war through fear of war and implied that fear was a necessary and natural balancing factor in all of life.

'Fear!' he replied. 'Fear is shit.'

He introduced her to Jung and Lorca and Hannah Arendt and was never contemptuous of her *naïveté*. He did try to force her to examine her preconceptions. He was the only one of the three occasionally to criticize her. She clung to him because she knew he had the best mind, and she reserved for him that part of her which wanted to think better of herself and to go forward. He seemed to represent some future attainment which involved great difficulties but was still comfortably far off and vague. He helped her to hold on to that vision of attainment. Therefore she wanted to protect him, even though she was unable to protect anyone. She did not want to sleep with him. He was the one she never slept with.

Truth was dark, lean, angular. He had a kind of rolling walk which was pleasant to observe, but he took no trouble with his appearance. His eyes were too large, his cheeks sallow, his neck scrawny, and his hair like a black Brillo pad. There seemed not to be enough of his face. He didn't care about food and never minded what he ate. He was all veins and tendons. Like Beauty and Goodness, he made no secret of his love for Cal.

One night in that autumn of their Sophomore year, Cal discovered how much she had hurt him. Late in the evening she tried the door to his room, but it would not open. He had locked himself in with a packet of razor blades and a bottle of Nembutal and was threatening to commit suicide because she would not be his lover. Goodness, Beauty and others present attempted to reason with him, alternately pressing their faces to the door and drinking Thunderbird. Cal sat in Goodness's grandmother's armchair, her knees pulled up to her chest, her arms wrapped around her knees, saying nothing, but sipping the Thunderbird when it was passed to her. She stared at the wall, not knowing how she ought to feel; feeling one thing and then another.

At five in the morning Goodness shouted that he intended to break into the room, and Truth finally opened the door. Then Cal unwound herself and went to Goodness's bed where she lay down with Fast Eddie the cat and pulled the covers over them both.

Goodness came and stood beside her. From her horizontal point of view his developing paunch appeared more exaggerated. His kind eyes seemed smaller.

'I'm not enough for you, Cal. Whoever thought you'd turn out a *femme fatale*?' He sighed. 'I guess I did.'

Cal looked up at him. 'I wish you wouldn't say things like that.'

Goodness was gaining weight, growing a beard. He was very comfortable to sleep with. Cal stayed with him, and let it be known she was still his, though she could not resist flirting and did so more and more, listening to other boys with complete attention until she erupted in a compulsive need to expose to them her innermost self.

The morning after Truth's attempted suicide she rose at seven and began her biology paper which had been due the previous day. At four the paper was finished, and she showed it to Truth. It was a report on a book called *Sick Minds, New Medicines*.

'It's about the use of drugs in psychoanalysis,' she told him.

He smiled at her. 'I like the title.'

The paper got an A minus. She had done it again with her blind intelligence. They pretended to be bitter and complained about the male professors. But they knew she never went to bed with any of them. She was interested in her peers because only they could reflect her back at herself.

The four of them lived in physical lassitude (athletics were not compulsory at Bruckner) and in emotional and mental agitation. Whatever happened to one affected the other three, and everything that happened was special. The world was packed with phenomena, symbolic yet personal, riddled with secret messages to be deciphered by them alone. And these messages arrived direct from the Power, whatever it was, that took a constant and avid interest in them. They held intense communication with the gods, whom they were sure were meddling in their lives. It was an absurd attitude, but they were not yet adults. Adults do not make unqualified identifications with cats or political causes. They do not feel branded by the books they read or translate life through them or embrace them like lovers. Adults see the world neither as code nor as secret garden.

In October 1962 Truth, Beauty, Goodness and Cal were still taking life in this unadult way. Their reaction to the Blockade of Cuba was therefore not surprising. They were convinced of the malicious intent of all parties. Like the other students at Bruckner, they had been tuned for three days to their radio. No one at the school attended classes, many of which had already been cancelled by professors anxious to keep close to their televisions. Everyone listened to the president's announcement that as of the 24th Cuba was to be quarantined. They saw for themselves the photographs of the missile bases and learned that Soviet ships were crossing the Atlantic with their provocative cargoes. Inside the claustral atmosphere of the university the crisis was inflated beyond its already perilous limits. A confrontation was inevitable and the result would be Armageddon. They had talked of it for years; it was what they expected.

Even Cal was worried, though she did feel as if she were watching herself in a film – a film about the end of the world. It was running an awfully long time. When would it be over? She remained at Flood Street where Truth was attempting to rouse the others from their lethargy.

'It isn't a question of politics any more,' he argued. 'It's survival I'm talking about. You live like creeps in your Bruckner dream. And in this dream all that's required is that you talk and read and talk and talk and talk. You spend your time elaborating your positions and your blame and joining organizations whose purpose is to do exactly the same thing. And so you think you're on the right side and that you've risked a little danger. Well, the dream is a trap and Bruckner is a trap and you'll just sit there talking as you die. Do you want us to be like them?' He gestured towards the hill. 'Well I don't. I want us to live.'

Beauty frowned. 'You're saying we should split?'

'Split! We should run like hell's behind us. Which it is. Jay has a car.'

Goodness sighed. He knew Truth was right. The entire Eastern seaboard was doomed, and eighty million people were living the last days of their lives.

'Where can we go?' he asked. 'Where's the safest place?'

Truth did not hesitate. 'Mexico,' he said.

They left that afternoon, stopping at the campus for Cal to pack a bag. Their friends were impressed by their valour. A few were envious of their escape. But no one else wanted to leave. No one had any plans. Ralphie Sabovic told Truth that he was crazy. Either there *was* no escape or nothing would happen. They'd come back and feel like assholes.

Truth, Beauty, Goodness and Cal were not worried about coming back. As they drove along the Mass. Pike, Cal beside Goodness in the front seat, they watched the landscape, the towns, the woods in autumn colours for what they were certain would be the final time. They were sad but not afraid. An unknown future with nothing to cling to but each other was a great romantic adventure.

The radio issued half-hourly bulletins on the progress of the Soviet ships. They would listen in silence then resume their speculations about Mexico. They might be forced to start life anew, as in the beginning. Now Cal would *have* to sleep with them all.

Beauty began to sing. The others joined in, Cal barely moving her lips. She was thinking how New England sunsets were best between now and Christmas. The wet light both heightened and softened the mad colours of the trees. Wooster and Springfield looked grimly poetic with the sun, like a descending firebomb, at their backs.

How lonely America was. It would be even lonelier soon. She had not called her parents. Perhaps she would never see them again. They were not taking the crisis as seriously as she, and would be worried by the idea of a trip to Mexico. They would not understand how she was perfectly safe and protected for ever by her three best friends. She might call them from a phone booth, only she didn't have any money. She tried to imagine what life in Mexico might be like and looked forward to the beaches and the swimming and to climbing ruined pyramids in the one pair of shorts she had brought. She planned her French paper which was due on Monday. The preliminary notes for it were secreted in her suitcase, as well as the book which was to be its subject – *Adolphe*. She watched the sunset like someone hypnotized, and thought about Mexico and the end of the world and her French paper. In her mind everything coexisted peacefully, without contradiction. She was ideally suited to be educated.

New York looked like a city on the edge of the universe, glowing with greasy light. From it you jumped off into nothing. Truth said it represented what Madame Blavatsky had called a Ring-Pass-Not. The half-hourly news broadcasts were having a peculiar effect on him – on all of them. There they were walking down Mulberry Street towards Hong Fats and no one hungry. Cal watched the people and played with her noodles, paid for by Goodness, and listened to him and Beauty talk while Truth made telephone calls. None of what they said made any sense.

Truth had not been able to reach his friends. He suggested leaving immediately for Washington, he could get Goodness some amphetamine. Instead they drove uptown to the Bronx and paid a surprise visit to Nancy Phoner's parents. Benjamin Phoner was a kind man, in appearance not unlike Truth. He was much admired among Nancy's friends because he had been blacklisted during the McCarthy purges. He had lost his professorship at NYU and now worked in his brother-in-law's furniture store. They'd had no money and no one dared do anything for them. He had been heroic. Cal was especially fond of him. When Truth explained how they were on their way to Mexico to escape nuclear holocaust Mr Phoner looked at him in disbelief.

'Go home,' he said impatiently. 'Finish the education your parents worked hard to pay for.'

They argued for two hours. Mr Phoner was convinced that the CIA had manipulated the military into its present situation, that Kennedy simply wanted to force Khrushchev to back down, that the Russians were in no position to attack.

When Mrs Phoner offered to make Cal a bed on the couch and Cal accepted and went off to brush her teeth, Truth put on his thin jacket and made for the door. Beauty followed him. Mr Phoner said at least they should wait twenty-four hours, at least they should think of Cal and protect her if they loved her as much as they claimed to. He said the very fact that they had come to see him meant they didn't want to make the journey. They were just seeking an authority figure to confirm what they already knew and to let them off the hook of their cracked commitment. Truth and Beauty said again that they were leaving. They looked wounded and worn out. Goodness said he must stay with Cal, he was sorry, why didn't they all meet here tomorrow.

'Goodnight, Mr Phoney,' snarled Truth on the way to the elevator.

At ten the next morning Beauty returned to the Phoners'. Truth was not with him. Goodness and Cal were in the kitchen with Mrs Phoner eating toasted bagels and reading the newspapers. They looked relaxed and happy.

'We're driving back to Bruckner,' they said. 'Are you coming? Whatever you do we love you and we understand. Mr Phoner lent us twenty dollars.'

The half-hourly radio reports confirmed that U Thant had flown to Cuba. As they drove past Springfield, not singing, they heard how Castro was refusing to allow international inspection of the missile dismantling. Even so, the tension had eased. By 3 November Kennedy had announced that the Cuban bases were being dismantled and Cal had received an A on her French paper. Goodness grumbled and Beauty was amused, but neither was behaving like himself, Cal could tell. She too felt distant, almost disembodied; relieved and yet let down.

They were worried about Truth. His absence was palpable, a collective ache. He telephoned every night from New York. During the calls Cal would sit in the big armchair, twisting her hair into a knot and letting it fall, listening to Beauty and Goodness trying to persuade him to return. The missile crisis was over. Why stay in Manhattan, smoking dope and sleeping somewhere different every night? Truth insisted that he would go on to Mexico. The crisis had been a sign, warning them and everyone like them that they must break out of the Bruckner dream. Sometimes he cried. He said he refused to concede that it was no longer possible to live heroically. He refused to allow the others to concede it. They said they could not understand why he thought they were conceding anything.

The next time he rang, Goodness snatched up the phone.

'We're coming to get you,' he said. 'We're leaving right away. Give me your address and just stay there and wait for us.' It was eleven-thirty p.m.

Leaving the apartment unlocked, they headed once more for the Mass. Pike. They drove as fast as possible, listening to all-night music stations and laughing and singing.

'My head is spinning,' said Beauty.

'Mine too,' said Cal.

The outskirts of the city had a sobering effect. They took a wrong turn off the Bronx expressway, drove around for an hour and made another wrong turn into a deserted industrial estate. They sat and looked at it, suddenly exhausted. The place seemed to emanate an almost radioactive glow.

'God, this is sinister,' whispered Cal. 'Where are we?' She had never imagined that being awake in a car at three in the morning could produce such feelings of desolation. By four they had found the apartment that belonged to Truth's friend who lived in a building on the Lower East Side. Second Street was funnelling a freezing wind into the broad barren channel of Houston Street, and inside the apartment the light was as cold and dead as the radiators. Truth sat on a cushion in a corner holding a grey cat.

'This is No-Name,' he said. 'He's a bum and a Buddha and he's coming back to live with us.'

Truth looked paler than ever. They hugged and kissed him but he did not rise, and they remained on their knees beside him, tenderly testing No-Name's ears and tail. Then Cal drew him to his feet and made him go with her to the car. He lay on the back seat, his Brillo-pad head in her lap, and clutched the cat who seemed secure in his future.

Goodness nibbled a No-Doze as the sun made its appearance in a smutty Hartford sky. Beauty sang along with the Vivaldi 'Gloria'. Their spirits were high because they sensed that something great had been accomplished. They were regarding this fourth and final journey as a triumph.

There was snow during the second week of November, then a warm spell. Stephanie complained of being lonely because Cal was always at Flood Street. She said Cal had drifted away and that she had become weird. Cal didn't realize how much Stephanie was hurt. She was held too tight in her quaternity. She lived with three men in a secret garden from which everyone else was excluded. They could not and would not be separated. Their friends turned and stared after them as they walked past. What had happened to them during that trip to New York?

They too began to wonder. They did no work and hardly ate and did not want to see anyone. They did not go to the movies or to SANE meetings. The other students, Bruckner, the whole world seemed a mirage. Truth said that a potent energy had been invoked and that they were all in its grip. They were exalted, they were displaced, and Cal was the most displaced of all.

'What's happening,' said Truth, 'is that we're having a collective hallucination.'

'We're under a spell,' Beauty replied.

'We ought to tell someone,' said Goodness.

Cal was frightened. So much had gone on without her noticing. What was it that had captured her mind? She felt as though a spirit were watching, as though it had come too close to bear, too close for their own good. She could feel the eyes and breath of the spirit. They *were* under a spell.

On 20 November the Blockade was officially lifted, but they paid no attention and felt no relief. They went to the office of Dr Wolff, professor of Psychology and expert in Eastern religion and philosophy. They told him how, since the journey to New York, an occult power had broken down the normal barriers between their minds and was causing them to see reality in the same twisted way. They told him that they were passionately in love with Cal and could not give her up, and that she might be crazy and they did not know what to do about it. They described to him how at first their unification had been beautiful, but that now it was terrible, that they wanted both to be set free and to remain in their present exalted state. What did he think was the matter with them?

Dr Wolff was interested. He took them seriously. He invited them all to tea, then told several of his colleagues that he had never met with anything quite like this four-way romance.

'Possession,' diagnosed Dr Wolff who knew a good deal about daemons in the brain. 'Her.' He put down his teacup and indicated the only one of the four who did not talk incessantly. Goodness spoke up like a man.

'I'm responsible for Cal,' he said.

'No,' Beauty interrupted. 'We all are because we're all in love with her.'

Dr Wolff made a sympathetic noise in his throat. He smiled at Cal who smiled back. He could see the daemon right there in her eyes. He was a big man with a sharp wit who commanded respect.

'Come and see me again on Wednesday. And don't smoke any grass and don't talk about this to anyone else.'

'We can't talk to anyone else.'

'We can only talk to you.'

'Come on Wednesday.'

Was the quartet becoming a quintet? Was Dr Wolff saving them from this dangerous romance or was he falling victim to its charms? They began to feel as though it was impossible to be separated from Dr Wolff.

They went for walks. They ate lunch in the cafeteria under envious eyes, aware of their uniqueness. Then one day Dr Wolff told Cal to come alone. The others waited for her at the entrance to the library, but she did not meet them. The afternoon light withdrew to concentrate itself in the setting sun, and still she did not arrive. No one had seen her. They were worried, and went to Dr Wolff's office which was closed until the Monday after Thanksgiving. Later she called at Flood Street to say she would spend the night in the dorm preparing for an exam.

Over Thanksgiving Goodness telephoned Cal in Rhode Island. She said she missed them all and hated Thanksgiving, that her mother was very irritating and that she was bored. He told her so many times that he loved her that he put her in a bad mood. Two weeks later at Flood Street she informed them in an offhand way that she had been going to the Psychological Counselling Centre. On Dr Wolff's advice.

'They'll give you pills and fry your brain,' said Truth. 'They'll tell you not to smoke grass and to quit SANE.'

'Please don't,' Beauty entreated. 'It'll destroy all your creativity.'

'It's interesting,' Cal replied.

Goodness asked her what had happened during her latest visit to Dr Lynch.

'He asked me how I felt, so I showed him a poem by Wallace Stevens which he said he couldn't understand.'

'And is this supposed to untangle you?'

'We talked after.'

'But you're so beautiful as you are.'

Cal shrugged. She was drifting away from him and from Truth and Beauty. They sensed the way she had come down out of their collective hallucination, which they remembered now with sadness. They likened themselves to a civilization that had reached its peak and must commence its inevitable decline. When they asked Cal about Psych. Counselling she would answer only that it was interesting. She could not say how it offered her a whole new way of talking about herself and describing herself. After all, she was only a small-town girl, bound to be entranced by the new and different reflection in the glass that was now held up to her.

'Cal,' Goodness approached her as she was lying on his bed studying for her mid-terms, 'I don't think I'm enough for you.'

His voice bore the trace of a whine, or so it seemed to her.

'Please don't say things like that,' she answered.

Truth was still the only one to be critical. His interpretation was that Cal wanted to see herself while simultaneously being distracted from herself. 'She wants to see herself better lit.'

One night, as she sat holding Beauty's hand, Truth looked at her fiercely and said, 'You've been going to bed with Ralphie Sabovic.'

Cal stared straight back at him and laid her head on Beauty's shoulder. Truth walked out and Beauty continued to read to her from an open letter of protest he had written to Dean Bags.

Beauty and Truth discussed the way in which they had been revelling in their hopeless love for Cal. Perhaps it was the idea of her that they loved. Her drifting away had blurred and weakened the focus of their feelings. Ideas and actions they had held in abeyance for months came to fill the place she left. They had been frustrated for a long time by Bruckner. Suddenly they were eager to seize their real destinies, free of the restrictions of academia.

During the Biology mid-term, which was compulsory for all Sophomores, they sat together in the deserted cafeteria drinking black coffee and reading *Evergreen Review* and borrowing cigarettes from the staff. At lunch they talked briefly with those who had survived the morning, then went upstairs to the lounge and spent the afternoon listening to Sam Daley improvise an ersatz Bach fugue. They leaned back lazily. They decided to leave school and go to New York.

Cal and Goodness joined them in the lounge. They had just finished the Renaissance Lit. exam and looked as though they had spent two weeks on a liferaft. Beauty and Truth explained their decision as Cal sat gazing at Sam, perfectly quiet and holding tight to Goodness's hand. She admired Sam as she had once admired Goodness – from afar, simply waiting to be noticed and seized. She had this feeling that Sam could tell her about herself. In her mind everything coexisted peacefully, without contradiction.

She went less often to Flood Street where there were no more parties. Goodness's new room-mate, Dexter Wapshot, was not a substitute for Beauty and Truth. Those two called or wrote to her from New York where they lived any old way, without money, just reading and going to films and staying up all night and getting crazier, she could tell. She missed them, and what they had done impressed her. They were the first of her classmates to take a year off. Eight months later students left in legions for the Lower East Side and the West Village. Cal adored New York; she imagined it as she read Beauty's letters.

'I am under severest pressure from my parents and Dean Bags to get myself shrunk. Bags says, "It will go well with you before the administrative board if you take corrective therapy." '

Don't, she thought. You don't really want to be re-admitted.

Goodness was by nature domestic, and he tidied the apartment and made it quite comfortable with more of his grandmother's furniture. He fussed in the kitchen, cooking elaborate meals for Dexter and Cal who sometimes failed to turn up. Then he and Dexter would eat alone under the kitchen light which now had a shade. He knew Cal was unfaithful to him but he did not dare to think how often. Once in February he met her going up the hill to the library. He had not seen her for six days and asked her point-blank about the other men in her life.

'I love the way everyone is so different,' she told him.

He could see her assessing him, thinking how fat he was getting. His back had thickened like the stalk of an old vegetable, and he hid his second chin under a beard. Deep in his florid face his eyes were still kind. He put his hand gently on her arm.

'You just want to get away from me, don't you?'

'No,' she lied.

Truth wrote her long letters which she guessed he had composed after hours of smoking grass because they were very abstruse and mystical. Cal gave up trying to decipher them and wrote back simply, 'This is what I think: the universe is order and it's chaos. Orderchaos. That's all.' What did he think he was doing? But she added the postscript, 'I miss you.'

Beauty wrote, 'With the passing months there is no longer any reality about you . . . I don't wish to be a Byron, wandering around the world never able to love because I once idealized someone. You cannot idealize something that is there, and so I am begging you to release me by sleeping with me. You have nothing to lose, never having loved me. I certainly cannot come out any worse.'

Cal felt embarrassed. Then she cried.

'What a stupid letter,' she said aloud through her tears.

Two years later Cal received a Bachelor of Arts with Honours. Goodness was not awarded Honours, but was admitted to a graduate school where he obtained a Ph.D. in English. He kept his beard, gained more weight, married and taught Comparative Literature at a college in Tennessee. Truth wandered the world. When he returned to America he drove a truck and rose high in the ranks of his labour union. Beauty developed an incurable illness and died in his twenty-fifth year.

Triptych

ALAN JENKINS

So this was the Isle of Pines – halfway
through Co. Kerry . . . The Isle of Pines!
It flares up in the mind
like a matchflame, and is gone.

We chafe each other for the hot, wet spark
and, now, land-masses melting, glaciers melting –
watched by satellite, miles above our heads . . .
Then wake up dead in our beds.

An archaeologist or hunter-gatherer, the first
to emerge from primeval forest,
is led by what's left of his nose
to a strangely glittering black barrow:

sheets of polythene are held in place by row
on row of tyres. Unnatural quiet. Unnatural dark.
Inside, a litter of bones, bottles, tins; a few
cyanide capsules in a box marked SHELTER.

*

A thousand million tiny fish
in a flap, helpless on the sheet –
which one will dare
the path between the barbed-wire fence

and the wall of heat?
(On one side, women stare
at blank eyes. Blank eyes stare back.
A Sad Sack

guard
will whip out his own Cruise
and demonstrate its use.
It is already hard.

Night and day,
a welter of woodsmoke, mud; the tents
of sticks and stones and black plastic rubbish-
bags; the darkening silos.)

*

I cycled five miles through potato-fields and forest,
past the Deer Haven, Canine Country Club
and Lobster Claw. – The hub
of the bicycle I'd borrowed

clicked and sang; she was behind, on an older model,
struggling a little. Halfway between the home of Robert Frost
and that of Robert Penn Warren, I walked in through maple
and spruce pine, and, with her beside me, rowed

my son across the moonlit lake. Hers,
by the wide brown eyes. The jagged silhouettes of firs,
the denser mass of mountain peaks. He bent close to tell me
that every river in Vermont was dry – the dripping oar,

his small voice the only sounds; we could see two hayricks
burning, cars in lay-bys burning. I struck out for the shore.
While she and I lay down among the melting rocks
he would water his one tree.

Chez Milou

AHDAF SOUEIF

Milou sits behind the cash desk. There is a grey checked rug on her knees and on the rug sits Athène. Athène is a comfortable dachshund the colour of expensive leather. She is sleek and plump but there is no doubt that she is growing old: you can see it in her eyes. Occasionally she ventures on to the floor and pauses briefly amidst the feet of the waiters. But then Milou gets anxious and leans over to look and call for her and Athène hurries back. She has to be helped on to her mistress's knee by one of the waiters – usually old Mahrous, the Nubian. All day long Milou cuddles Athène. Milou's manicured fingers have thickened but she still wears her grandmother's heavy Russian rings. Her hands are mottled with liver-spots and they are hesitant on the cash-register. They lie heavily on Athène's back, absently stroking her smooth length, fondling the drooping ears or scratching the worried brow as the old dog whimpers quietly.

Milou might have married Philippe, but that was long ago. Now, all day Milou watches the frayed red velvet curtains screening the entrance to the restaurant. She knows all her customers, though she never smiles and only nods sternly to the oldest and the most regular. The young tourists who stray in and park their backpacks by the door puzzle over this large, grim woman with the rinsed red hair, who never leaves her seat. Yet despite the slight frown that Milou's features settle into when her thoughts wander, her customers find her a benign presence – and they come back.

To her left and slightly to the rear so that she cannot see him unless she turns round, old Monsieur Vasilakis sits in a corner of the restaurant. He sits at a round table with a small black and white television flickering soundlessly on a cutlery cabinet in front of him and a carafe of red wine always at his elbow. Monsieur Vasilakis is nearing ninety and almost all the friends who used to occupy the other chair at his table, share his wine and stare companionably at his flickering TV, have passed away. Milou usually knows exactly what he is doing even though her gaze is fixed firmly in front of her. Today, he too is aware of his daughter's corner: the cash desk has been extended by a table covered by a white linen cloth and a chair has been placed beside Milou's. Milou observes the red curtains with particular purpose; she is expecting a friend. Well, Farah was too young to be quite a friend; it was her mother really who had been Milou's friend and, since their friendship had dated from Latifa's wedding night, Milou had known Farah since she was born. Latifa's wedding night. Milou did not actually shudder or indeed feel anything much at all. But she remembered. She remembered the shame and the misery which for years that phrase had evoked in her;

the shiver moving up her back into her shoulders and arms until her fingers tingled with it, the cold emptiness in her stomach that she had had to rub and press into something she could bear. Latifa's wedding night: when she had fled down the dark servants' staircase and into Morsi Hamed's apartment to find his daughter, the bride, in the bathroom pulling off her veil and demolishing the elaborate chignon her hair had with such trouble been pinned into. 'I hate this,' Latifa had stormed, 'and so does he. We'll wear the stupid clothes and sit on the platform to be stared at like monkeys but I don't feel like *me* with this *thing* on my head and I'm not having it – ' Then she turned and saw Milou properly. She drew her in and bolted the door. She sat her down on the edge of the bathtub and made her drink some water and Milou told her everything. How strange that then it had seemed that she must die; that tomorrow could not happen. And now it was as though the whole thing were a film she had seen. A film that had moved her for a while.

Milou had first seen Philippe amid the ululations and the clash of cymbals at a friend's wedding in the Greek Orthodox Cathedral on Shari El Malika Street. Milou was twenty then. She was tall and well built and handsome. Her father, Khawaga Vasilakis, sitting over his wine after their last customer had gone – watching her as she strode through the darkened restaurant folding up the white linen tablecloths to take home for Faheema to wash – her father would often tell her then that she had her mother's shapely legs and her exuberant auburn hair. He always made this observation sadly. Then he would shake his head and bite the ends of his drooping grey moustache as he stared into his glass. Milou knew that her mother was French, had been a dancer, had been beautiful – maybe still was. She had abandoned her husband and the one-year-old Milou for – of all things – a Turkish soldier: a black-eyed, whiskered brigand who had swaggered off his ship and into the Allied Restaurant in Alexandria one fine day in '27 purposely to wreck Theo Vasilakis's life. After three years of alternately swearing to smash the whore's face if she dared show it in the Allied and of vowing that everything would be forgiven if only she would come back, for, after all, she was the mother of his child, Theo could bear Alexandria no longer. He sold the restaurant and took Milou and Faheema, the black maid who looked after them, to Cairo. He never saw his wife again and he withstood all friendly pressure to remarry. He opened Chez Milou (instantly 'Shameelu' to the locals) on the Rue Abd-el-Khaleq Sarwat and looked forward to the day when his daughter would be both an adornment and a partner in the restaurant. Now that Milou was both, her father watched her constantly and lived in terror of the swashbuckler who would come to lure her away and ruin her father's patched-up life for the second and final time. For a swashbuckler it would have to be. You only had to look at the girl – the long, strong legs, the lean waist, the straight back, the broad forehead, wideset eyes and brilliant hair – to see the swarthy, muscled, sweating, tobacco-spitting son-of-a-bitch who would claim her. Khawaga Vasilakis's paunch trembled with apprehension and distaste and he chewed on his moustache.

But Milou saw Philippe amid the incense and the burning candles in the Greek

Orthodox Cathedral and thought he looked like an angel: the boy – he could hardly be called a man – was so fair and so still. He sat at the far end of the pew on the other side of the aisle; the bridegroom's side. He was so separate that he appeared to belong more to the shining byzantine icons on the walls than to the mass of breathing, moving people around him. Milou could see only his head in a three-quarter profile. His face was pale and fine-featured, gleaming straight black hair rising smoothly from a white brow. His nose was chiselled. His mouth wide, his lips narrow and ascetic. She could not make out the colour of his unmoving eyes. But it was a quality of serenity, a combination of his utter stillness and the way his head shone like an illumination in the dim cathedral that so captured Milou.

Having no mother to do this work for her, Milou managed to find out who he was and – despite her dismay at confirming that he was indeed only seventeen and still at school with the Jesuit Frères – she contrived an introduction. Milou found that Philippe stood a few centimetres taller than herself. She found that his eyes were green-grey and that his voice was mellow. His French was chic, more chic than her own, and his Arabic more broken. She found that even close up his skin kept its luminous quality. She imagined that there was something extraordinary – extra-mortal almost – about him, and longed to reach out and touch his face just on that fragile, contoured cheekbone and rest her fingertips in the shallow dips at the outer corners of his black-fringed eyes. She found out that he was the son of Yanni Panayotis, the grocer, and therefore that he was a neighbour of one of her father's oldest friends: Morsi Hamed, who owned a furniture shop in the market off Ataba Square.

Philippe bowed his head slightly, as though the better to hear anything she might say. He smiled and his eyes said that something amazing had happened. Milou surprised herself; she had never before felt this rushing frailty, this tremulous energy, and it never occurred to her that he had not felt it too.

The year was 1946 and the victorious Allied soldiers were everywhere in the city. Khawaga Vasilakis thought his daughter showed remarkable acumen when she announced that, since their business was doing so well, it was foolish to go on buying provisions piecemeal from the neighbouring shops; from now on, she declared, she would buy what they needed once a week, wholesale, from the market.

Yanni Panayotis's grocery store was on the very outer fringe of the market – almost, in fact, in Shari el-Khaleeg – that wide road which until so recently would turn into a river in the season of the flood. Milou had never been that far from the Rue Sarwat before and the first time she went, Faheema, who knew all the roads and alleys of the city, went with her. They walked down King Fouad Street and stared in the windows of the *grands magazins*, then across Opera Square, through the very tip of the notorious Azbakiyya district, across the busy swirl of Ataba Square and into the teeming, narrow Mouski. Faheema started to point out grocers in the alleys along the way but Milou would have none of them. It had to be Yanni Panayotis's store they went to and his was the furthest one of all. Faheema, who was neither young nor green, and whose breath was getting shorter as she hurried to keep up with her striding charge, began to grow suspicious. What would a grocery store have that would make a normally reasonable girl march ardently to the end of the world for it like this? There was only one answer possible. Faheema pursed her lips, collected her *melaya* round her and puffed after Milou.

Yanni Panayotis was a big man with a great deal of shaggy black hair streaked with silver. He made up for his broadening forehead by growing a wild beard and moustache. He liked the looks of both women and sat them down in his dark, cool shop and offered them tea and chocolates. From then on, Milou always went to Shari el-Khaleeg on Sunday. She went one week and then the next and the third time *he* was there. He was helping his father stack a delivery of large tins of white cheese and Milou sipped at her scalding tea and watched his broad back move under the fine white cotton shirt as he bent and straightened and lifted and reached. She glanced at the grey linen trousers shaping themselves around him as he squatted down in front of the cheese, but then she bit her lip and kept her eyes on the sawdust-strewn floor. When he had finished, Philippe took out a pressed white handkerchief from his pocket and wiped his brow. He was formal as he declined his father's offer of a cold drink: 'I will leave you to conduct your business.' He bowed over Milou's hand: '*Enchanté*, Mam'selle, a most happy opportunity.' He smiled into her eyes, and left. Yanni turned to Milou, shrugging and spreading his hands wide, and saw at once her passion for his son in the girl's high colour and rigid posture. Ah. So that's it, he thought. It is for this that it is Sunday, always Sunday; the little Philippe has lit a fire –

'And what a fire that will be,' he commented to his wife that night. 'The girl is beautiful and her hair is in flames already.' Nina turned down the corners of her mouth and pouted at the husband who, after two married daughters and a son who might, if he wished, grow whiskers and a beard, could still sweet-talk her back into bed with him on a Monday morning when the shop was closed and the boy had gone to school and Nina was in her flowered silk dressing-gown, belted to show off her still-tiny waist. She would glance up at the mahogany display cabinet hanging in the corner above their bed with her bridal veil and its crown of orange-blossom inside it and remonstrate that it was unseemly to behave like a honeymoon couple and draw the blinds in the morning after twenty-five years of marriage and what would the neighbours think? Khawaga Yanni grunted affectionately as he nuzzled his moustache into his wife's neck: 'They will say, "The old fool is still crazy for her" – and they have a right, no? Is that not so, little one? Ah, my little one – ' and Nina would hold him gently and let him love her and think what a wonderful stew she would make for his lunch. Now she pouted and stared down at the *petit point* in her hand: the girl is too old; she is four years older than Philippe. Yanni should not be easy-going on such matters. A man can tire easily of a wife older than himself. Of course, on the other hand, she has no mother or brothers to make trouble and, when Monsieur Vasilakis – God grant him long life – goes, she will be the sole owner of a restaurant in a very good part of town.

The discussions continued and Milou's visits to the shop continued. Philippe left the Frères and joined the Faculty of Commerce and still every Sunday morning Milou would walk across town to the grocery store on Shari el-Khaleeg, take tea with Khawaga Panayotis, and hire a *calèche* to carry her and her provisions back to the Rue Sarwat. Sometimes she began to despair, to lose heart – but then she would see him. And each time she was freshly convinced that he had 'intentions', that their glance had met for a fraction longer, that his smile had asked a question – a question she longed to answer. Until Latifa's wedding night.

Days before, cross-legged, on the floor at Milou's feet with her mouth full of pins and her hands full of shiny, emerald green taffeta, Faheema urged her to make a move: 'You either get him out of your head or you sort him out. A woman has to manage, you know. Three years have passed and it's "I'm sure I felt him press my hand", "Today he actually touched it with his lips". What's this no-good talk? Is this child's play, or what? Maybe he's still young and doesn't understand how things work. Some of your men are like that, you Greeks. Except – look at his father: there's a man for you, a man who fills his clothes. But you're not going to spend your whole life waiting. He doesn't speak? You've got a tongue. Make a little skirmish. See what clay he's made of – '

To get to the roof terrace where the wedding party was being held, guests had to go through Morsi Hamed's flat, out of its back door and up the wrought-iron, unlit servants' staircase. The stairs had been freshly washed for the occasion and gleamed black in the darkness. The garbage pails that normally stood on the landings had been kept indoors and the cats – who lived off the garbage – stayed away. The large terrace was hung with coloured lights and a marquee at one end provided a multicoloured backdrop for the bridal dais. The drums beat out and the accordions wailed for all the neighbourhood to hear and the hired, white-robed *sofragis* circled with silver trays of iced sherbet and chocolates and almond-filled sweets. Milou excused herself from the bride's younger sister, Soraya, and slipped away. Later, she tried to determine what had made her choose that particular moment – but she never could. She just remembered how she had leaned over and whispered a few words to Soraya, then, exchanging a look with Faheema, sitting with the other women-servants on the carpet at the foot of the bridal bower, she had picked the skirt of her gown off the floor and headed for the stairs.

Milou turned a corner of the staircase and saw a man climbing up out of the dark towards her. She stood still as Philippe, unaware, continued up the stairs. Then, he must have heard a rustle, or perhaps he felt her breath, for he stopped. He looked up – and there it came again: the smile that barely touched his lips but came through his eyes.

'*Bonsoir.*'

At no other point in her life did Milou look as radiant as she did then: gathering her softly rustling dress, bare arms white against the green tulle of the bodice, her '*Bonsoir*' was the merest whisper. Philippe stood to one side to let her pass, for of course he knew that it would be most improper to linger on the stairs, and Milou lifted her skirt and came slowly down. The music pulsed down the stairwell. Milou drew level with Philippe. She turned as though to pass him sideways because of the narrowness of the stairs – and then she stopped. She was so close that she felt her breasts brush against him and her skirt fall around his legs. Milou lifted her face and his eyes looked into hers. She whispered his name and her hand let go of the crushed taffeta and rose to rest lightly against his cheek. Now, now he must surely – but Philippe, too well bred to step back, simply stood unmoving and Milou's hand drew away, went to her own face, her throat, then clutched at the skirt again as she whirled away, stumbled down the stairs and into the bathroom where Latifa was tugging the grips out of her hair.

Milou frowned at the red curtain which was opening to admit a pretty young woman in a short-sleeved red cotton dress with matching open shoes and sunglasses pushed to the top of her head and holding back her dark shoulder-length hair. 'Chèrie!' said Milou and held up her hands. Athène woke up and growled deep in her throat.

'Tante Milou!' Farah said, bending to hug Milou's shoulders and kiss her on both cheeks. Farah sat on the chair next to Milou, asked a passing waiter for some iced water, fanned herself with a magazine, tickled Athène's ears and began the ritual complaint about the parking and the heat: 'I've parked at the Opera and walked all the way up. But it's absolutely the only place and I'm going to see Tante Soraya later so I guess it makes sense.'

'She's still in your grandfather's old flat – God have mercy on his soul?'

'Oh yes. She's still in Ataba. That's one thing that doesn't change, thank goodness. It's all exactly the same as when my grandfather was alive. Even his bed is still there. Oh – ' remembering, 'should I go and say hello to Monsieur Vasilakis? Or will I disturb him?'

'Don't bother,' said Milou. 'He won't know you anyway. He's become even more vague since Faheema died. He was used to her.'

'God grant him long life.'

'Ah, well. He's certainly granting him that,' agreed Milou.

'But . . . things must be difficult for you, Tante Milou?' Farah said uncertainly. Milou was silent, considering her fingers on Athène's back. She was not smiling. Farah stood up.

'I'm going to go and greet him.'

Milou did not look round as her guest bent over the old man and said his name gently. Watery, red-rimmed eyes shifted from the still-life of flowers on the television and looked up.

'I'm Farah, M'sieur. Do you remember me?'

Theo Vasilakis nodded several times and returned to the screen. Farah laid a tentative hand on his shoulder.

'They haven't changed this picture for three days,' he complained. 'Between every two programmes this is what we get. They do have other tableaux: some with trees and some with birds; swans, you know,' his hand moved in the air, waveringly expansive, 'but they've been using *this* for three days. People can get bored like this. Eh. Well . . . ' He watched the flowers resignedly. Mahrous the Nubian paused.

'It's all right, Set Farah,' he said gently. 'The Khawaga is fine. You go and sit with Set Milou. See what you would like for lunch. The fatta is very good today – '

'I'm going to eat fatta, 'Am Mahrous?'

'Yes. Why not? Don't talk to me about a regime; you're thin as a stick. You could do with some flesh on you. Go and sit with Madame and I'll get you a good lunch. Leave it to me.'

'What about the Khawaga?'

'He knows you're here. If they don't change this picture soon he'll come and sit with you. Go, go, don't worry.'

Farah went back to her chair. Athène was asleep again, or at least her eyes were closed. Milou looked up and smiled.

'So. Tell me, Chèrie, how is Maman?'

'She's all right,' Farah shrugged. 'I guess she's happy where she is; away from us all.'

'*C'est dommage ça*; her staying away like this. And it can't make things easier for you? Especially now?'

'No. Sometimes I'd like to talk to her. And it's harder living with my father when she's not there. Although I suppose in a way it isn't really since they were getting on so badly – I don't know. Tante Soraya helps a lot, though – with the practical things; like looking after Teddy for me. And I go stay with her sometimes when it gets too claustrophobic with Daddy. I feel much more comfortable at my grandfather's – at her place, really. You know, having grown up there and all that. But I can't actually talk to her – '

'She dotes on you. You've always been her child – '

'But she's so bitter now. And sort of – hard. She's always irritated with Uncle – her husband. And she's completely disappointed in her son and tells him so – all the time. She keeps pressuring me to go back to "Teddy's father" and when I say we were unhappy together she looks at me like I'm mad and says, "So what? Who's happy in this world?" '

'Your mother seems happy – '

'Yes, but *she*'s doing it all the wrong way round; discovering freedom and the pleasures of living alone now, after a million years of marriage. Still, she has a right. She says she reads in bed till she falls asleep and she sleeps with the window open and she doesn't bother to cook but eats readymade salads and fruit – ' Farah giggled.

'And Papa? He is not unhappy?'

'Oh no. He's not bothered. I mean – I suppose he'd have preferred it if she'd stayed around and gone on being exactly as he wanted her to be. But since she started, you know, speaking up for herself, I guess he thinks he's better off on his own. You can't really tell with him, though – '

'Aren't you going to have any lunch or what?' Farah got to her feet. Monsieur Vasilakis was standing next to her. 'Well? Aren't you going to offer your friend something to eat?' The question was querulous.

Farah glanced at Milou and answered quickly. ' 'Am Mahrous is bringing me some lunch in a minute. Won't you join us, M'sieur?'

'Mahrous, Mahrous, he's no use any more, the old idiot. He's gone senile.' Vasilakis was glancing around him as he muttered.

Farah picked up a chair from the nearest table. 'There you are, Monsieur Vasilakis. Please sit with us.'

Now she was between the old man and his daughter.

'Where is the food for your guest?'

Farah glanced at Milou's set face and unease built up inside her; an old familiar unease. For years she had heard her grandfather use this tone to the daughter who had elected to stay and look after him. For years she had watched Tante Soraya's face set in just such a closed look as this one. Mahrous appeared with a tray.

'That's the spirit, Khawaga!' he beamed. 'You join the ladies and give the telly a rest. There's nothing on it but empty talk anyway, *and* it's all repeated.' He set the dishes down in front of Farah. 'I'll go get the Khawaga's wine. Have a glass of wine, Set Milou, with the Khawaga,' he urged.

Milou shook her head. The carafe and one half-full glass were placed on the table. 'Eat in good health and happiness,' Mahrous smiled at Farah. 'You bring good company to us and light to our restaurant.'

'And what about you?' Milou stroked Athène and continued as though there had been no interruption. 'What about you, *ma petite*? Are you better off on your own too?'

'Oh, Tante Milou,' sighed Farah, poking at the stuffed courgettes. 'It is so difficult being a divorced woman here. I didn't think it would be like this.'

'It's just because you haven't got your own flat.' Milou lifted a hand from Athène and reached over to pat Farah. 'When you have your own flat it will all be different.'

'But I'm *never* going to have my own flat.' Farah put down her fork.

'You've already bought a flat – '

'Yes, but the man hasn't even started building yet. It's all on paper. If he starts *tomorrow* it won't take less than five years and I'm practically thirty already. I really never thought it would all be so difficult.'

'Everything is difficult now. Everything.'

Monsieur Vasilakis nodded. He put down his glass and leaned forward, a hand on each knee. 'Everything's changed. Life has become difficult. Very difficult.' He shook his head. 'In the old times, it took fourteen different types of fish to make a bouillabaisse. I used to pick each fish personally. Nowadays what can you find? Three, four types maybe. Impossible to make a *vraie* bouillabaisse. Your father, he understood these things; he would tell me from the night before: Khawaga Theo, tomorrow we eat bouillabaisse – '

'Papa, do you know who this is?'

'Eh? Of course I know who this is. Morsi Hamed's daughter – '

'Morsi Hamed's daughter's daughter, Papa.' Milou's voice was flat.

'I know, I know.' The old man was impatient. 'You've always been friends together, you two. Even though she married and you didn't.' He turned to Farah. 'Your daughter must be *une belle demoiselle* by now, eh?'

'Farah has a little boy, Papa. His name is Teddy. He's almost three?' turning to Farah.

'Almost. And he's utterly gorgeous. I would have brought him with me but he's spending the day with his cousins. He's my whole life now, Tante Milou. I don't know what I'd have done if he wasn't with me. I can't imagine how some people go through life without ever – oh. Tante Milou. I'm sorry – '

'It's all right, Chèrie.' Milou patted Athène and scratched the dog's throat. 'Don't worry. That's all very, very past now. But what about men, then?'

'Men? What men?' Monsieur Vasilakis had turned to see what was happening on television, but now he turned back, suspicious. 'You're married, child. My daughter herself went to your wedding – '

Farah touched Milou's arm gently. 'I am divorced, Monsieur. My husband and I have left each other.'

'Divorced, divorced, that is all one hears nowadays. Nobody has patience any more.' Monsieur Vasilakis sorrowed. 'It wasn't so in our day. You waited. Maybe one partner makes a mistake. The other one waits. If one pulls a bit, the other lets go a bit. That way the world can go on. Life wants patience. Eh . . . so you're divorced? A waste of the money your father spent on your wedding. He had a big wedding for you, I know. Milou was there. A man who knew how to do things, your father, a proper man.'

When her father had been silent for a few moments, sucking on the ends of his moustache and shaking his head sadly, Milou repeated quietly, 'So, my dear. What about a man?'

Monsieur Vasilakis came to again. 'Stay away from men.' He looked earnestly at Farah. 'Sons of bitches all of them. He has form and looks impressive and inside he's wormeaten. Leave them alone. Especially now. There *used* to be men. Why the King himself used to dine here. And Eden. He ate at that table over there – with Montgomery. Anthony Eden, you know?' He nodded at Farah and she nodded back. Then he turned slowly in his chair to look at the television.

'I'm not interested, Tante Milou. No, truly. The few – two men in fact – that I sort of could like are already married, firmly married. I've had one proposal and you should have heard it: "As for the fact of your being a divorcee, I am prepared to overlook it", and he was supposed to be "progressive". No. And besides, I don't want any conflicts around Teddy. There was – ' Farah paused. 'I did think of an "arrangement" – '

'An "arrangement"?'

'A marriage of convenience, I suppose it's called. I'm fed up with all the emotional stuff and I know I'm not going to be in love again; I don't want to be. But I do need a set-up – I need somewhere to live – '

'What are you talking about? This is a theory? Or there is a real person somewhere you are thinking of?'

'Oh I'm not really thinking about it any more. But yes. There is someone. But it's really too ridiculous.'

'Is it someone from the club? An old friend from school? What is ridiculous?'

'Oh no, no, nothing like that. It's a neighbour – of Tante Soraya's. You might even know him – '

Milou stared at Farah.

'Do you know him, Tante Milou? Monsieur Philippe? Panayotis? Tante Milou?'

'No. No, not really.'

'Well, they've been Tante Soraya's neighbours for ever. He's really quite old, I suppose, although I don't know exactly *how* old. He doesn't look too bad though – and he has a very gentle manner. Teddy likes him. But I must say the main thing that made me think was the flat. They are magnificent those flats, Tante Milou: the high ceilings, the cornices, the long corridors. And his flat has even got some amazing pre-war wallpaper which looks as though it was put up yesterday. And then of course there's all of that marvellous old furniture that his mother had when she was a bride absolutely light years ago. Imagine. But I know it's wrong to think like that and anyway there's something kind of spooky about it all – how come you've never met him, Tante Milou?'

'I have – met him. At occasions: weddings and so. That's all.'

'Well, there's only him and Nina – that's his mother. He has sisters but they've been settled in Greece for ever and his father has been dead a long time. But Monsieur Philippe still lives with Nina. It's quite strange really, when you think of it, because Tante Soraya says that he's also always had the same job ever since he graduated; some small accountancy job. She won't really talk about him though – just says "Philippe never changes" and that's the end of it. But she did tell me that he wouldn't take over his father's business when old Monsieur Yanni died – '

'Yanni, eh? Old Yanni the grocer?' Monsieur Vasilakis only half-turned round. 'He was a good man too, God have mercy on him, like your father. We didn't see much of him here, but Milou used to buy all our groceries from him. Every week. He had a shop at the very end of the Mouski. Every week she would go there and come back with the groceries in a *calèche*. He gave her good discounts; for old customers, you know, and Greeks together. His daughters went back to Athens, but he had a son, too. A beautiful boy, they said, *and* he went to university. But we don't know anything about him – '

'Didn't you like the fatta, then, Set Farah?' Mahrous was grieved at the pile of bread and rice left on the plate.

'It was delicious, 'Am Mahrous, but I could never finish it. I'm afraid I picked out all the meat, though.'

'This won't do, Set Farah. This won't do – '

'And I've eaten up my vegetables.' Farah smiled up at the old waiter removing the plates.

Milou looked at Farah. 'When you say you considered marrying – this man, he has asked you?'

'Oh I'm not going to marry him, Tante Milou! I was just, you know, playing with the idea.'

'But has he asked you?' Athène stood up and tried to get off her mistress's knee but Milou held her collar.

'Oh no.'

'Well then?'

'But he would if I wanted him to.'

'But he is Christian, Orthodox?'

'He would become a Muslim.'

'But how do you know? How do you know he would?'

'Tante Milou. One *knows* these things. There's definitely something in his eyes when he looks at me, and when I meet him on the stairs or he comes home from work and finds me chatting to Nina he always looks as though something wonderful has happened. I don't talk to Tante Soraya about this kind of thing but Nadia, my youngest aunt, noticed and said she thought Monsieur Philippe had a *tendresse* for me.'

'Nadia? Now she's really your father's darling, isn't she?' Monsieur Vasilakis was animated. 'He would bring her in here when she was only so high and sit her properly at the table and let her order whatever she wanted! Ah! What a world! "The last of the bunch is always pure sugar," as they say. How would I know? I only had Milou.' Monsieur Vasilakis drooped again. He put out a shaky hand for his glass. 'She was everything to me. Everything.'

Milou held on to Athène's collar. 'Tell me,' she said, straightening up. 'Tell me. If you thought a man had a *tendresse* for you, but he wasn't doing anything about it. And you wanted to hurry him up a little, so you made a move, an unmistakable move; one that nobody could pretend had been a misunderstanding. And he ignored it – ignored you. What would you feel?'

'It can't happen,' answered Farah firmly.

'But if it did?'

'It can't. But if it did, then – I suppose I should simply not think about him after that. But it's a lovely word, isn't it, Tante Milou?'

'What?'

'*Tendresse.*'

'Ah,' said Milou. '*Tendresse* . . . yes.'

from Solomon

MICK IMLAH

. . . I published my desire – and instantly
Squads of intent castrati sallied out
To smash through pickets of disgruntled beaux,
Whip up my standard over remote quarries
And ply my summons in the virgin seam.
No magnet was more natural: I pulled –
Earth's surface ached – and soon, what trickled up
Invisibly, in secret tributaries,
Swelled to a general and an inward flood;
And from the Torrid Zones and the Frigid Poles,
From dizzying scarpways and the viperous marsh,
From poultry farms, pig farms and paddyfields,
From school assemblies, from production lines
Whose very spanners grieved for their grip again,
Over the convent wall and under the wire,
From the weak pleas of parents, there converged
To crown the whole horizon where they came,
A tightening circle of exquisite girls;
On foot, on horseback, some on camels, some
In cages, some in wheelchairs, all compelled
Like Eastern kings, by my will's hanging sign,
To pitch their tents about Jerusalem.

A world of wives! The colours of the map
Made visitable suburbs of themselves,
And every day I'd venture in fresh fields
To sample some exotic variant;
For each submissive Turk was her own shade,
And no Swede would repeat her neighbour's hue;
So every Sunday I could call to view
An original rainbow arched over the week,
Whose seven elements combined anew,
As sun meets shower, in brief entanglements
Designed by Solomon. This way my palette
Flourished, like Adam's lexicon of beasts.

Forget their names? – Of course; a woman's soul
Appeared to me, and is retrieved by me,
In terms of colour. Names have unwieldy,
Shared, defective, ageing histories,
Betokening much beyond the split second
A sexed animal needs to express itself.
For example: when the *English* come to mind,
I see shy maids with little pastels wrapped
Like apples in a basket, and undo
Layers of reserve like linen to let through
Cathedral greens; the brass of trumpets blown
Through blazed cheeks; stipple winking from a pool;
Blood on the dairy floor, and the pale buff
Of broken pots in sheds; the pebbled blue
Of winter skies; the quick flare of blue
Fired by the kingfisher through evenings dim
With smoke and midges; wet dawns, dripping mint
And tufted heathers, and a sense of moss
On the inside of things, and rust, and gloom . . .

So much for England, then. And so it went –
Till after the fiftieth carmine, after the hundredth
Clichéd rose, and all the tract between,
I planned a mural of my million brides
In a rainbow shape, to span the pearly start
And purple end of chromatology . . .
Too late, I called an artist in, who sighed
And cuffed bits of soiled pigment from the wall:
Colours (he lectured me) *blossom apart*
But they corrupt each other; mix them up,
You'll always get the same, dull, mineral brown.
(And so it had proved in life; my single mind
Had come to fuse the bright particulars
That women brought, in a brown, saming fog;
And yet, my habit overruled my sense,
Or sense my judgement, and at each day's dawn
Boredom got up and smacked me in the face.)

It suddenly seemed a mixed lot – never to know
The simple conjugation of the mass
Of choiceless men and women – he and she
Boarding each other like a bus in sunshine
(Snug in the fastness of their married berths
They sleep together now, like slotted bolts);
But who on earth governed a sum of parts
Equal to mine? – The Queen of Sheba? – She
Aspired; and for a brave, tenacious month
Fought not to shiver in the freezing gulf
Between good looks and my remote greatness.
It did amuse me briefly when she framed
Infantile riddles on the abacus
(*What has ten holes, that when the first is shut
The other nine are opened?* – though of course
I knew both answers, my sole reply
Was to let these fingers irresistibly
Confound her reckoning). How the subsequent
Dependence wore her charm away, until
I had to banish her, you'll understand;
You'd find her knitting now, in a seaside town,
A fifteenth set of hangings for my bed –
Which will be beautiful, like her, but show
Tiny irregularities of design.

Questo Backwater: Lampedusa's Sicily

DAVID GILMOUR

Sicily is a land of memorials. Public buildings across the island are stamped with marble slabs commemorating 'immortal heroes' and their 'prodigious triumphs'. The lives of obscure deputies and insignificant mayors are recorded in grandiose phrases: 'glory of Sicily', 'honour to his country'. Even those 'patriots' who brought misery to their island have had their deeds re-written and enshrined in pompous lettering.

Giuseppe di Lampedusa's plaque is on a wall in the former Caffè Mazzara in Palermo, above the table where he wrote during the mornings of his final years. Placed there in 1978 by the Rotarians of west Palermo, the plaque describes how Lampedusa 'amid the clamour of life, wrote pages and pages of *The Leopard*, exalting in his art that beauty which shone in his soul', thereby producing a 'wonderful synthesis of truth and poetry'.

Anyone acquainted with *The Leopard* is likely to assume that the Sicilian Rotarians had not read it, or else had forgotten its contents when, twenty years after the book's publication, they decided upon commemoration. A cardinal of Palermo described *The Leopard* as one of the three factors which contributed to the dishonour of Sicily (the others being the Mafia and the social reformer Danilo Dolci), but few Sicilians have agreed with him. To most of them, Lampedusa is a great Sicilian writer, a source of regional pride and a name to be quoted in guidebooks and travel brochures. Perhaps this is an instance of what he termed the *fierezza cieca*, or blind pride, of the Sicilians: to be proud of the achievement and yet not to notice that it was done partly at their expense. For Lampedusa had a wide repertory of sarcastic remarks which he aimed at his fellow islanders: it would be difficult to find three consecutive pages in *The Leopard* or any of the shorter works which did not contain some deeply contemptuous reference to modern Sicily.

Lampedusa was a shy and reticent man who could seldom find anything to say at cocktail parties or in his club. Few of his acquaintances realized that his courteous and mild-mannered exterior concealed a powerful intelligence which was busy dissecting their weaknesses. But in private, with his cousins or a small circle of close friends, he was ruthless about Sicilian deficiencies. He used to refer to Sicily as '*questo* backwater' or as 'Peru', although he had never been to South America and knew little about it. Goethe's view of Sicily ('To have seen Italy without having seen Sicily is not to have seen Italy at all, for Sicily is the clue to everything') was incomprehensible to Lampedusa who had more sympathy with Ruskin's opinion that it was pointless to

The Villa Lampedusa in Palermo

visit the island just to see imitative works constructed by second-rate craftsmen. There was little about Sicilian life that did not provoke some sarcastic jibe: the targets were as varied as the provincialism of the local newspaper, the *Giornale di Sicilia*, and the island's sex life. Sicilian virility was in his opinion a myth and the endless boasting masked rare and inhibited performances. Another myth was the Sicilians' great intelligence. If you asked groups of Piedmontese and Sicilians to solve a problem, he said, the Piedmontese would take a long time but eventually would solve it, whereas the Sicilians would come up with rapid answers – all of them wrong.

One of the principal problems about Sicily, he believed, was that its inhabitants had a distorted geographical perspective, which placed themselves at the centre of civilization. An example of this failing comes in the short story 'Lighea' when the protagonist is described as 'one of those Sicilians who consider the Ligurian Riviera . . . a kind of Iceland'.

The *campanilismo*, or provincialism, of the Sicilians was one of Lampedusa's most frequent grumbles and a source for many ironic remarks. Life in Palermo was so unbearably stagnant that he advised friends to read Conrad as an antidote. Yet at the same time he realized that most of his acquaintances were too provincial to appreciate Conrad's writing or even to understand his life. 'A lady whom we all know,' he once recounted, 'was returning to Palermo with me by car after an absence of *two* days. On reaching Porta Felice she made the sign of the cross and thanked the Lord for allowing her to see her native city once more ("*O tu Palermo, terra adorata!*"). How is it possible that this lady could ever be interested in Conrad, who for twenty years wandered around the Pacific, or Kipling, who could spend half a year in London and the other half in India?'

This provincialism was also, according to Lampedusa, at least partly responsible for 'the time-lag of a century in our artistic and intellectual life'. 'A century' is perhaps an exaggeration even when referring to Bourbon Sicily, although the failure of the Enlightenment to have any impact on the island (in strong contrast with Naples) lends support to his view. During his later years, with modern communications and the beginnings of the new European community, Lampedusa found the time-lag even more astonishing. 'Not only do the works of modern English writers not reach Palermo,' he once complained, 'you cannot even hear their echo. Flaccovio [a bookseller and publisher] condescendingly displays in his window as "novelties" *The Cocktail Party* and *The Family Reunion* which are twenty years old. One knows Graham Greene exists through his fame but not in any tangible way through his books. To find a copy of a recent book one has to go at least as far as Rome, or else endure the torment of "ordering" (which two times out of three is unsuccessful).'

Lampedusa's views on Sicilian characteristics reappear in *The Leopard*, the short stories and the memoir of his childhood. Sometimes they are stated plainly as the author's viewpoint: Sicilians are accused of 'a niggling and hair-splitting rarely connected with any real understanding of the problems involved'; their 'quick wits' are deceptive, they merely 'usurp the name of intelligence'. But similar opinions are also given to his principal, partly autobiographical characters. 'If Sicily is still as it was in my day,' remarks La Ciura in 'Lighea', 'I imagine nothing good ever happens there, as it hasn't for three thousand years.' Later the same character describes it as 'a lovely land, though inhabited by donkeys'. In *The Leopard* Don Fabrizio criticizes Sicilians not so much for their lack of intelligence as for their vanity, laziness and 'terrifying insularity of mind'. 'In Sicily,' he explains to a Piedmontese official, 'it doesn't matter about doing things well or badly; the sin which we Sicilians never forgive is simply that of "doing" at all.' Several pages later he tells his astonished visitor: 'The Sicilians never want to improve for the simple reason that they think themselves perfect; their vanity is stronger than their misery.'

Lampedusa's widow used to say that Don Fabrizio was not an autobiographical character, and various critics have warned against treating his views as if they also belonged to his creator. Yet Lampedusa did share most of these opinions: the pessimistic interpretation of the island's history, the scepticism about the Risorgimento, the unflattering view of the Sicilian character – and repeated them in conversation. Moreover, Don Fabrizio's strictures are accompanied by numerous asides from the author, inserted into the text to support the prince's case: interventions designed to inform the reader of such Sicilian traits as their disregard for truth, their ignorance, their 'impermeability to anything new', their idleness which was 'the purpose of power'.

From general observations on the Sicilian mentality, Lampedusa regularly descended to more specific failings. He was particularly intolerant of the islanders' noises: 'the sagging Girgenti accent', 'the harsh consonants', 'the guttural grunts Sicilians use in anger'. Nor was their singing any better: he complained of a song 'transformed into a kind of Arab wail, a fate to which any gay tune sung in Sicily is bound to succumb'. And he grumbled that there was no mirth at harvest-time, none of the '*stornelli* singing of Tuscan girls at vintage' or 'the Livornian threshing punctuated by feasting, song and lovemaking . . . ' (In fact there was a good deal of singing during both the vintage and the grain harvest; the gathering of the olives, however, was a more melancholic ritual.)

Occasionally, one of Lampedusa's characters stands out in decency and dignity from the rest. As he declares in 'Il mattino di un mezzadro', however, this seldom happens, because 'a person of sensitive feelings [is] a human species very rare in Sicily'. Individuals may have been exempted from the continuous polemic, but groups and classes were irredeemable. The corrupt middle classes, without any of the civic qualities of their counterparts in northern Europe, were the most consistent target, their 'tenacious greed and avarice' being an important theme in *The Leopard*. But the working classes are also portrayed with little sympathy, especially the peasant 'men of honour' whom he described as 'violent cretins'; and Lampedusa's aristocrats are usually frivolous and ineffective with 'frothy and infantile imaginations'. If membership of a social class gave a person traits he could not easily discard, so might political beliefs. One disagreeable character in *The Leopard*, Ciccio Ferrara, possesses the 'deluded and rapacious soul of a Liberal', which in the context of Sicily in 1860 is not as unfair as it might seem: many middle-class 'liberals' supported Garibaldi in order to grab Church property when the ecclesiastical estates were broken up.

Don Fabrizio ascribes these failings to the violence of climate and the misfortunes of history. Lampedusa's works are full of references to those months – 'apocalyptic Julys' and 'inexorable Augusts' – which make the Sicilian summer 'as long and glum as a Russian winter'. The sun's damaging power is conveyed in a rash of adjectives – 'tyrannous', 'crude', 'brash', 'drugging', 'leaden', 'implacable' and 'appalling' – and the sun itself is seen as 'the true ruler of Sicily . . . which annulled every will, kept all things in servile immobility, cradled in violence that has the arbitrariness of dreams'. The case against the Sicilian weather is powerfully put and almost plausible. But, in fact, a Sicilian July is incomparably less glum than a Russian February and the island's summer, savage though it can be during rare days of sirocco, is very much less than 'six feverish months at a temperature of 104°'.

Historical misfortunes were a more convincing source of Sicilian inertia. Since early classical times, Sicily has been too small and weak to defend itself, and yet too large, too strategically important and (until the later Middle Ages) too rich to escape the interest of foreign powers. Its destiny has thus inevitably been colonial. 'For over twenty-five centuries,' says Don Fabrizio, 'we've been bearing the weight of superb and heterogeneous civilizations, all from outside, none made by ourselves, none that we could call our own.' Frequent foreign invasions produced a sense of fatalism among Sicilians. Unable to resist the invaders and mesmerized by 'magnificent yet incomprehensible' monuments, they turned inwards on themselves, managing nevertheless to retain both a sense of inferiority and an arrogance towards the rest of the world.

Many critics, most of them sympathetic to the Italian Communist Party, complained of Lampedusa's view of Sicily which seemed to deny the island any possibility of an optimistic future. Yet no one was in a better position to write about the place than he. Almost uniquely among Sicilian writers, he actually lived in Sicily; he was not like Verga, trying to describe the Sicilian 'reality' from Milan and asking his friends to send him phrases in dialect to make his work sound more authentic. Lampedusa lived in Palermo and yet was able to preserve a certain detachment in his observation of Sicilian life. It was indeed strange that someone so 'un-Sicilian' should have stayed in an uncongenial place where he had few friends and few people who matched his intellectual interests. He stayed partly from lethargy and partly for atavistic reasons. His sense of tradition and feeling for history held him back, as did his nostalgia for the land (especially his family's land) which he had loved as a child before he went to England and France and returned with the conviction of Sicilian inferiority.

He stayed also on account of his mother. Lampedusa may not have been typically Sicilian, but like all married islanders he had to play his part in the complicated triangular relationship of mother, son and daughter-in-law. A successful marriage in Sicily often depends less on the bond between a husband and his wife than on the relationship between the mother and her daughter-in-law. In Lampedusa's case the triangle was disastrous, the other points occupied by difficult and formidable women who could not stand each other. Within a year of their marriage in 1932, his wife had returned to Latvia (she was half-Baltic and half-Italian) and refused to live again in Sicily until the Baltic states had been annexed by Stalin. During the 1930s Lampedusa travelled disconsolately between Riga and Palermo but spent most of the time with his mother in Sicily. Not until he was nearly fifty (and his wife had come back) did Lampedusa and his mother live in separate houses.

Yet there was also a more positive and perhaps barely conscious reason for his reluctance to settle outside Sicily. For Lampedusa the island was a place of contrasts and extremes – a country 'in which the inferno round Randazzo is a few miles from the beauty of Taormina Bay'. It had a certain magnificence which set it apart from more prosaic places, a grandeur corrupted by history but still visible in decay. Lampedusa believed in Sicily's essential greatness which had been ruined over 'twenty-five centuries' of mismanagement and neglect. The Sicily he loved was the classical island, the wooded land of the Greek colonists, the fertile country which under the Romans produced higher wheat yields than it does today. It is no coincidence that La Ciura, his important, largely autobiographical character, was a Hellenist.

In a letter to his wife in 1942, Lampedusa described the wooded corner of Capo d'Orlando, where his cousins lived, as an Arcadia, a pastoral Greek landscape far removed from the noisy cities and arid hillsides of the rest of Sicily. He loved it because it had withstood the depredations of history and reminded him of the 'archaic and aromatic countryside' which the Greeks and Phoenicians had encountered. The island's immortality is also evoked in 'Lighea' when he describes 'eternal Sicily, nature's Sicily': 'the scent of rosemary on the Nèbrodi hills, the taste of Melilli honey, the waving corn seen from Etna on a windy day in May . . . the solitudes around Syracuse, the gusts of scent from orange and lemon groves pouring over Palermo . . . during some sunsets in June . . . the enchantment of certain summer nights within sight of Castellamare bay, when stars are mirrored in the sleeping sea and the spirit of anyone lying back amid the lentisks is lost in a vortex of sky, while the body is tense and alert, fearing the approach of demons.'

Contrasts between classical times and the degraded Sicily of recent centuries are made in both 'Lighea' and *The Leopard*, often through mythological references and allusions. Yet Lampedusa's attraction to the island was not confined to its Greek past or to its Arab and Norman periods when it was one of the most civilized and prosperous regions of Europe. For all his sarcasm about the nineteenth and twentieth centuries (when it was one of the poorest and least civilized regions), there is a strange, almost hidden pride in his attitude to modern Sicily. The place may have been vain and ignorant but at least it was not mediocre. It may have been violent, irrational and deceitful, but it had mystery and a certain style. The old aristocracy may have been useless, but there was a grandeur in its uselessness: Don Fabrizio in his 'voluptuous torpor' is more impressive than the worthy Piedmontese official who wants to change things.

In contrast to those Sicilians he criticized for their bizarre perspective – those who in Don Fabrizio's words 'remain convinced . . . that the civilized norm is here, the oddities elsewhere' – Lampedusa placed the 'norm' in northern Italy and measured Sicily against its standards. The results were mixed, but Sicily did not always lose. His attitude to the northerners is apparent from his language, his belittling use of adjectives, his habit of using diminutives in such a way that a Milanese count becomes a *contino* rather than a *conte*. By employing a drab, mediocre mean as the 'norm', Lampedusa was able to illustrate his own double-sided view of Sicily: certainly it was a place of violence and excesses but it had also a sort of warped greatness that was not despicable. Bound to his island by history, ancestry and upbringing, entangled in a relationship in which love and hate nurtured each other, Lampedusa cared desperately about its decadence. That relentless bitterness towards Sicily, which permeates everything he wrote, could only have come from someone who loves what he knows to be irredeemable.

Giuseppe and Alessandra di Lampedusa

A. TORRES

MONTEVIDEO
34 SUR

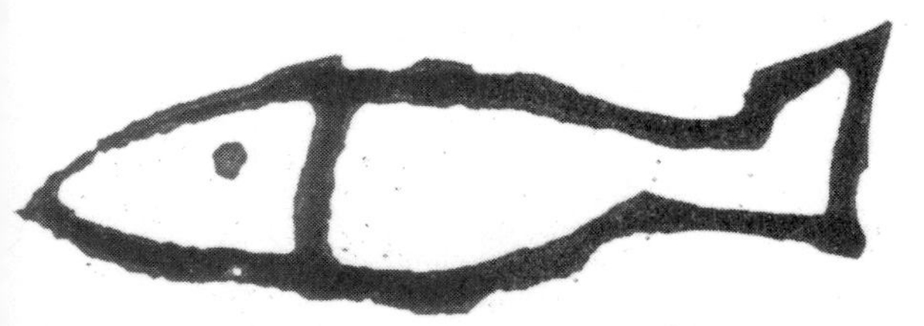

SUR

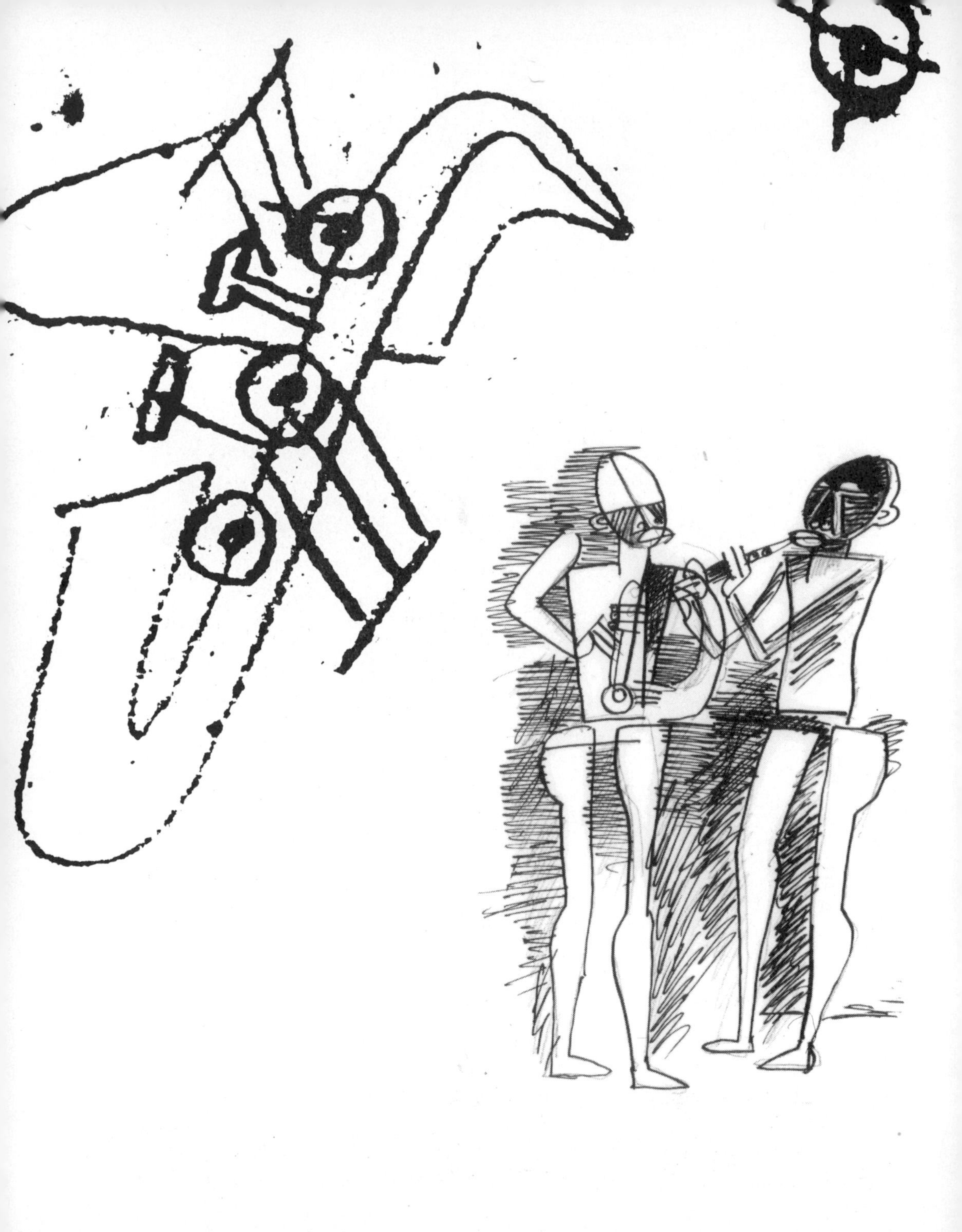

A Blockade Memorial

CAROL RUMENS

There were platoons of tents: not one was closed.
Inside, in each wound's dark, we knew there'd be
Pale puzzles like ourselves: a flawed Yorick

At last conversant with his mess of props.
But when we dared to peep, the ossuary
Held simply straw, the light dormition of roses.

*

Since graves were everywhere, we couldn't see them.
The walkways bore them off to a last farewell
– A frayed red hand, waving up from the ground.

We trod on oak-leaves, stars, the splashed confetti
Of monstrous brides. The verb 'to die' is vast
– A city. But 'to die for the motherland'

Has no visible end, works in all tenses,
State-like, and makes them present: there are always
Live feet going over and over the dead.

*

An east wind, solid with processional ghosts
Carrying brands that first lit glowingly,
Then blanched, the faces of the crowd, swept through us

And drove us to the gates, the sheltering temples.
They frowned in pity, gathering the shades
Into their smaller, denser, human forms.

*

Here stood a country looking for itself.
First, it would find a baby's fist of bread
– The daily ration for 900 days –

And then, a diary. If the power-lines ceased
Their faintest song, and tyre-tracks, slithering,
Curved, for whatever reason, into silence,

If dry tongues ached against walls and shoe-leather
– How could a diary speak?
Somewhere there are girls who still know how.

*

She was called Tanya. Round her once had lived
Her family. True to girlhood courtesy,
She dipped her pen, listlessly, carefully,

As each one died, redeemed their gravelessness,
Making a loss-shape from the name and date
Until she had exhausted all her time

And reached the final name,
A child brought up to wait politely, take
The last turn in the complex grown-up game:

Everyone's died. Only Tanya's left.

*

Past the necropolis the earth lay snow-stilled
And empty, free to grieve in her own way
– Northerly, reticent. A concealed flood.

In moments we were tearless and absurd.
High-kicking, floundering through the half-whisked whites,
To storm the silver woods, our boot-tops foaming.

*

We found a pool. Dark water shivered thinly.
The adolescent birch trees seemed to step
Suddenly back, not liking to admit

How passionately they'd dwelt on their reflections.
Such slippages and slynesses and rumours!
We heard them, then: the ice-locks liquidly

Yielding, the wind more westerly
With each gust. But the lost weight of the starving
Still drifted from the camps: who'd cup its grains?

Distant, triumphal chords kept touching us
Like old soldiers, vaguely fingering
Their medals, asking why there's so much dust

On swept and watered stones. And spring, too young
To hear them, stoops to the tents with a light breath:
She wakes the roses, snips the bandages.

A Chronicle of Small Beer

NAN GREEN

It was early in 1937 that George and I were shopping in Leather Lane, London. He said: 'I've got to go to Spain.' I said: 'Yes.' By chance, the Spanish Medical Aid needed someone to ferry a truck out to Spain and George drove it.

My sister Mem, on being told the news, wrote to me: 'How history does knock one about . . . ' to which I replied: 'This is where we start knocking history about.' Harry Grisebrook, my brother-in-law, sent a letter full of heartfelt abuse for George for 'deserting' his wife and family. 'Listen,' I wrote back full of outraged pride, 'George and I are thinking of more than our own children; we are thinking of the children of Europe, in danger of being killed in the coming war if we don't stop the Fascists in Spain.'

'Holding the fort' was not easy, but not nearly as difficult as it might have been if I had not had support from the Party and other anti-Fascists. Our (Jewish) landlord instantly reduced the rent we paid for our flat by one-third. I got a job in a nearby office from whence I could come home by four o'clock to meet the children from school. I continued to serve as Branch Secretary, cycling round to visit every one of our sixty-three members at least once a month.

Early in July, Wogan Philips came to see me with a proposition. It seemed they needed someone like me (an organizer) to assist the Medical Aid units from Britain which had plenty of nurses, doctors, ambulance drivers and stretcher bearers but not enough administrative personnel. He had brought a request that I should go out to Spain; he himself had been wounded and did not intend to go back. The son of a peer, he was not without resources. He proposed to free me to go to Spain by paying for my children to go to any boarding school of my choice.

I walked up and down for a whole night of turmoil, trying to decide what was best. If it had not been for the existence of A. S. Neill's Summerhill School I could never have contemplated sending the children to boarding school. But I believed in Summerhill and knew that they would be in an atmosphere in which their father's action in going to Spain would meet with full sympathy and approval.

I don't know. To this day I don't know whether I did right to go. But anyway I went, intending to return in no more than six months, and staying, in the event, for almost a year. The children were fitted out for school and both left happily, hardly finding time to say goodbye when the train pulled out. Wogan stood me a slap-up farewell lunch at the now defunct Holborn Restaurant, saying, 'You'd better eat as much as you can because you won't get anything like this in Spain,' and that very evening I caught the train for Paris, with two heavy suitcases containing a few clothes and a vast quantity of medical supplies.

Paris was the scene of the International Exposition where, before catching the night train to the Spanish border, I stood spellbound by Picasso's *Guernica*, noted the competitive vulgarity of the German and Soviet pavilions, and snorted in disdain at the British contribution – mostly tweeds, pipes, walking sticks and sports gear, I seem to remember.

By the afternoon of the following day I was in Barcelona, with the address of my destination on a piece of paper, the suitcases, next to no money and a few words of Spanish. There were no trams and no buses; there was a temporary power cut and it was Sunday in any case. Failing to get through on the telephone, I set off dragging the suitcases and, by showing people the paper at every crossroads and following where they pointed, eventually reached Calle Balmes, the reception centre for Medical Aid people.

The wild enthusiasm which had characterized Barcelona twelve months before was no longer so much in evidence. The Anarchist *Incontrolados* had been brought, to some extent, under control, and the hardship was beginning to leave its mark on the scene. People looked tired, drawn and often shabby – but gallant and not down-hearted. Buildings were pitted with the pockmarks of machine-gun fire. Dust and rubble gave off that acrid smell which became so familiar to me in embattled London four years later. An incredibly battered tramcar was proceeding slowly through the street; it had served as an armoured car with which, during the first days of the Fascist rebellion, a group of workers had successfully stormed one of the public buildings. Now, decorated with slogans and banners, it was accompanied by a group of gay young people collecting for the Red Cross. I was told this happened every Sunday. And carnations were being sold in the flower stalls on the Ramblas.

My destination was already arranged. Next morning I was given a *salvo conducto*, a sheet of paper entitling me to travel there. Travel, how? At all exits to Barcelona there were guard-posts which stopped every vehicle leaving the city and loaded them with passengers to wherever they were going – a kind of military hitch-hiking. After an hour or so of waiting I was shoved on to an open lorry with about twenty others and we set off. After spending the night at the convalescent hospital in Benicasim, I went through the same process next morning and later in the same day found myself at Huete, in what was called 'the English hospital'. To my profound astonishment, I found George there.

Now George had left for Spain with the firm intention of joining the International Brigade as soon as he had delivered his lorry, and I had only a vague idea that he was still retained in the medical service. (Letters were censored, and one sent the replies to a code address.) He had sent me some carefully guarded accounts of battles in which he had participated, of the death of Julian Bell and that of Izzy Kupchik and others we knew, and a vivid though typically understated account of his first experience of aerial bombardment (strafing) in which he described how he lay in a ditch and 'experienced a sudden fondness' for his hands – the hands, don't forget, of a cellist.

A little while before my arrival he had crawled under his ambulance to examine a choked feed of petrol on a mountain road, and freezing petrol had run down his arm, taking off an area of skin. He had been sent to Huete for treatment and was almost recovered. Meanwhile he was appointed Political Commissar of the hospital.

George was a good commissar. Part of his job was to promote the welfare of patients and staff, and on this day he had arranged a concert for such patients as could walk or be carried to the large 'recreation hall' – formerly, perhaps, a chapel in what had been a monastery. He had bought himself a cello; a Bavarian lad with an injured leg played the violin (by ear); the village plumber was an excellent guitarist though equally illiterate musically; and a Catalan patient, also with a leg injury, played the

bandurrion (a sort of mandolin). George taught them tunes, and they already had quite a credible repertoire. A departing patient had left behind an accordion. Early in the afternoon George showed me this, and said that I should play it with his orchestra that evening. 'But I can't play the accordion!' I protested. 'You will by tonight,' he replied firmly. The keyboard side was of course easy since I had had piano lessons as a child. I learned a dozen or so chords during the afternoon and dutifully took my place in the orchestra that evening. It must have sounded dreadful.

Next day I was introduced to my job: assistant secretary. The chief administrator was British, as were the surgeon in charge, theatre sisters, ward sisters (who included three New Zealand nurses) and one or two ambulance drivers. Tremendously devoted work was done by the Spanish people. The training of village girls as nurses and wardmaids was speeded by their eagerness to learn and their devotion to the work, which far outran the expectations of our nurses. Like Cromwell's men, they knew what they were fighting for and loved what they knew.

This is a chronicle of small beer. I can only tell what I saw and experienced. One day I watched George trying to shift an enormous cupboard with the aid of two very young stretcher bearers, Spaniards. They pushed, pulled and heaved without making any difference. 'It is impossible, George,' said one of the lads. 'To Communists nothing is impossible,' George replied. One more heave, and the cupboard moved.

A fiesta was planned; I think it was to commemorate the October Revolution. A bar was set up in what had been the crypt of the monastery and was now the garage for ambulances. To make an inspection pit, a few flagstones had been removed, uncovering some human bones. An American artist, one of our patients, devised a banner to hang at the back of the bar, depicting caricatures of Franco, Hitler and Mussolini, and hung some of the bones beneath the banner. The point was raised, might this not antagonize the villagers, to whose ancestors maybe the bones belonged? Being in the aftermath of my personal repudiation of the Christian religion, I was vehemently in favour of leaving the bones there. 'I don't like finding myself on the opposite side to my wife,' said George, and proceeded to remind us of the meaning of the Popular Front. The bones were taken down and re-interred, and I swallowed my lesson without too much difficulty.

In December, George at last attained his desire and was discharged to go to the front and join the British Battalion. At almost the same time, I was appointed administrator of a hospital for convalescents at Valdeganga, which had in the past been a hydropathic hotel, being located by some hot springs of chemically impregnated water which emerged nearly boiling from under the ground. It had been a health resort for rich people; there were marble bathtubs with silver-plated taps in the shape of swans' heads.

My job at Valdeganga was not an easy one. The hospital was paid so much per head of patients – consequently if the number of patients fell we got less money per month to run it and to remain solvent we sometimes had to lay off staff, mainly girls from the nearby village which was an anarchist stronghold. Angry deputations on behalf of the temporarily unemployed followed. Rightly or wrongly we suspected Huete, which was supposed to send us its convalescents, of hanging on to them unnecessarily for the sake of *its* solvency. At intervals, when a battle raised the number of injured, they would send us a new batch of patients and then we could bring the staff up to full strength again.

The village girls, mostly wardmaids and kitchen hands, slept together in two dormitories and, as it was winter, and a mountainous situation (snow fell that Christmas, very unusually), they often shared beds for warmth. As a result, scabies broke out amongst them. It became necessary to decontaminate them, their clothing and their bedclothes simultaneously. The majority of girls possessed only one pair of corsets which they refused to give up. The Austrian medical officer bullied them, I was for more gentle persuasion; Frank Ayres, a Yorkshire railwayman who was the Political Commissar, explained and explained and explained, and eventually we won the battle.

I believe that due to the altitude we were all infected with a touch of 'mountain sickness' and lived in a permanent state of mild excitement. The physiotherapist (an excellent one), a refugee from Austria who had done all her training in England and had joined the Communist Party there, possessed a Teutonic political rigidity and started a whispering vendetta against Frank because he flatly refused to remove some anarchist literature from the patients' library. This was at the height of the Soviet-inspired hatred of 'Trotskyism', which spilled over into the Communist movement everywhere and made heresy-hunting a righteous crusade for many members.

All round the hospital, on the mountainsides, lavender grew wild. When you walked, brushing against the stunted plants, you released their lovely perfume. The villagers were, except when agitated about the wardmaids, immensely friendly. We gave a children's party for New Year, 1938 (how we managed it, I don't remember, but we gave them each *one chocolate*, something which most of them had never seen). In the remote village of Valdeganga there had been a great deal of intermarriage – it seemed as if all the children introduced each other as 'my cousin', and a number of them had a common feature of the two middle fingers of each hand being joined together. At the end of the feast, one child started singing in rhyming couplets a well-known tune and this was taken up by one after another, each providing a new verse. It began, 'Long live the English hospital, long live all the wounded!'

The village had a very small power station, the manager of which used to come to the hospital on Saturday nights with his wife for our weekly dance. He played the fiddle and she the piano. Half or more of our patients were sufficiently mobile to dance, but there was great difficulty about partners for them. Village girls in those days could not be *touched* before marriage by any man but their fathers or brothers, and to have danced with a stranger was likely to ruin the chance of a husband. I prepared, and recited each Saturday night, an earnest speech pleading with the girls to regard these wounded men as their brothers, but only a few of the bolder ones responded; the rest danced with other girls, while our poor patients danced with one another.

The fiddle player was called up and his wife left the village to go to her parents. Out came the old accordion, and for two or three hours on Saturday nights I sat on the bar at one end of the recreation room, sawing away at fox-trots, *paso dobles* and the everlasting 'Over the Wave', only about ten tunes in all. The kind bartender (a patient) used to keep filled at the side of my stool a tin mug of very rough, sweet vermouth. It was my weekly trial of strength-in-the-head to pack up my instrument at the end, sling it over my shoulder and walk in a dead-straight line to the door and across to the hospital.

An elderly Canadian called Arthur Tazzaman who was ill with gastritis and suspected the cooks of poisoning him – in the end I had to form a rota of people to sit with him at mealtimes and exchange plates as soon as we were served – conquered his pain and disability to the extent of rescuing three wrecks of motor vehicles that lay about the roadsides on the way to the hospital and, with the help of everyone who could hold a spanner or recognize the parts of an engine, built the three wrecks into one complete new truck. He almost wept with anxiety each time he saw it being driven out of the hospital by our slap-happy Spanish drivers, and with relief each time it came back unharmed.

Frank Ayres had returned from England to wind up the English section of the hospital at Uclès – newly adopted by the Spanish Medical Aid Committee. I don't know how Uclès came to be chosen, but it represented the ceaseless effort in London to keep or present the medical missions as politically 'pure'. A fresh batch of nurses, hand-picked for their non-Left character and background, had been sent to this new venue and a lot of money was poured in to assist the hospital with equipment and other things it needed, including improving the sanitation (which was deplorable). In fact, so 'uninvolved' were the Spanish staff and management that they leaned heavily to the Right. (When Franco's troops arrived in 1939 after the Republic's defeat, some of the doctors got out their Fascist blue shirts from their suitcases and went out to greet them.)

Old Frank took me with him to Uclès where we found a half-built septic tank; a dry moat round the whole building, into which had been thrown soiled dressings and bits of amputated limbs, and which was now the home of a large rat colony; an empty ward with a notice over the door saying it was to be the new Leah Manning Ward, and a general sense of hostility towards us. There was no job for me. I undertook, while I waited for some direction from Barcelona, to do what I could to raise the morale of those poor British girls who had been thrown into these shambles: one of my daily jobs was to de-louse them when they came off the wards. They were not permitted to go on night duty. I remember one of them weeping – she had a patient who was paraplegic, and one night a rat had got into his bed and gnawed his leg which of course had no sensation in it. She had procured four big tins, filled them with disinfectant and set the legs of the bed in them. The night nurses had removed the tins because they 'looked untidy'.

I remember May Day, 1938 because I broke down for the first time. There was no one in the house. I had had no letters for nearly a month. I didn't know where George was. I started thinking of previous May Days, the gay flowers and slogans, of pushing my darling children in their double pushchair from the Embankment to Hyde Park, and began to weep overwhelmingly. I went into the kitchen, put my head into the roller towel on the back of the door and the floodgates opened. Gruff, practical old Frank found me and brought cups of strong tea and aspirins. Many years later he told me that up to that moment he had regarded me as admirably efficient and stony-hearted, but then my tears had warmed his feelings into affection.

Soon the official call came for me to go north. How to get there? The road was cut off. The Spanish authorities refused, quite rightly, to give me any sort of safe-conduct papers. I can't remember how, but Frank managed to arrange for me to travel to Marseilles on a British battleship, the *Sussex*, as ostensible escort to one of the British nurses who was being invalided home. I flew from Marseilles to Barcelona; it was the first time in my life that I had ever been on an aeroplane.

There was a job ready and waiting for me. I was to go to the front, as secretary to the chief medical officer of the 35th Division.

Barcelona was showing the signs of siege. People's faces were drawn and pale. The civilian rations were even more exiguous than the meagre allowance we received as military. Everyone carried a little cotton bag, containing their daily ration of dark unpalatable bread, which was no longer served in restaurants. The port was bombed daily. The children, or a goodly number of them, had been evacuated to places further up the coast, to those heroic 'children's colonies' which continued to care for them.

I set off for the front. The front at that time seemed to be the absolute keystone of the fight against Fascism and war. Hitler had to be stopped. Even my small contribution might be of help.

Though we did not know it, preparations were beginning for that last great campaign of the Spanish People's Army, the crossing of the Ebro. I reported to the HQ of the 35th Division Medical Corps and was introduced to Dr Len Crome, the chief medical officer. My job was to type his dispatches in formal Spanish, to keep the divisional medical records and turn them into usable statistical information, and to stamp every official document which left the HQ with an official rubber stamp that was hung round my neck and stayed there until I left the front four months later. I also acquired a sack of tea, a Primus stove and a small quantity of sugar. I have sometimes thought that the serving of tea at all hours of the day and night, which made me a sort of welfare officer for our unit (the HQ staff, doctors, ambulance drivers, mechanics, cooks, etc.), was perhaps my main contribution to the battle of the Ebro.

The HQ of the 35th Division Medical Corps, when I joined it, was located in a decrepit farmhouse. As I sat typing one day in a small dusty 'office' upstairs, a tall, bushy-bearded, bespectacled figure walked in. It was George. A totally unexpected encounter for us both. We embraced, hurriedly exchanged news and talked of the children . . . Then he had to leave. But at least I had seen him. He was *alive*!

We were on the move, nearer again to the river we were soon to cross. My office was now the open air and my quarters a mattress on which, if the weather was good, I slept out of doors (otherwise in a bell tent along with several men).

We were in a little mountain village called Bisbal de Falset, almost overlooking the Ebro. Not far from us, though we did not see them, the units of the 35th Division were preparing for the crossing. In the first days of July, for the sake of morale, and to celebrate the 14th, it was decided to hold a fiesta for the village folk. There were to be speeches, a children's day and a sports day. The sports day was remarkable. There was only one flat surface in the whole village: the main road which passed at the end of the main street. This became the racetrack, the athletic ground and the football field. Our lot (the medical people) played a group from the fortifications unit which was stationed there too. The event was intermittently interrupted by convoys of huge lorries coming down the main road towards the river, laden with arms and ammunition. Everyone knew where they were going, and what for, but nobody said a word. (The crossing of the Ebro, a day or two later, took the enemy completely by surprise. There were no quislings in Bisbal.)

We crossed the river one night after the first of the troops. With Crome and his adjutant, we drove down steep hairpin bends through the dusty dark, but all along the route we could hear, and sometimes see, the local peasants laying down swathes of branches to fill up the potholes, and hacking away at the rocky sides to make the corners more manoeuvrable for heavy vehicles. We just made it by dawn.

It was a scene of desolation, with still-unburied bodies lying by the roadside, shattered dwellings and huge piles of jettisoned material, papers, suitcases, bedding, even rifles, showing the haste with which the enemy had made his getaway. We set up our first HQ at (I think) Flix, in the buildings of a power station where the (German) technicians had left us some well-built slit trenches in which to take refuge when the bombardment began, which it soon did.

Each day the doctors in charge of four front-line dressing stations sent in their lists of the day's casualties; my job was to type these out, classify them into various categories (head wounds, leg wounds, amputations and so on; the base hospitals to which the wounded men were sent, the weapons which had caused their injuries – mortars, shells, bullets and others) and turn these figures periodically into graphic form, with the aid of a box of watercolours and some drawing instruments. The casualty lists were sent off every day at four o'clock to the higher command, where they would be co-ordinated with those from other divisions and matched to reports from base hospitals which revealed, for instance, how long it took for a man with a compound fracture of the tibia to work through his treatment and get back into action, or the urgent need for more tin helmets, of which there were shockingly few. There were a lot of casualties; an avalanche of work descended with which we could barely cope (though I still went on making tea) and for an agonizing few moments every day I scrutinized the lists for George's name.

When planes came over we had no need to identify them as the enemy or 'ours'. A glance at the sky was enough. If it was one of ours, the sky would be full of bursts of anti-aircraft fire, while if it was one or more of theirs – and they often came in formation – an occasional puff of smoke was all that could be seen.

The bridges across which all our supplies reached us were under incessant bomb attacks. Sometimes all of them were damaged and could not be repaired for hours or as much as two days, though the fortification units slaved heroically. One of the most urgent requirements was blood for the transfusion service (then in its infancy). Being fortunate to be a universal donor and a sedentary worker, I was recruited to give some of my blood by direct transfusion – an unforgettable experience. Lying down beside a seriously wounded man, on the point of death, I watched as the colour came back into his lips, his breathing improved and he turned back towards life. During those early days of the Ebro campaign I gave 200 cc of my blood three times in little over three weeks. I felt no ill-effects, except that my legs seemed rather heavy for a day or two afterwards. On each occasion I received (by regulation) a *vale* – a piece of paper entitling me to a tin of condensed milk and an egg. Neither was available. But on the third occasion Kozar (a mechanic), sitting by his generator, had seen someone running to fetch me to the operating theatre and by the time I emerged he had managed to snare a rabbit and was cooking it in his little frying pan. It was so fresh that the heart, lying in a saucer beside him, was *still beating*.

Its first onslaught over, the 15th Brigade got a few days' rest. I visited the British Battalion, a raggle-taggle bunch of weary men, scattered over an arid hillside. George was there, unharmed. We spent two evenings together and one whole night, on a louse-infested sofa.

But the long, slow, desperate and heroic retreat of the Spanish People's Army battling against the overpowering superiority of the Fascists, aided by German and Italian troops and war material in growing force, had begun. We lost ground. There were a few hours when our hospital and HQ were actually between our own and the enemy lines. We had to retire quickly, back towards the river where we set up in yet another derelict farmhouse, not far from a railway tunnel which had been converted into a hospital, for safety from the air.

Crome was replaced by a medical chief from the crack 5th Regiment (the Communist regiment which had throughout covered itself with glory and was a byword for courage and military efficiency). Enrique Bassadone was a contrast to the easy-going but nevertheless highly efficient Crome, who had a devastating irreverence for bureaucracy, and liked to surround himself with eccentrics and oddballs. Enrique, highly professional, with a batman to keep his spotless uniform in order and wait on him at table, didn't approve of women and always addressed me in the third person – while I replied in the second person, the universal habit in Republican Spain.

At this time we received the news that the Republican government had decided, in view of the endless shilly-shallying in the League of Nations about foreign troops on both sides – equating with the utmost cynicism the comparatively few volunteers who had come to Spain to risk their lives in the fight against Fascism with the armies of conscripted men from Germany, Italy and Portugal (not to mention their aeroplanes), to withdraw *all* the members of the International Brigades and send them home, and propose a proportional withdrawal. This, disregarding the fact that a great many of the volunteers had no home to go to, having come from Fascist countries to return to which would mean imprisonment and death.

We were to be sent home. George had sustained a slight head wound, but he had insisted on returning to the battalion to take part in the final action with his British fellow-soldiers. He came through our HQ and we spent an hour or two together eagerly discussing which of us would reach England first, and how it would come about, who would see the children first – and we agreed that George should not shave off his beard until they had seen it.

The 22nd of September had been fixed for the withdrawal of the British Battalion; our little group in the Divisional HQ (mostly drivers, mechanics, American and Canadian) were to engage in training of their Spanish successors and we had no date fixed for our departure. George was joyous at going back into the lines for his final swipe at the Fascist enemy, and sent me a note on his return to the battalion, repeating his conviction that the desperately wanted war supplies must 'even now' be pouring in.

The 22nd September came and went. Though I was still at the front, I sighed with relief that George was not on the casualty lists I had studied daily with dread.

On the night of the 23rd, two chaps came and wakened me.

'George is missing,' they said.

Due to an unexpectedly severe enemy attack, the British had been asked to spend one more day in helping to repulse it in the Sierra de Pandols. In spite of desperate resistance, they had been forced to retire and, when the time came to call the roll, George had not answered.

I didn't say anything. I pulled up the sheets around my suddenly icy-cold shoulders and lay down, trying to grasp the thunderbolt. It must not, it could not be true. He-might-be-alive-he-might-be-dead repeated itself with bewildering monotony in my waking thoughts for the rest of my stay in Spain and for the following months, gradually changing to despair.

We left the front a couple of weeks later, having handed over our jobs to our Spanish successors. We drove back across the river in an open *camion* and I recall the sudden surprise and delight I felt, as we drove through the first village on the far side, to see women in the streets! I hadn't seen another woman for weeks, and wished I could get down and embrace them – there you are, my sisters, my dear ones, weep with me! We stopped in Asco, where I began to telephone all the hospitals to which casualties might have been sent, spending hours shouting down crackling, buzzing, intermittently silent lines. Finally, there was nothing to do but to go home.

The Catalan chauffeur who drove us to the border was preoccupied with worry about his little son, who was sick. At the French guard-post I begged and pleaded to be allowed to enter France, buy some condensed milk and cross back to the Spanish end – about twenty yards – to give it to him; it was surely harmless to introduce sealed tins of condensed milk into Spain? The official refused. We made our way to a café for a meal. I ate two bits of a white roll and some fresh butter (neither of which we had tasted for months) and then was absolutely unable to get another morsel down. In Toulon I bought a pair of shoes, my *alpargatas* being almost worn out. Then we took the train – I don't even remember whether for Calais or Le Havre.

When I reached England I went straight to Summerhill to see the children. *What* was I going to say to them? 'Daddy isn't coming just yet, we don't know quite where he is' was the best I could do. I had to give them hope but not too much hope. One doesn't tell lies to one's children, but what is the truth here? He-might-be-alive-he-might-be-dead . . .

That afternoon there was a tea-party: someone's birthday, I think. I sat and watched my two eat their jelly, sandwiches and cake. In between every spoonful or mouthful Martin looked across at me with such blazing love in his bright brown eyes – so like the look in his father's grey ones when he used to sit beaming at me in the early days of our marriage, saying 'I'm doting on you!' – that I could hardly bear it. Frances refused to admit to herself that her father might not come back. She buried it inside where it began to canker. She experienced an *adult* grief but had no outlet for it.

I went right on working for Spain – 'merely changing the front and the weapons' as the International Brigaders put it. The war was not yet lost. The fight was still going on. Food, medical supplies, everything was needed more than ever, and the political struggle – 'Save Spain – Save Peace' – more urgent still. My daytime job was at the National Joint Committee for Spanish Relief. I shared a small basement flat in Bloomsbury with Winifred Bates and together we formed a voluntary group: 'British Medical Units from Spain' in which we organized all the nurses, doctors and others who had returned to speak at meetings, to hold meetings, to raise funds and write to the press, local and national. Angela Guest, always original and daring, by herself upset a tin of red paint on the steps of No. 10 Downing Street, to represent the blood of the Spanish people. The struggle became more and more desperate and now doubt began to creep in as to its outcome.

Doubt meanwhile was stealthily coming over my spirit. As the days wore on and there was no news I began to know in my heart that if George had been alive he would somehow by now have managed to communicate with me though I invented all sorts of fantasies to keep alive some hope.

Then the long nightmare came to an end. Early in March, when the end was drawing near in Spain and the exodus from Catalonia was about to begin, I got an official letter from the Republican government telling me that George had died on 23rd September 1938. Winifred, who watched me open the letter, told me afterwards that she knew what it contained because my face went grey.

What I built up in the next few hours was the determination not to show that I was shattered: for the sake of the children, who must discover that I could now cope with being both father and mother to them, and for the sake of George, upon whom no blame must fall. Pride, pride in his having given his life for the cause we all held dear, must be the keynote.

Frances, poor sweet, could not accept the news. She continued to tell her schoolmates fantasies about the cake she was going to bake for her daddy when he came back. She became actually ill, ran a mysterious high temperature, and A. S. Neill sent for me. The very day I got there, he had, with characteristic wisdom, sent a girl who was an orphan to play with her in bed. The conversation turned to fathers. 'I haven't got a father,' said Sally. 'That's funny, neither have I,' said Frances. I had brought her something she wanted – a grass skirt in which to dance like a Caribbean girl. She looked at it and wept. 'What is the matter?' I said. 'Don't you want it after all?' She burst into tears and flung herself into my arms, saying, 'I only want Daddy.' Now we were able to cry together.

Martin, I think, with the resilience of a younger child who had not grasped what it meant, actually took longer to work the loss out of his system (if he ever did). Two years later I found him in bed one night, staring at the ceiling. 'What's up, can't you get to sleep?' I asked. 'I am *trying to remember Daddy*,' he replied. 'Ah,' I said. 'I don't have to try because you are so like him that whenever I look at you I can remember him very well.'

Back to March 1939.

One morning the *Evening Standard* put out placards saying 'ON TO BARCELONA'. Blazing with anger, I rang up the editor and accused him of Fascist bias. The placards disappeared with the next edition. That day, or the next, I had lunch with Dr Audrey Russell, a member of the National Joint Committee. As we waited to be served, she looked at my hands which were clenched into fists, trying, I suppose, to hold back the Fascist advance. 'Unloose your hands,' she told me. I did so and unloosed a flood of tears. I'd thought until then that I'd cried all my tears.

The Chamberlain government recognized that Franco and the exodus from Catalonia had left thousands of refugees in deplorable camps on the beaches of southern France. The National Joint Committee quickly set to work to send relief, and in particular to collect money for the chartering of an entire ship to send refugees to Mexico, whose government had generously offered asylum. I was enrolled and we stumped southern England, speaking and collecting funds.

A French vessel was chartered, the SS *Sinaia*, whose usual run was to take pilgrims to Mecca. It could hold about 2,000 passengers. A group left for the camps, to draw up the passenger list with great care – to make sure that whole families were enrolled and to try and ensure that the list reflected the political composition of the Republican side, without bias towards any particular group.

Leah Manning suggested I go as an observer on the ship, and the Committee agreed. Hastily borrowing a number of white coats, to make me look a bit professional on board, I packed up and set off for southern France where the ship lay ready. A covey of British VIPs were there to see her off.

The voyage took twenty-three days. My job, I discovered, was to see to the feeding of the very young children. On the first day, a group of (refugee) doctors surveyed all the infants and children under two years of age and allocated them to one of five or six diets. Supplies of various kinds of infant food had been brought on board. I co-ordinated the diets into quantities, and every three hours descended to the galley where I stirred, with the aid of two hardworking Spanish girls, great saucepans full of milk and different paps, distributing them in a made-over barber saloon to the mothers, either in bowls or in feeding bottles which had to be sterilized between feeds. I hardly ever got up on deck.

At Madeira, where the ship stopped to take on water, the captain asked some of us who possessed passports to go ashore and buy him some wine. Sir Richard Rees,

William Brebner (a Quaker observer) and I, together with Georges Soria, a French journalist who was to write up the voyage for the French press, went off into the hills to some cellars, furnished with tables and chairs made from barrels, and 'tested' glass after tiny glass of Madeira. Having made our purchases (I have absolutely no palate and could not tell one from another, but someone must have been proficient), we returned a bit tipsily through Funchal, where we were held up by a procession of Fascist Youth, dressed in black shirts and jackboots. Soria, with whom I had up to that point spoken only in French, suddenly leant over my shoulder and called out in excellent English: 'Fuck them all!' to my great delight.

A Shining Example

HELEN SIMPSON

The two women faced each other across the garden table like rival queens from a pack of playing cards. Mrs Leversage obviously ruled the clubs and spades, with her coal-coloured hair catching rookish blue lights from the sun.

'So that was why I left Fowler and Crabpiece,' she concluded. 'The job was simply not creative or fulfilling enough to warrant my staying. You, Jane, of all my friends, would understand that.'

Jane looked down at her lap in gratification at being so included into the blessed company of Mrs Leversage's friends. Here was a most unassuming queen of hearts and diamonds. The only rage-red item which qualified this girl for such a title was her hair, which crackled in a silent blaze around her white cheeks and forehead.

'What exactly did you do at Fowler and Crabpiece?' she asked in a respectful voice.

'A great deal of liaison work and co-ordination,' snapped Mrs Leversage. 'It's difficult to describe, but, my God, they certainly squeezed every ounce they could from me. Some nights I was there until seven o'clock. It was *exhausting*. But I wouldn't have minded any of that if there had only been more frankness and less jealousy flying around. Certain people simply closed their eyes and refused to recognize my talents. When that happens, it's time to leave.'

'Do you mean, you wish you could have been more *in charge* of things?'

'Well, naturally responsibility arrives hand in hand with recognition of one's talent and value to the company as a whole. But that's not really the point. I don't think you've quite grasped the issue, Jane.'

'I'm sorry. I've never had that sort of job. I don't really think about my work except as work. It's just something I have to do for the money and I'm glad when Friday comes. But of course your work isn't really *work*.' She struggled, wrinkling with effort, hurrying on as she saw Mrs Leversage's face shift into opaque displeasure. 'I mean, you don't need the money. You're doing it for another reason altogether. A *creative* reason!'

Mrs Leversage shifted in her chair and searched the girl's face for satire. She saw nothing but admiration and a desire to please. The mention of money had touched her on the raw. Only last night her husband had been twitting her about the expense of the working wardrobe which she had purchased before starting at Fowler and Crabpiece; she had not stayed long enough to recoup even half its cost from her salary.

'Your mind is too full of money,' she said shortly. 'There are other things in life.'

'Sorry,' muttered Jane. She fiddled with the glass ring she was wearing, twisting it so that its refracted lights fell in a shower of arrows on to the darkness of the bay tree by their table.

'What on *earth* are you wearing on your finger?'

'Only my diamond ring,' said Jane, with an attempt at playfulness.

'Let me give you a piece of advice,' said Mrs Leversage, soberly. 'If you can't have the real thing, go without. Cheap imitations are as bad as lies. I'm surprised at you, quite honestly.'

'But it's just a joke,' protested Jane. 'Jim bought it for me when we were in Brighton last weekend. He sang me that song about A man that looks on glass, On it may stay his eye. I can't remember the rest, but we *pretended* it was a diamond, you see.'

'I fail to understand the pleasure to be gained from pretence,' said Mrs Leversage, increasingly judgemental and apocalyptic. She extended one sallow jewel-laden hand to the centre of the table for their mutual examination.

'*That* is the real thing,' she said heavily. The diamond above her wedding ring sparkled busily, full of its own expensive inner lights. Jane stared at it obediently. She felt that the morning had gone wrong, but could not tell how or why.

'Are you sure your friend Jim values you at your true worth? Because you're an unusually beautiful girl, you know. Exquisite. That eggshell complexion with the Titian hair. No need to look so bashful. False modesty is as unattractive as false jewellery. I really must introduce you to my friend in television. He's in charge of casting the new production of *The Haycrofts of Haycroft Hall*.'

'Do you know *television* people?' breathed Jane.

'Of course I do, my dear,' said Mrs Leversage with a glittering laugh. 'You must come along to one of my little parties and I'll make sure you meet the useful ones. But first, you must *promise* me not to wear that monstrosity!' She laughed again, and stood up. 'Shall we take a turn around the garden?'

Jane followed the sulky high-heeled figure across the lawn. She herself lived in the basement flat of the house next door, and access to the garden was not one of the landlord's little generosities. The Leversages' house, of course, had retained its late eighteenth-century integrity, remaining unpartitioned and unsullied by property developer or tenant. Jane considered the garden to be its greatest glory, so clean and full of birds and rich freshness that it was like Eden after her own daily London scene.

'Oh, you are so *lucky*,' she breathed, staring at the drops of taut-skinned rainwater which sat on the glossy leaves. It had rained in the night, and all the plants were still wet and extravagantly green. The lawn glinted like an emerald. Violent sunshine lit the individual delicacies of each grass blade and every leaf in this wealthy frondescence.

Mrs Leversage had instructed her gardener to plant as many separate varieties of flower and shrub as was humanly possible in the space, and the result was a thickly embroidered spectacle, a *mille fleurs* tapestry in the medieval manner, an impossibly detailed treasury of newly minted shrubs, saplings, creepers, bracken and enamelled flowerets.

The two women moved lazily from plant to plant, Mrs Leversage inspecting each one with a beady eye for less than perfect health. Jane traced their outlines with her fingertips and sniffed at them like a blind girl. She had forgotten the sharp conversation and her own unease in a kind of verdurous ecstasy.

'I would never want to go anywhere else if I were you,' she said. 'Such a lovely garden and house. I think I would be perfectly happy.'

Mrs Leversage paused at a rose bush to snap off a fading crimson head.

'Tell me about Jim,' she said smoothly. 'What exactly do you see in him? Would I be right in deducing from my own chance observations that he is – if you will excuse the hackneyed image – something of a rough diamond?'

'Jim is Jim,' said Jane stupidly. 'I don't know. I don't seem to think like that.'

'It is never too soon to start asking yourself, "What do *I* want from this relationship?" You must say to yourself *constantly*, "Am I getting as much back as I am putting into it?" '

'We have quarrels sometimes, if that's what you mean, but I suppose most people do,' said Jane, her face clouding tenderly. 'I met him at a party. He'd had a bit to drink, and he was singing with his eyes shut. He has a lovely voice. I liked the way he said the words of the song. We moved in together when this flat came up.'

Mrs Leversage raised her eyebrows and remained silent. They continued their walk to the end of the garden, where pear trees grew in fruit-clustered ladders up the brick wall. This orchard corner also sheltered green peaches, under-ripe damsons, and one old apple tree loaded with early burnished fruit. Mrs Leversage raised an elegant arm and plucked down two apples. She polished them graciously against the sleeve of her silk dress, then offered one to Jane. She watched the girl's teeth broach the fruit's white sparkle.

'Of course, things are different these days,' she said deliberately. 'But I'm not all that much older than you. Maybe ten years. Twelve at most. I would never have agreed to live with a man without at least the offer of marriage. What *is* there to look forward to otherwise? The woman is always the loser in such a relationship. She leaves the man no incentive. As my mother used to say, "Why buy a cow when you can milk it for nothing?" '

Jane felt suddenly tired and close to tears. Her pleasure in the garden had evaporated. She could not remember saying anything in particular, but knew she must have made a bad mistake somewhere along the line. She had unintentionally offended Mrs Leversage, who had been so kind in asking her to lunch on her day off. She glanced at her quickly, noticing the discontented fold of her mouth, and the sinuous restlessness of her hands around the apple.

'Is it true that real diamonds will write on glass?' she asked, with a great effort to return to less painful ground. Mrs Leversage's face cleared. She even smiled. Jane beamed back in relief.

'Yes, my dear. They are the hardest natural substance known to man. How strange that you should ask that! You've reminded me of the first man I nearly married. He was young, he had a brilliant future ahead of him, and he was wild about me. One evening he proposed to me – I remember it was at the Caprice. Do you know it? No. Well. *Anyway*. He gave me the largest solitaire ring you ever saw. I wouldn't say yes or no. The diamond mesmerized me. I hesitated, then accepted. But, as the evening wore on, I knew I had made a terrible mistake. To cut a long story short, I made some excuse, slipped away from the table, escaped from the restaurant to where his car was parked a few spaces away and . . . Can you guess what I did?'

'No,' said Jane earnestly.

'On the windscreen in large letters I used the diamond to scratch the words, "Sorry. No go." And I have never regretted doing that. Because, remember, Jane, it is *so* important to be true to oneself. I cannot emphasize that enough, my dear.'

'What happened to the diamond?" breathed Jane.

'I still have it,' said Mrs Leversage with a misty smile.

They sat in thoughtful silence for some moments.

'That diamond was the perfect medium for my message,' mused Mrs Leversage. 'I have always refused to be forced into compromises. What is it Shakespeare says about integrity? Something to do with a jewel. I'm sure he must have meant a diamond.'

She gave Jane's cheek a playful pinch, then sauntered back towards the house. She was pleased with herself again.

'Let's have some lunch now,' she called back over her shoulder.

Jane stayed another moment, lifting her face to the garden-spiced breeze. She snuffed the air like a cat or a dog. Its rich warmth made her wish foolishly for the brine-freshened gales of her last weekend in Brighton. The sun was at its height, pulling all the moisture in the garden back to itself. The heat and dampness produced giddy scents, and insects hummed greedily. A bee boomed like a threat in her ear. She took to her heels, across the lawn, and into the cool house.

'I hope you don't mind taking pot luck like this,' said Mrs Leversage as they sat in the sepia shades of the dining-room over the elegant remains of last night's dinner. Jane's eyes were still dazzled by the garden, and in this interior gloom she could make out little but the sharkish whiteness of Mrs Leversage's smile.

'It's absolutely delicious,' she replied in docile gratitude. They were attacking the broken coral ramparts of a salmon mousse.

Mrs Leversage poured the rest of a bottle of chilly white wine which had been left to languish after the arrival of the champagne last night.

'There is something so sad about eating leftovers on your own. Don't you agree?' she apostrophized in her habitual dinner-party manner.

'I never seem to have much left over because of Jim's appetite,' said Jane seriously. 'But I always throw out some bread for the birds, even though he tells me off for being wasteful.'

'I'm not sure how well Beef Wellington stands repetition,' said Mrs Leversage frostily. 'So I will content myself with a little of this deliciously ripe Brie. But help yourself, my dear, by all means.' She hesitated, then opened a bottle of claret which had been termed perfectly acceptable by her wine merchant but which her husband refused to drink.

'What number of wedding anniversary was it, Mrs Leversage?' asked Jane, tearing her eyes away from the rosy slices of beef on her plate.

'Our fifth,' said Mrs Leversage, with downcast eyes and a modest smile. Then she looked up dramatically from under her brows, transfixing Jane with a needle-sharp stare.

'We have the perfect marriage,' she said, with considerable simplicity.

Jane gave a tentative smile, rapidly replacing this with what she hoped was a more appropriate expression of awe. She thought of the fat man she had met once or twice in the street, and of the pale brown eyes prominent behind their bifocals. Toad-coloured was how she had described them to Jim. She blushed.

'I hope one day, Jane, that you will find happiness like this with a man,' continued Mrs Leversage. 'I think, if you will forgive me for saying so, that you are not critical or exacting enough. You must put a man on his mettle to find out just what he is worth.'

Jane paused in mid-mouthful and considered this.

'Whenever I have a five-pound note, I slide it into my purse so that the Duke of Wellington's face looks over the flap. Because he has the same look about the eyes as Jim. Is that a good sign?'

Mrs Leversage's face became enigmatic to the point of sphinxdom.

'I don't think you have taken my point,' she said coldly. She cut herself a long sliver of cheese, then pushed it aside. 'Beware egocentricity, Jane,' she said. Her eyes were very green as she stared at the girl. 'You only talk of how *you* feel. You should surely be more aware of how *he* values you.'

Jane looked troubled.

'I don't think he's the type to show his feelings,' she said. 'I think it's something to do with him coming from the North.'

'I can see I shall have to *show* you what I mean,' said Mrs Leversage. 'Wait here.'

Jane watched her stalk from the room, slightly unsteady in her high shoes. She tried to think why she felt so strange, and held her wine glass against her flushed cheek to cool herself. When she pushed her chair back and stood up, the room span gracefully around her shoulders for a moment.

Over by the mantelpiece, the afternoon sun spilled into the air like golden tea. Jane stood in its warmth and blinked at her reflection in the pier-glass. The wine soared in her head and she was impressed by her own beauty. She lifted her hand to touch the flame-coloured hair, watching the fair-skinned heroine in the mirror do the same.

Her eye became distracted by the forest of precious objects between her and the flattering shadow. Pale cards engraved with a wealth of invitational gold were propped against the central clock and its ormolu cherubs, clustering beyond to bronze satyrs and *bonbonnières* milkily enamelled with lovers. A procession of parties, weddings and celebrations shimmered with the confident promise of happinesses which Jane would never see. It was like hearing familiar music from a long way off, and not being able quite to make out the tune. A tear stole pleasurably down her hot cheek. From the kitchen came the whirr of the grinder.

'Thank goodness,' she murmured. 'Coffee.'

The fragrance of the beans combined with the night-faded persistence of cigars. She wished she could take this lovely sophisticated combination back to her own flat, which smelled musty because of the damp, and of meals more prosaic by far than the ones consumed in *this* house.

'No, stay by the looking-glass,' said Mrs Leversage. She set down the tray, then took up the shallow box in front of the coffee pot.

'I hope this will show you what I have been talking about,' she said, advancing towards her, fiddling with the catch of the box.

The lid flew open. Jane stared. Mrs Leversage smiled. The gems flashed their dazzling faces into the afternoon.

'My fifth wedding anniversary present from Adrian. Fifteen emeralds, and two hundred and fifty diamonds. See how thoughtfully he chose those variants on the number five. Emeralds for my eyes. Diamonds because they are *my* stone.' She pointed to the variously faceted gems. 'Brilliant cut. Marquise. Pear-shaped. Trilliant. See the straight square lines of the emeralds; except for that exquisite cabochon specimen on the clasp.'

Their brilliance reminded Jane strongly of the rich wet garden that morning.

'Just like a tree after it's been raining,' she said reverently. 'In fact, trees *are* diamonds, when you come to think of it. Trees turn into coal after a few thousand years, don't they?'

Mrs Leversage shot her a sharp look, taking in her heightened colour and vagueness.

'And then coal turns into diamonds, although it takes a very long time,' Jane rambled on.

'We must see how they look on you,' said Mrs Leversage curtly. 'Face the looking-glass. I'll fasten it.'

Jane turned obediently, staggering against the fender. She steadied herself and watched as Mrs Leversage drew the diamond collar around her neck, fumbling under the weight of auburn hair as she tried to snap the clasp shut. The necklace was cold against her collar-bone and she shuddered.

'Keep still,' said Mrs Leversage, 'or you'll make me drop it.'

'Sorry. A goose walked over my grave.' Jane giggled foolishly, then swept her hair up on top of her head in an attempt to help.

'*There*. Stay like that, Jane. Stay quite still.'

They faced the reflection in the mirror. Jane's arms stretched long and white above her head, and her hands were invisible, buried in the hair they held aloft. Her gem-encircled neck looked not her own. She felt embarrassed at showing the soft marigold hair under her arms, and blushed.

It was very quiet in the room. She saw Mrs Leversage's face behind her in the mirror. Mrs Leversage was staring at her in such a hard bright way, with such an astonishingly unpleasant smile on her lips, that Jane blurted out, 'Can't I go now?'

She felt a gliding movement at her side, a warm pressure beneath her armpit. At the same time she saw in the mirror a sallow jewelled hand snake to and squeeze at her breast.

There was a moment of undiluted bafflement before her brain connected the image with the sensation.

'No!' she roared, only it came out as a mewing noise. She wrenched away, catching a glimpse of her own crimson face in the mirror, and, banging her ankles clumsily against the fender, lost her balance and fell headlong. The patterns of the Turkish carpet shot up towards her face and she clutched at the fire screen and irons which were in her immediate downward path. There was a racket of clattering brass and splintering wood as she hit the deck.

Into the silence which followed, Mrs Leversage's words fell like solid objects, plangent and metallic.

'You're going to be very sorry if you've damaged that necklace. Very sorry indeed.'

Leunig

Leunig

NO
UNDERSTANDING
ANY
TIME
Leunig

The first condoms of spring

From the Coast of Bohemia

LACHLAN MACKINNON

Battered raffia, Russian vines are dangling
like an abandoned therapy, for my doctor's garden's
Rousseauesque foliage is late this spring.
The only hope for it is time's cure-all
and I reach the end of another consultation. Home:

children have drawn with charcoal on the stones.
I am not incurably sad
although I have forgotten all my games
and remember only a silver Colt I lost in my sandpit
and found rusted, the trigger-action gone.

Somehow the one my grandfather sent
by chance for my next birthday never felt the same.
It is like my friend's Czech friend insisting
I spit upon your Shakespeare
with his filthy geography.

Do you suppose we could have been restrained
if we had had that legendary coastline?
You couldn't call a Colt the equalizer now.
The stick-men stare blindly, eyes bigger than their heads.
The bedraggled, tangled garden is bowed with longing.

Second Thoughts on Consistency

HANS MAGNUS ENZENSBERGER

Once upon a time there was a Black American revolutionary by the name of Eldridge Cleaver. He spent some years in jail, wrote a few books, became a Black Panther, went into exile, attempted a comeback as a revolutionary designer of men's trousers, and has not been heard of since. During the 1960s, however, Cleaver coined a memorable phrase. 'Baby,' he said, 'you're either part of the problem, or you're part of the solution.'

To many people, and for a long moment, this seemed an apt maxim. Clear-cut, unequivocal, uncompromising, it had the deceptively simple sound of a Bible quote. For some years to come, it was adopted by politically minded people, not only in the USA, but also in Europe and in what is sometimes called, rather sweepingly, the Third World. The only trouble with Cleaver's handy dictum is that it does not happen to be true. First of all, the solution is nowhere in sight. There does not seem to be such a thing. Of course, there is a huge supply of quick fixes – zillions of little remedies are being offered by outfits as diverse as IBM, EST and the KGB – but even their promoters would hardly claim that they merit the majestic singular of Cleaver's phrase.

More importantly, however, it has become exceedingly clear that everybody is 'part of the problem'. Supposing, for the sake of argument, that you were able to identify the 'good' side in any or all of the many conflicts which beset the world and, granted that you would be willing to take it, this would in no way entitle you to feel justified, since you would inevitably continue to participate in the web of situations, arrangements and traditions which are, precisely, 'part of the problem'. In stating this rather obvious fact, I do not wish to imply that the 'baddies' cannot any longer be identified. On the contrary, this is fantastically easy. What I find nearly impossible is the obverse operation. To point out a 'goodie' does not any longer seem to be feasible, least of all when a mirror is used in the process.

This is a very disagreeable state of affairs, especially for concerned intellectuals, who for a century or two have thrived on basic tenets like the following: it is good and necessary to seek first principles. It is difficult but laudable to hang on to them at any cost. Compromise in the face of adversity, rollback and reaction is bad. A radical should be radical. Opportunism is sinful. Consistency is good.

I should like to think, though I cannot be sure, that these rules were laid down in simpler and harder times than ours. A man who was a devoted communist in 1912, for example, was certain to be faced with difficulties but he could hardly be blamed if he thought of himself as 'part of the solution'. The same may be said of a Spanish anarchist of the 1930s, or of a Kibbuznik starting a new life in Palestine. A few of these men and women are still alive, and if you meet them you will find that they inspire a feeling close to awe. Unfortunately, their deep conviction has been inherited by a much lesser breed. Ever since the early 1960s, a peculiar type of intransigent has made his appearance, a type who is very much a part of our problem, since he is uncommonly close to ourselves, our work, our milieu and our private lives. He is easy to recognize, but difficult to define, since he comes in a great number of varieties. I cannot be sure about America, but in Europe we have seen them all: the stern critic of monopolist state capitalism tucked away safely in a state-run university with tenure for life; the slave of intellectual fashion coming out strongly against intellectual fashion and its minions; the well-endowed bureaucrat of culture with a sickening fondness for 'subversive' artists; the revolutionary video freak documenting his own uncompromising misery on endless tape; the peace research fund director bullying his elegant female office staff, and so on. Needless to say, all these people are full of principles. Indeed, the hazier their identity, the keener they are on the rhetoric of commitment. They all cherish a radical stance, untarnished by considerations arising out of their everyday existence.

Now it might be thought that there is nothing new in all this. The hypocrite and the Pharisee are, after all, well-established and ancient types in the comedy of manners. And indeed, if this were just another instance of self-righteousness and a double standard of morality, we should be confronted with a cast of quite familiar characters out of an Ibsen play. The point, however, is precisely that we are not dealing here with individual characters or with a subjective deficiency, but rather with an absence of character and with an epidemic of objective proportions. The people I have in mind do not embrace principles because they believe in their inherent truth. They use them as a blunt instrument with which to bash others. Principles are needed only for the purpose of defining others as opportunists, careerists, sellouts, moral, political or aesthetic renegades. The only person beyond suspicion is the fellow who has got hold of the microphone and who represents, for the moment of speaking, a higher reality of which, alas, he himself is not a part.

It is hard to identify this sheriff of conviction, this watchdog of basic values, this guru of principle. Indeed, it may turn out to be impossible. Speaking about him involves a moral paradox: this is a phenomenon which you risk becoming a part of the moment you speak about it. No amount of sincerity will save you from the condition of moral schizophrenia which has become a universal of our intellectual existence. The very claim to a state of superior ethical grace is self-defeating.

Not many people are prepared to resign themselves to such a state of profound and permanent moral ambiguity. There is a heavy demand for idols who would not be part of the general quagmire, and a supply-side economy will not fail to provide what is needed. This is why we find, in our cultural market-place, an unlikely assembly of cult figures who are supposed to be beyond suspicion. What they do for a living is of secondary importance. They may be philosophers or therapists, mystics or ideologues, artists or criminals, gurus or terrorists. The main demand made upon them is that they be part of the solution, not of the problem, that an unquestioned integrity can be ascribed to them, that they be untainted by doubt, compromise and equivocation. The result of this search is a curious Hall of Fame, a Madame Tussaud's of post-modern morality, crowded with figures such as Sid Vicious and Mother Teresa, Castaneda and Einstein, Samuel Beckett and Josef Stalin, Charles Manson and Eric Fromm, John Cage and Henry Abbott, Jian Qing and William S. Burroughs, Karel Woytila and Ulrike Meinhof, the Reverend Moon and Professor Beuys.

What is it, then, that we are so keen on that we want to acquire it at almost any cost, even if it means looking foolish, or crazy, or obscene? It must be something utterly lost. I believe that it is consistency, the notion that there ought to be a large degree of congruence or at least compatibility between what we are, what we think and what we do. Consistency is not a simple concept, and I am not sure of its status in Anglo-American philosophy. German theory, however, has been traditionally very strong on this notion, for which German philosophers have developed the term *Konsequenz*. This is, first of all, a logical category. In any rational discourse, your judgements were supposed to follow from certain assumptions or first principles. In other words, you should not simply jump to conclusions or defend any old phrase which happened to pass through your head as if it were a valid proposition. Contradictions would have to be avoided, overcome or at least explained. Very soon, and rather imperceptibly, this rule acquired moral overtones, and finally it became a postulate, an ethical imperative, and even something of an obsession, at least in Germany.

Mine is a civilization which historically has been prone to the belief that to possess principles and to act them out to their utmost consequences is good. Possibly this has to do with the Reformation, with the turn the Protestant ethic took in Prussia; in any event, it is a recurrent theme in the rosary of German idealism, from Kant to Fichte, from Fichte to Hegel, from Hegel to Marx. But I refuse to believe that we are dealing here with a specifically German obsession. After all, the utopian thinkers of Renaissance Italy, the theologians of Imperial Spain and the French Jacobins have indulged quite heavily in the passion for consistency at any cost. And in our own century, dozens of nations, from Korea to Chile, from Cuba to Bulgaria, not to mention Nazi Germany and the Soviet Union, have organized their social systems on the basis of principles which are odiously threadbare and ludicrously hypocritical but which happen to be thoroughly consistent. (It is interesting to note that the models on which most existing one-party systems are constructed are of German origin.)

Entire continents are filled with the monotonous drone of unequivocal speech. In this type of rhetoric, decisions are always 'irrevocable', support is invariably 'staunch', the laws of history are 'iron', and determination is 'unflinching'. People who long for consistency are notoriously easy to organize in larger groups, in schools, churches, armies, sects or parties. The man who desperately wants to be 'true to himself' will end up, paradoxically, by surrendering to a collective identity. The intimate resolve to adhere to a set of principles and to follow them to their utmost consequences is no moral safeguard. Indeed, there is often something schematic, something reminiscent of the bureaucrat, about an all-too-blatant devotion to principle. Those who pride themselves on their loyalty to ideas should remember that you cannot betray abstractions; you can only betray people.

Consistency, as a logical category, is empty. It is possible to be a consistent vegetarian, a consistent thief, a Trotskyist or a Mormon, a dandy or a Fascist. It is therefore not quite clear how consistency ever could lay claim to the status of a moral postulate. Another little problem arises as soon as you ask yourself whether consistency is to be understood as a demand on your thoughts or on your actions, or on both. In the first case, the risk to the outside world is minimal, but you may well end up a crank. Schelling's theory of electricity, for example, is entirely based on deduction. It follows, with a great deal of precision, from the first principles of his *Naturphilosophie*, and is thus quite unblemished by empirical observation. With all due respect to a great mind, it must be said that it is complete nonsense, albeit of an entirely harmless and even entertaining kind. The point here is that consistency places an enormous strain on learning, and makes it excruciatingly difficult for you to change your mind. If you then extend your postulate to include the way you act, you may be in for some real trouble. The idea of Schelling fixing a light bulb according to his theories is almost too much to bear. And yet this is a relatively innocuous example. Quite a few brave and decent people, a decade or so ago, concluded from principles which I cannot call unsound that the best way to deal with napalm was to bomb Dow Chemical. Most of them have learned by experience to think otherwise, even at the cost of consistency. Those who refused to pay this price would seem to be in for a lifetime of attacking Dow Chemical with home-made explosives.

But even if you just happen to mind the slashing of welfare or of food-aid programmes to desperately poor countries, you ought to think twice before claiming consistency. Any such claim will expose you to a particularly obnoxious sort of blackmail which has become very popular in certain quarters. As soon as you voice your objections, some horribly well-groomed politician is sure to get up and say: this is all very well, but it is just talk. If you are so keen on foreign aid, or on the welfare of the poor, why not do something about it? Why not live up to your principles? Be consistent! If you happen to be a Christian, for example, the least one may ask for is that you go and spend the rest of your life in an African leper colony instead of sitting here and getting on our nerves. And if you don't like capitalism, why not go away and fight like Che Guevara?

This type of argument is not an argument at all; it is an echo of the voice which you can hear on the streets whenever a potential suicide is crouching high on the window-sill of an office building. It is the mob shouting: what are you waiting for? Why don't you jump? In Germany, long ago, there was a most courteous gentleman by the name of Adorno who had an answer to this cry. He said: 'The ability to distinguish between theory and practice is a great achievement of civilization.'

Now, given the confusing state of affairs which I have been describing, I should like to point out some of the advantages and even joys of inconsistency. I do not claim that inconsistency, in itself, is a virtue. There is something neutral and rather unassuming about it, and I dare say that it can be abused. I am not advocating incoherent babble, and I rather like rational discourse. Besides, the case for inconsistency cannot be made consistently without incurring a logical conundrum.

Instead, I would suggest that we owe our lives to vacillation, indecision and unprincipled action. You would not now be in a position to mind what I am saying, or to agree with it, if it were not for the late Mr Khrushchev, who behaved, as we all know, like a disgraceful opportunist in 1962. Did he not back out with his rockets? Wasn't he simply yellow, as they say? Did he not throw overboard the most sacrosanct principles of Marxism–Leninism? And no one in the whole Kremlin had the guts to stand up and say: selling out to imperialism is bad. No, all these old militants just thought of one thing: they wanted to save their own skins, and in the process they happened to save our skins as well. Consistency would have dictated a quite different course of action. It generally does. Let me just mention a few examples:

Take any economic doctrine whatsoever, apply it, proceed logically with your project, and you will eventually destroy the very economy you had set out to save.

Act out the fundamental tenets of capitalism to their ultimate consequences, and you will end up with a state of civil war and/or a Fascist dictatorship.

Attack the social system you live in by any means at your disposal, and you have terrorism; defend it by any means, and you have the Gestapo running the place.

Be a rigorous ecologist and defend nature against man with no holds barred, and you will end up leading a Stone Age existence.

Build communism, be uncompromising about it, and your militancy will take you straight into what is rightly known as the socialist camp.

Go in for economic growth at any price and you will destroy the biosphere.

Join the armaments race, be consistent about it, and you will blow yourself to pieces.

Etcetera.

In this sort of situation, which has become quite commonplace, principle isn't any longer what it used to be. For those who are still looking around for a maxim to follow, I would suggest the following: consistency will turn any good cause into a bad one. It is a luxury which we cannot any longer afford. For philosophers who are interested in keeping their thinking as straight as possible, this must be an unwelcome thought, but for people at large it will not come as a surprise. In our parts of the world, a vast if not vociferous majority of citizens has come to realize, I believe, that their only chance of survival is based not on one or two Big Ideas, but on a constantly changing set of marginal options. They are quite prepared to face a lengthy and contradictory process of muddling through, of trial and error. Even in Germany, a society traditionally much given to principles, the last decades have seen a deep change in attitude. Social scientists have taken little note of this process, perhaps because they prefer to deal in Big Ideas or in statistical data. Nations as diverse as the Greeks and the Japanese, the Swedes and the Venezuelans, indeed most of the peoples who are given a chance to choose, will opt for the blessings of a more or less social democracy – not, I think, because of any deep-seated ideological conviction or loyalty, but because they feel instinctively that a sort of halfway house has become their only alternative to barbarism and self-destruction.

And now a word about ourselves. I hope you do not mind my using the first person of the plural form. Let us avoid categories such as 'the intelligentsia' or, even worse, 'the cultural workers', and just think of ourselves as a set of people who make a living by coming up, every now and then, with a new idea, a new image or a new shape. It is easy to see why the end of consistency is not something which we would relish. The state of affairs which I have tried to sketch goes against the grain of our most cherished habits. One of our main satisfactions in life has always been our ability to carry our ideas to extremes. Ever since we have existed as a social group – that is, for at least two centuries – we have been gainfully employed in going too far. Historically, the winner amongst us has always been the fellow who went further than anybody else. Never has this game of ours been played with greater fervour than in the first half of the twentieth century. In the heroic times of modernism, the logic of consistency was extremely powerful; the whole prestige of the avant-garde depends on its single-minded courage, on its determination to follow an ideological or aesthetic theorem to its very end.

It is true that not much blood was shed in the process. The radicalism of the Euro-American avant-garde did not lead to massacres. At worst it led to a certain amount of intolerance, sterility and dreariness. Thus we can afford to look back without anger to those bygone days. There is even something touching about those black squares on the walls of galleries and museums, and about the critics who saw in them the culmination of art history. Some of us still remember the times when poets who filled a whole book with lower-case i's and e's were considered the salt of the earth. Treatises were written on the 'objective state of composition' as applied to the man who gave a one-hour talk 'On Nothing' in front of breathless audiences.

All these games, however, were innocent only as long as they were practised as an indoor sport. When architects started to write manifestos demanding that our cities be scrapped, this gave rise to shrill debates which must have been great fun. When they turned out to be consistent enough to reduce our living space to an unending pile of cubes, this had rather dire consequences, especially for the unfortunate people who were doomed to live and work in the ensuing concrete dreams. And wherever advanced political theories were consistently applied, things took a decidedly tragic turn.

SECOND THOUGHTS ON CONSISTENCY

In the late 1950s, the Political Science department at the University of Paris had become a very cosmopolitan place. All sorts of things were being taught: the political economy of underdeveloped nations; the importance of central planning; the modernization of traditional tribal societies; the dynamics of anti-colonialist revolutions . . . It is therefore not surprising that the lectures and seminars of the faculty were largely frequented by a motley crowd of students from the former French colonial empire, from Vietnam and Morocco, from Madagascar and Somalia, from Algeria and Guyana.

Some of the more radical teachers had come to the conclusion that liberation movements in the poorest parts of the world would have to undo the structure of the colonial societies inherited from the age of imperialism if they wanted to put an end to the endemic misery of their countries. It was no good, they said, to do away with foreign domination and to take power without destroying the very fabric of the existing social system. The radical solution which they advocated had three major aspects.

First of all, the relationship between town and country had to be reversed. Urbanization was a plague introduced by the colonial powers. The parasitic cities siphoned off the productivity of the land. Industrialization would require a huge amount of foreign capital, and it would inevitably favour the local bourgeoisie. It should therefore be postponed. Absolute priority should be given to agriculture.

Secondly, a poor country must take care not to be integrated into the world market. Terms of trade would inevitably follow the pattern of international capitalism and perpetuate its domination. For a considerable length of time, isolation was the only solution. The economy must be geared to self-sufficiency. A subsistence economy would bring initial hardship for the more privileged part of the population, but it would permit autarky and thus, in the long run, put an end to exploitation from abroad.

Lastly, it was necessary to protect underdeveloped countries from the baneful cultural influence of the West. It was held that the educated élites in post-colonial nations posed a threat to independence, because they clung to the ideas and values of the metropolis. Merchants and functionaries, teachers and doctors were especially dangerous elements, since they had adopted Western ways in their formative years and would infest the whole nation with their thoughts and their lifestyles. This corrupting influence would have to be stopped, and the bourgeoisie would have to be liquidated as a social class.

This programme, which was advocated mainly by teachers from North Africa and Asia, and which was influenced by the Algerian war and by Maoism, is remarkable for a number of reasons. One of its more baffling aspects is the fact that it is curiously self-referential. Quite clearly, its proponents belonged to the educated élite in their own countries; they had spent their formative years in European schools, and their ideas are in great part derived from Western traditions. It would thus seem that they were, in terms of their own theory, at least as much part of the problem as they may have been part of any future solution. Granted that their ideas were based on their experience in several poor countries, the empirical data they could draw upon still did not make any sense unless they were interpreted. And for this interpretation, they depended on principles which they took over from European thought. Being progressive people, they did not avail themselves of the obscure dogmas and the ideological patent medicines which the West has produced in great abundance; they did not pick up political messages such as racism, chauvinism and anti-Semitism, which are very much part of our heritage. No, they took the very best we had to offer: the basic tenets of the French Revolution, the teachings of the Enlightenment, the idea that it was both necessary and possible to abolish the extremes of injustice, oppression and exploitation.

Among the students attending those courses were quite a few who came from South-East Asia. They took down and memorized every word which was said. One of them was called Kieu Samphan, another Jeng Sary, and a third one Saloth Sar, better known by his *nom de guerre*, which was Pol Pot. They all graduated with honours, packed up their notebooks, and went home. Fifteen years later they started to put into practice what their professors had taught them. They were very earnest, very devoted; their consistency cannot be doubted. The results are known to everybody who reads newspapers or who owns a television set, and the only open question by now is whether the Khmer Rouge's experiment has claimed half a million or two and a half million lives. I try in vain to imagine what their teachers feel when they happen to think of their former pupils.

Mind you, I am not saying that it is a crime to follow a line of thought, *any* line of thought, to its ultimate logical conclusion. We are all extremely curious people who cannot bear to leave unthought anything that is thinkable, and we dearly wish to know where our latest hypothesis might lead us. That, after all, is part of our work. Neither is there anything abominable about the fact that most of our trains of thought will sooner or later take us to a dead end. In a finite world, this is only to be expected. And if some of us feel like spending a lifetime in our respective blind alleys, this may seem a boring exercise, but, as long as it remains purely a matter of theory, I do not see why we should object to it. The little parable which I have just told goes to show, however, that some people are unable or unwilling to draw a line between theory and practice. They are so desperately consistent that they don't know a dead end when they see one. The fact that there is no way ahead inspires them to an ever more frenzied activity. The result, as we have seen, may well be murderous.

It must be said that there is a much simpler and less violent way out of a blind alley. Once you are sure that you have reached the end, and with a bit of foresight you can find out well ahead, you can turn around and try another thoroughfare. The trouble is that people who have been nurtured on principles often feel that such a course of action spells defeat or even betrayal. Many of them have reached positions of great power. I am thinking of Mr Castro, Mr Begin, Mrs Thatcher and Mr Khomeini, to name just a few. In their respective dead ends, they hang on to their anachronistic dreams – terrifying remnants of those heroic days when a man could still imagine himself to have been in the right, just because history was on his side, and because the bad ones were against him. In other words, by being sufficiently principled, and militant, and brave, a person could become, as it were, infallible.

Some of us may deplore the passing of the Age of Consistency. They might find some consolation in military science. The classic teachers of strategy have always held that there is no greater feat in warfare than an orderly retreat from an untenable position. Only a fool bent on self-destruction will call such a move an act of cowardice. I would rather go along with Paul Feyerabend when he says: 'Stamping out opportunism will not make us better men; it will just make us more stupid. What we ought to get rid of is rather our tendency to dream up, in our egoistical way, some sort of "good" or "rational" or "responsible" life, which we then try to force down the throat of other people in the guise of objective values.'

Inconsistency is not the answer to our predicament, but it has its advantages and its enticements. It cannot be preached. It increases our freedom of thought and our freedom of movement. It is good for our imagination. It is fraught with intellectual risks. It also takes a lot of training, but, if you put your mind to it, you may end up not only being less afraid, but even less afraid of being afraid. Inconsistency might even provide a much-needed dose of irony and a measure of gaiety in the face of the prevailing mood of depression. We can never know what we have at the back of our minds, but most likely it is more than our principles allow for, and more than consistency will tolerate. Alas, the end of ideology is not in sight, and its monotonous noise seems to go on for ever. Among all the static and the clutter, the anachronism and the propaganda, nothing could be more tempting, and, perhaps, more helpful, than the forbidden fruit of our brains.

Let me now jump to my conclusion, which may turn out to be quite different from yours. A tirade against consistency, however timely, may well bring comfort to the scatter-brained. Immersed as we are in the daily mash of the media, half-dazed by the relentless passage of trends and styles and quirks and fashions, exposed to the most banal and most routine sort of amnesia, an apology for the jellied mind is hardly what we need. To defend the charms of inconsistency is to ask for trouble. Misunderstanding being an essential mode of communication, some of you must have concluded that I have been making a plea on behalf of the Man without a Memory. I would therefore like to conclude with a tale in praise of obstinacy. Obstinacy, you see, is not a matter of principle. It does not need an ideological framework, and it does not offer justifications. The obstinate man is a modest animal, devoid of missionary ambition. He does not usually depend on a theory, and his deeds cannot be said to be derived from abstract postulates. His thoughts do not show up in opinion polls, and the technicians of political control will have a hard time in making him out. He is also very difficult to organize. In short, he is a dangerous animal, and, needless to say, there is no moral guarantee, there is just a possibility, that he will do some good. 'You go on talking as long as you like,' the obstinate man will say. 'I know what I want, and I'll keep my thoughts to myself.' Then, when he walks out of the door, he will drop a cryptic phrase. He will say: 'There is no other way.'

Take the inconspicuous man, for example, who is boarding the express train from Munich to Constance – for, although we can do without idols, we still need examples. Just look at him sitting across the aisle, in the smokers' compartment, a quiet, friendly fellow looking out at the dim November afternoon. It gets dark early at this time of year. He has grey eyes, he is in his mid-thirties, his clothes are old but neat, he looks like a craftsman, you can tell by his deft and slender hands. A mechanic most likely, or a joiner. In his spare time he will go to his club and play the guitar or the accordion, and if he has some money left he will spend an evening at the small-town dance hall by the river. No, he does not read newspapers. Every now and then he will go to church on a rainy Sunday, but he does not really care deeply about religion, neither is he very much interested in politics.

Finally the train arrives in Constance. He gets off and passes the lakeside. He obviously knows his way, but he does not seem to be in a hurry. There is an old suburb with overgrown gardens and warehouses. It is now a quarter to nine. In a minute or two, he will have reached the Swiss border. Two officers from the nearby customhouse walk up to him and ask him for his papers. He produces his passport. It turns out that the document has expired a few weeks before, and thus they ask him to empty his pockets. No contraband is found, but there are a few shreds of paper in his pocket, an old badge issued by the Red Front militia ('It is just a keepsake,' he will explain later); furthermore some bolts and screws and springs, and finally there is a picture postcard showing the interior of a Munich beer cellar called the Bürgerbräu. The customs men don't quite know what to do with him. In the end, they ask him to come along for a routine check.

While he is sitting down on a bench in the office shed – the wall calendar is showing the date of 8 November 1939, and it is now exactly 9.10 p.m. – a bomb is exploding in Munich, three minutes after Adolf Hitler has left, earlier than he had planned, the beer cellar where the big November rally of the Nazis has been held. Georg Elser had spent four months making the bomb before planting it in a pillar of the Bürgerbräu vaults.

Elser, born on 4 January 1903 in Hermaringen, and murdered in the Dachau concentration camp on 9 April 1945, the most dangerous of Hitler's enemies, did not belong to any organized group, nor did he act on the orders of any party. In planning, preparing and executing his attempt to kill Hitler, he was entirely on his own. There is no trace of his story in the textbooks used in German schools. In the scholarly works of German historians, Elser figures in a footnote if he is mentioned at all.

Experts will tell you that we are living in a society made up of outer-directed zombies, and that there are entire generations of us who suffer from anomie, narcissism and loss of self. They may well have a point. But I think that obstinate man is still very much with us, just as he was forty or 400 years ago. You will meet him at the next street corner if you look out for him. There is no specific sociological setting where you could place him. Obstinacy is not a privilege of the intellectuals, rather on the contrary. I believe that it will never go away, but I cannot offer any proof for this contention. I cannot explain where people like Elser come from, what makes them tick, or what may be the source of their determination. Like most of the things worth bearing in mind, this is an open question.

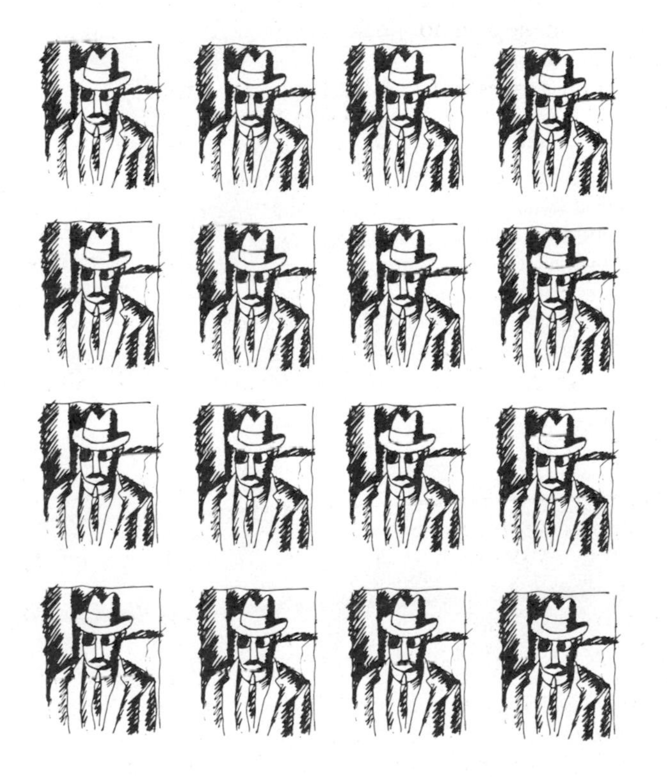

The Devil

DEBORAH MOFFATT

For a while I lived in Seattle, with my cousin Laverne. I went there to go to the university, but I didn't like it. I wanted to *live*, and being a student didn't feel much like living, so I dropped out and got a boring job selling clothes down at the Bon Marché. I didn't care what kind of job I had, as long as I was earning enough money to go out at night. A guy that I met at a disco told me that I should be a model; I was pretty enough, and I'd make better money. It turned out he ran a modelling school, so I went to classes there for a couple of weeks, but it was just a complete waste, because the guy that ran the school never told me that I was too short to be a model. I figured it out for myself, after I'd spent all that money on classes.

Laverne had been living in Seattle for three or four years before I got there. She lived with her boyfriend, Adrian Dick. They had a kid, Marla, and just after she was born Adrian left Laverne for a gorgeous Chicana woman from the Yakima valley. Laverne is pretty, but nothing like that Chicana, who was really something; so feminine, and small, and delicate. Laverne is large, and kind of hard-looking. She's Indian, and most of the women on her reservation are like that: big and strong. You don't want to mess with them. (I'm not Indian, even though Laverne and I are cousins. We're related by marriage, not blood.)

I guess it wasn't too easy for Laverne after Adrian left her. She had to take care of Marla, and she had to work. But Laverne is tough; she can handle anything. She started taking classes at the university, and got a work-study job, and cheap university housing. When I moved in with her, I promised to help with Marla and the house and things, but it didn't really work out that way. I mean, I was so busy with my job and modelling school, and I was going out almost every night, to discos and bars and parties, and I had a lot of boyfriends, but since Laverne didn't want me to bring guys back to her place I usually spent the night somewhere else, so I wasn't around all that much. But she didn't complain because at least I was good about paying my share of the rent.

Sometimes we would go back home together. I'm from Tolliver, and Laverne's reservation is near there. I didn't like going back to Tolliver, but Laverne said I should go see my old man, so we would go visit him just for a little while and then we would go stay with Laverne's family for a night or two. Her folks would take care of Marla so that we could go out together, and that was about the only time that Laverne ever got out for some fun.

Going to see my father was always a drag. Tolliver's the pits, nothing there but a dirty old tavern and some churches. My father lives out on a ranch all by himself. My mother ran off when I was a kid and drank herself to death in Spokane. My father is old now, and senile or something. He gets me confused with my mother, stares at me and says, 'You're no good, nothing but trouble, all that drinking and all those men.' But that's not *me* he's talking about; it's her. My father gives me the creeps, he really does, so I don't go see him very often, now that I don't have Laverne telling me I should.

Laverne's parents are different: they're younger, and nice and easy-going. When we stayed with them, Mrs Bill would always cook a huge meal for us, and Mr Bill would drive us all around in his big four-wheel-drive truck; he'd take us to lakes where we could swim, or to rodeos and powwows in nearby towns, or anywhere we wanted to go.

It was when we were over at Laverne's reservation that we first heard the story about the Devil-man. It was summer; I suppose everybody was thinking about the Devil because it was so hot. Anyway, the story goes like this: a good-looking man comes into a bar, and maybe he picks up a girl, or maybe he just has a drink, and then he goes away – by himself or with a girl – and then somebody says, 'Hey, that man had hooves, did you see?' or horns, or a tail, and then everyone realizes that he was the Devil. The night that we heard the story, down at the Wooden Nickel, where we always hung out when we were over there, everybody was talking about the Devil-man, and how he'd been seen in Yakima, and Euphrata, and in Wenatchee.

When the tavern closed, I bought a couple of six-packs to take with us, because we were going on up to the stick-games. Laverne drove us in her father's truck. They have the stick-games in an old shack way up on a hill near the forest. The road out there is twisty and pretty rough, but Laverne was driving all right, so I guess she hadn't had too much to drink by then. I was pretty drunk, though.

Whenever there were stick-games on, we always went, because it was something to do and also because Laverne is really good. That night, as usual, she was making a bundle. (Stick-games are a kind of gambling.) I was drinking most of the beer we had brought – Laverne never drinks when she's playing. I was getting a little bored, watching the game, because to be honest I could never really tell what was going on. They get really carried away, playing and singing their songs. The sticks are bones, carved and decorated, and when the singing stops you're supposed to guess who is holding them, and in which hand, I think. Sometimes I would feel a little out of place at the stick-games. I was usually the only white person there. Nobody would hassle me, but they wouldn't pay any attention to me, either, so I would get bored, and then I'd drink more than I really wanted, because there was nothing else to do.

And then, that night, two guys, complete strangers, came into the shack, just walked in like they owned the place. One of them kneeled right down in the dust and joined the game. I didn't like the look of him. He was wearing mirror sunglasses, so you couldn't see his eyes, and he had a big hat that he wore tilted forward, so you couldn't see the rest of his face either. I liked the way the other guy looked, though. He was tall and thin and he had wide brown eyes; he looked part-Asian, Filipino maybe. He must have liked the way I looked, too, because he came over to me and offered me a beer, which I accepted, of course. 'Thanks,' I said. 'Where'd you guys come from?'

He didn't answer, just smiled and turned to watch the game. I tried to watch too, but I couldn't concentrate with that good-looking guy beside me. After a few minutes I felt his hand on my back. I started to move away, but he whispered, 'Hey, girl, where you going?' So I stayed where I was.

The other guy – the one with the dark glasses and the big hat – was really cleaning up. He was a better player than Laverne, even. She was losing all her money, but she didn't seem to care. She kept on singing and playing like everything was all right. The strange man was talking to her, making her laugh, but I couldn't hear what he said. I was distracted by the man beside me, who was rubbing my back. It was starting to turn me on, the way he touched me.

Then he took hold of my arm. 'Come on. We're going for a ride.'

I went with him. I don't usually go off with strangers, like that, but I was drunk, and he was *so* good-looking. He had a Trans-Am, and he drove fast, really fast. I was scared, but I didn't say anything. At least we weren't out on a main road. He drove into the forest, to a small pond. I don't know how he found that pond; it's supposed to be secret, because it's sacred. I'd been told about it, but I'd never been there before. Only the members of Laverne's tribe are allowed to go there. But this stranger drove right to it, and said, 'Here we are. Get out.'

He laid a blanket on the ground and then pulled me down on to it. We made love. It was really something. I thought I was going to die, it was so good. It was dawn when we finished. The sky was purple.

'What's your name?' I asked him.

'You can call me Joe.'

'You never said where you come from.'

'You ask too many questions, girl.'

I tried to think of something to say that wasn't a question. 'Your friend plays stick-games pretty well,' I said.

'He ain't my friend. You want to know about him?'

'What about him?'

'He's been in the pen fifteen years. Just got out.'

'Oh yeah? What was he in for?'

'Murder. He killed his woman.'

I shivered. 'How come they let him out?'

'They didn't *let* him out; he got out.' Joe climbed on top of me. 'Ain't you tired of talking?'

We made love again. The sun rose and burnt my eyes. My head hurt. I was sweating. I felt sick. Joe picked me up and threw me into the pond. 'Come on,' he said. 'We gotta go.'

He dropped me off at the edge of town. I gave him my phone number in Seattle; he said he'd be in touch.

'What about your friend?' I asked. 'Aren't you going to look for him?'

'He ain't no friend of mine,' Joe said, and tore off in his Trans-Am, showering me with dust.

As soon as I got inside Laverne's house I knew that something was wrong. The place was empty. Laverne usually slept on the living-room couch, but she wasn't there. Marla's crib was empty too, and so was Mr and Mrs Bill's bedroom. I looked all around the house, but no one was there. I felt sick again, not from the beer I had drunk but from embarrassment, thinking that they were all out looking for me. God, what if they'd found me out there by the pond with that guy, stark naked and everything? I got goose-bumps from the shame. I sat down on the couch and tried to figure out what to do. I decided that the best thing was just to stay put; sooner or later they would come home and find me there. I lay down and fell asleep, and didn't wake up until some time in the afternoon. There was still nobody around.

I went down to the Wooden Nickel. 'You serving food?' I asked the woman behind the bar.

'Yeah. What you want?'

'I don't know. Fried eggs, and potatoes? And coffee, please.' I went over to a table beside the window. The tavern was hot, and smelled of stale beer and cigarette smoke. Flies buzzed around my head and made me dizzy.

The woman brought my coffee. 'Watch out, it's hot,' she warned me. 'Bad about Laverne, eh?'

I spooned sugar into the cup. 'What about Laverne?'

'Don't you know? She's down in Spokane, at the hospital. It's fifty-fifty she'll live. Didn't you hear about the accident?'

I sipped the coffee; it burnt my mouth. I dropped the cup and started to cry.

'I told you it was hot,' the woman scolded. 'You'll have to pay if you want another cup.'

Later Laverne's father filled me in. 'All I know,' he said, and his voice was slow and sad, 'is what they told me. Them that was up there at the stick-games; what they told me. You weren't there?' he asked, and his eyes kind of hazed over, with tears or sleep. I guess he was pretty tired. He didn't get back from Spokane until midnight, and he came alone; his wife and Marla stayed down there, with Laverne.

'I went out for a drive with a friend,' I said. 'Laverne was still playing away when I left.'

'They said she went off with some strange man,' Mr Bill said. 'They went in my truck. She was driving. She'd been drinking.'

'Not much,' I said quickly.

'Everybody saw her go off with that man.' Mr Bill wiped his face with his hand. 'I don't understand.'

I could see he didn't like the idea of his daughter running off with some strange man, but, after all, Laverne was no virgin; she'd been around. He knew that.

'You see,' he said, opening out both hands in front of him and staring, puzzled, at his palms, 'that man is gone.'

'Dead?'

'No. *Gone.* Disappeared. They say – the police say there was never anyone in that truck with Laverne. Not a trace of the man, no fingerprints, nothing. Like he never existed.'

When Laverne got out of the hospital she stayed with her parents for a while, and then her father helped her build a cabin out in the woods, on some land that he owns. She lives out there all alone now. Adrian Dick has Marla; he got custody of her after the accident. He said that Laverne wasn't fit to be a mother, because she drove around drunk with strange men.

I had to leave the apartment in Seattle when Laverne's lease ran out. I was going out with Joe by then, and we got a place together. He turned out to be real bad news, though. He told me I was so pretty, I should get into the movies. He said he knew some people in Hollywood, and that if I saved up some money he'd take me down there and help me get started. So I saved and saved, but it wasn't easy, because it costs a lot to go to discos and bars and things, and we went out almost every night, and usually I paid for us both. When I had enough money saved up, Joe told me to give it to him, he'd take care of it, and, next thing I knew, he was gone with the money.

After that, I went to stay with Laverne. I thought maybe she had the right idea, living out in the country on her own, with no men to mess up her life. I wanted to relax and just do nothing for a while. But I didn't like it. I missed being around other people, and going out at night, and men – I really missed men, most of all. I even missed Joe. And Laverne was funny. I mean, she acted strange. I think the accident messed up her brain. She hardly ever talked to me, and never looked right at me, just stared into space and smiled to herself all the time. It was creepy.

Also, there were strange noises at night, which scared me. When I was lying in bed, trying to sleep, I would hear stamping and loud breathing, or a sort of low coughing, right outside the cabin. I would lie there, petrified. What if some lunatic was out there, preparing to attack us?

So I had pretty much decided to leave the cabin, because I was just getting too nervous out there. And I was bored, too. And then I saw the tracks. I was outside wandering around in the sun one morning, feeling glad to be out in the woods after all. Laverne's cabin would be a good place to live if there were guys around, and a bar nearby, and if Laverne wasn't there. That's what I was thinking that morning, when I noticed the tracks.

'Hey, Laverne, come see!' I called. 'You got deer out here, did you know? They're coming right up to the cabin at night.'

She came outside. 'Yeah? What did you say?'

'I said you got deer here! Look.' I pointed to the tracks. 'See?'

'Yeah, I guess. Maybe.'

'Well you do! I know deer tracks when I see them! Here I've been so scared at night, all those funny noises, and it was just deer.'

'Oh,' she said, rubbing her toes across the tracks. 'Nothing to be afraid of.'

'Hey, don't! Don't erase them! Maybe the deer will stop coming, if they see that we've found their tracks. They'll smell us, or something, you know?'

But she kept on rubbing out the tracks, one little hoofprint after another, like she had to; she couldn't stop. She didn't even seem to know what she was doing, just worked away, staring into the woods over my shoulder.

From LANARK, A Filmscript

Alasdair Gray

RIMA'S ATTIC

A DOWNWARD CLOSE-UP OF TWO BLUE-STRIPED MUGS ON BARE FLOOR-BOARDS. EACH CONTAINS BLACK COFFEE ESSENCE AND BROWN SUGAR. BESIDE THEM IS A SUGAR BOWL, A BOTTLE OF CAMP COFFEE ESSENCE, A HALF-FULL BOTTLE OF BRANDY. RIMA'S HAND POURS BOILING WATER FROM A SMALL ELECTRIC KETTLE INTO EACH MUG, SETS THE KETTLE DOWN, LIFTS THE BRANDY AND ADDS SOME TO BOTH.
PULL BACK TO SHOW—

AN ATTIC WITH SO LOW A CEILING THAT ONE CAN ONLY STAND UPRIGHT IN THE CENTRE. A MATTRESS MADE UP AS A BED COVERS A QUARTER OF THE FLOOR. LANARK'S SHOES, PULLOVER AND TIE ARE BESIDE THE BED. HE LIES ON IT WITH BACK ON THE PILLOW, SHOULDERS AGAINST WALL, WATCHING RIMA WHO SITS ON THE BED-FOOT WITH HER BACK TO HIM. HER DUFFEL-COAT HANGS ON A HOOK ON THE DOOR IN THE WALL BEYOND HER. A CHEST ON THE FLOOR LEFT OF THE DOOR HAS A TABLE LAMP ON IT BESIDE TWO OLD DOLLS: A CHINA BABY AND CLOTH DUTCH MAN. A SWISS PENDULUM CLOCK, CHALET-SHAPED BUT HANDLESS AND MOTION-LESS, HANGS RIGHT OF THE DOOR AND A STRINGLESS GUITAR LEANS IN THE CORNER. ON THE WALL FACING THE BED A ROW OF HOOKS SUPPORT HANGERS WITH RIMA'S OTHER CLOTHES ON THEM. HER SHOES ARE IN A ROW ON THE FLOOR BENEATH. ELSEWHERE THE WALL HAS SMALL CHILDISH CRAYON SKETCHES OF GREEN HILLS AND BLUE SEAS PINNED TO IT. →

A TWO-BAR RADIATOR WITH CURVED REFLECTOR SHIELD IS PLUGGED INTO THE SAME WALL-SOCKET AS THE KETTLE.

DESPITE THE POVERTY OF THESE PROPERTIES THE APPEARANCE IS COSY AND PLEASANT. RIMA ALMOST SMILES AS SHE TURNS TO HAND LANARK A MUG, SAYING:

RIMA: You probably wont refuse to drink it.

LANARK: Thanks.

HE SIPS. SHE TURNS HER BACK TO HIM, NURSING THE MUG ON HER LAP. HE STARES AT HER.

LANARK: You're kind to me. (SHE DOES NOT MOVE.) Did you come to this city long ago?

RIMA: (DRILY) What does "long" mean? (SHE SIPS.)

LANARK: Were you small when you came here?

SHE SHRUGS. HE PUTS DOWN THE MUG, GOES TO HER ON HIS KNEES, LAYS A HAND ON HER SHOULDER. HER ONLY REACTION IS TO CLOSE HER EYES.

LANARK: (TIMIDLY) Do you remember a time when days were long and bright?

A TEAR TRICKLES FROM UNDER ONE OF HER EYELIDS. LANARK CANNOT SEE IT. HE PUTS HIS OTHER HAND ON HER OTHER SHOULDER.

LANARK: (SOFTLY PLEADING) Let me undress you?

SHE DOES NOT MOVE. HE UNZIPS THE DRESS AT THE BACK AND DRAWS IT DOWN TO HER WAIST. HER SHOULDER-BLADES, UNDER THE BRA-STRAP, ARE GREEN WITH SCALES AND PRICKLES.

LANARK: (DELIGHTED) You've got dragonhide! Your shoulder blades are covered with it!

RIMA: (STILL NOT MOVING, AND WITH CONTEMPT.) Does that excite you?

LANARK: I have it too! Here!

HE SHOWS HIS GLOVED HAND. SHE FACES HIM.

RIMA: (HARSHLY) Do you think that makes a bond between us?

HE PLACES A FINGER ON HIS LIPS, PLEADING FOR SILENCE, AND CONTINUES UNDRESSING HER.

A SHORT SEQUENCE OF CLOSE-UPS SHOW RIMA'S HEAD AND SHOULDERS AS, WITH OPEN EYES, SHE ENDURES, NOT SHARES HIS LOVEMAKING. IT SOON ENDS. HE COLLAPSES FLAT BESIDE HER AFTER A FINAL GRUNT OF RELIEF.

LANARK: (GASPING) Thanks! Oh thanks!

SHE STANDS UP AND LOOKS DOWN AT HIM.

RIMA: Well? Was that fun?

HE GAZES AT HER, CONFUSED, THEN DEFIANT.

LANARK: Yes! Great fun!

RIMA: How nice for you.

TALKING, SHE TURNS AWAY AND PULLS ON JEANS AND A SWEATER. THE CAMERA CONCENTRATES ON LANARK AND HIS GROWING HORROR.

RIMA: You're not much good at sex, are you? I suppose the best I'll ever get is Sludden.

LANARK: You told me .... you didn't .... love .... Sludden.

RIMA: I don't, but I use him, sometimes, just as he uses me. He and I are very cold people.

LANARK: Why did you let me come here?

RIMA: You wanted so much to be warm that I thought you perhaps were. You're as cold as the rest of us, really, and even more worried about it. I suppose that's what makes you clumsy.

LANARK COVERS HIS EYES WITH HIS UNGLOVED HAND.

LANARK: You're trying to kill me.

RIMA: Yes, but I won't succeed. You're terribly solid.

DRESSED NOW, SHE BENDS AND SLAPS HIS CHEEK BRISKLY.

RIMA: Come on. Get up. Get dressed and get out.

HE STARES AT HER THEN STANDS AND ADJUSTS HIS TROUSERS AND SHIRT, NOT LOOKING AT HER AT ALL. SHE HANDS HIM HIS TIE, WHICH HE STUFFS INTO A POCKET, AND PULLOVER, WHICH HE PULLS ON. THE SHOES ARE THE SLIP-ON SORT. HE PUTS HIS FEET IN THEM. RIMA GOES TO THE DOOR, TAKES HER DUFFEL COAT FROM THE HOOK, OPENS THE DOOR AND STANDS BESIDE IT, HOLDING UP THE COAT FOR HIM TO SLIP HIS ARMS IN. HE STARES AT HER.

RIMA: (IMPLACABLY) Goodbye, Lanark.

HE WALKS STRAIGHT PAST HER OUT OF THE DOOR.

THE STAIRS

A LOW-ANGLE SHOT FROM MIDWAY UP. LANARK, STONE-FACED, DESCENDS BLOCKING ALL VIEW OF THE TOP.

RIMA'S VOICE: Lanark! (A PAUSE) Lanark!

HIS HEAD DESCENDS OUT OF VIEW, REVEALING HER AT THE STAIRTOP, COAT IN HAND.

SOUND: THE STREET DOOR IS OPENED.

RIMA: Lanark, take this!

SHE FLINGS COAT INTO THE CAMERA: BLACKNESS.

SOUND: STREET DOOR SLAMS.

FOG & SNOW

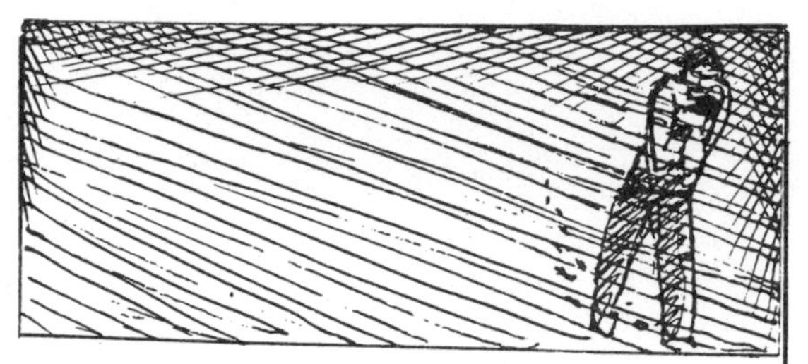

SOUND: FOOTSTEPS IN FROZEN SNOW.

A DIM HUNCHED FIGURE EMERGES ON THE RIGHT AND BEFORE VANISHING OFF RIGHT WE RECOGNIZE LANARK, COATLESS, CLENCHED GLOVED HAND PRESSED TO CHEST, OTHER HAND CLUTCHING WRIST OF IT.

SOUND: THE DRONE OF AN APPROACHING TRAMCAR.

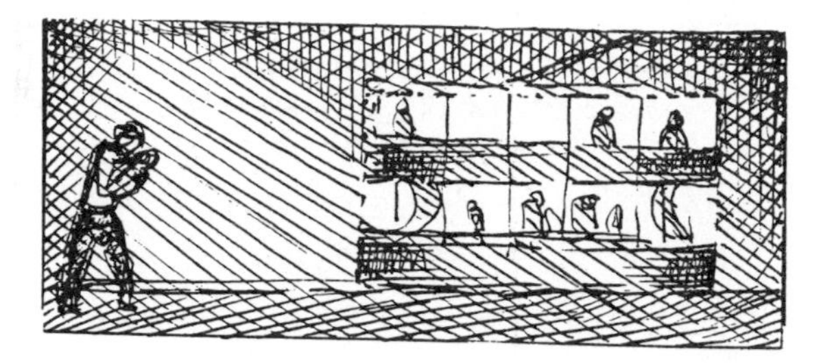

DIM HUNCHED LANARK TRUDGES IN PROFILE FROM LEFT TO RIGHT WHILE THE REMOTER SILHOUETTE OF TRAMCAR PASSES RIGHT TO LEFT. LANARK CLENCHED HAND SHAKES SPASMODICALLY, AS IF TRYING TO BREAK THE GRIP OF THE OTHER HAND.

SOUND: WOMEN TITTERING.

FOG THINS RIGHT TO SHOW 3 WOMEN WITH A COFFEE-STALL BEHIND, ONE OLD AND FAT, ONE OLD AND WIZENED, ONE YOUNG IN FUR COAT AND HAT. SOUND: FOOTSTEPS IN SNOW. LANARK EMERGES LEFT. THE YOUNG WOMAN WAVES AND CALLS.

GAY: *Lanark!*

HE HALTS, STARING. TRACK TO THEM AS SHE APPROACHES SAYING:

GAY: *Lanark, where have you been? Sludden's been looking everywhere for you. He wants to tell you something.*

LANARK STARES AT HER. HIS GLOVED HAND SQUIRMS. HE TIGHTENS

HIS GRIP. IT GOES INERT.

GAY: (SMILING SLYLY) I know why you're wearing a glove, I've got one too! (HE STARES AT HER) I'll show you my disease if you show me yours. (HIS MOUTH OPENS.) Everyone has a disease

SHE TUGS HER GAUNTLET OFF AND AND PROJECTS HER LIGHTLY CLENCHED FIST TOWARD HIM. CAMERA MOVES SLOWLY INTO CLOSE-UP AS SHE UNCLENCHES HER HAND AND THE PUPILS VANISH FROM HER EYES. SLUDDENS MOUTH IS IN THE PALM. IT SPEAKS.

SLUDDEN'S VOICE: (TINY AND CLEAR) You're far too serious, Lanark.

LANARK: Oh. Oh God.

SLUDDEN: You worry too much.

CLOSE-UP OF GAY'S HAND AND FACE.

LANARK'S VOICE: Oh this is Hell.

GAY'S MOUTH FALLS OPEN. SLUDDENS VOICE COMES OUT OF THAT TOO, BUT DEEP AND HOLLOW.

SLUDDEN'S VOICE: But you're trying to understand life and that interests me.

SOUND: LOW SOLEMN ORGAN CHORDS CORRESPOND TO BACK-TRACKING FOOTSTEPS.

CAMERA BACK-TRACKS UNTIL GAY APPEARS HANGING IN THE THINNING FOG LIKE A PUPPET, HER TOES A FEW INCHES ABOVE THE SNOW.

SOUND: STRONG ORGAN MUSIC.

ZOOM BACKWARD TO PASS, THEN SHOW FROM IN FRONT, LANARK RUNNING BLINDLY TOWARD THE CAMERA LIKE ONE NEAR THE END OF HIS EMOTIONAL & BODILY POWER.

THE NECROPOLIS

THE CAMERA ZOOMS BACK BEFORE HIM THROUGH THE STONE PILLARS OF A HUGE OPEN WROUGHT IRON GATE. LANARK SLOWS TO A HALT BETWEEN THEM AND, BREATHING DEEPLY, GLANCES BEHIND HIM FOR THE FIRST TIME. NOTHING IS VISIBLE THERE BUT

SOUND: ORGAN MUSIC, SOLEMN AND EERIE.

HE TURNS AND THE CAMERA TURNS WITH HIM, KEEPING HIM CENTRAL AS HE SURVEYS A SNOW-COVERED HILLSIDE OF BLACK MONUMENTS, THE TALLEST AND MOST CLOSELY CLUSTERED ON THE SKYLINE. THE WEIGHT OF THE GLOVED HAND MAKING IT HARD FOR HIM TO KEEP BALANCE. HE NOTICES THIS AND LIFTS THE HAND CURIOUSLY TO HIS FACE.

SOUND: END ORGAN MUSIC.

CUT TO CLOSE-UP.

THE HAND HAS SWOLLEN. CLAWS PIERCE THE ENDS OF THE GLOVE FINGERS.

WITH AN INDRAWN CRY LANARK THRUSTS THE CLAW AS FAR FROM HIM AS HE CAN, PRESSES HIS FACE WITH THE HUMAN HAND, STUMBLES TO THE GATE PILLAR AND CRIES THROUGH CLENCHED TEETH —

<u>LANARK</u>: *Let me <u>out</u> God, Let me <u>out</u> God, God let me <u>out</u>.*

— STRIKING THE PILLAR WITH HIS BROW EACH TIME ON THE WORD <u>OUT</u>. THEN HE DROPS HIS ARMS, LEANS BACK ON THE PILLAR. HIS BROW IS BADLY GRAZED, HIS EXPRESSION UTTERLY HOLLOW.

<u>SOUND</u>: A DISTANT MELODIOUS BELL CLANGS RESONANTLY ONCE.

HE LOOKS UP. THERE IS A BRIGHT LIGHT SUDDENLY ON <u>THE HILL</u> AMONG THE HIGHER MONUMENTS. HE PULLS HIMSELF ERECT & STARES AT IT.

<u>SOUND</u>: A FAINT IRREGULAR MUSICAL THRILLING NOISE, OF A SORT TO AROUSE CURIOSITY WITHOUT THE LEAST TOUCH OF DREAD. THE BELL CLANGS AGAIN.

LANARK WALKS TOWARD THE LIGHT. CUT TO —

LANARK CLIMBS A STEEP PATH TOWARD THE LIGHT. CUT TO —

HE ENTERS A SPACE SURROUNDED BY OBELISKS. THE LIGHT COMES FROM THE FAR SIDE OF A MONUMENT IN THE CENTRE.

<u>SOUND</u>: THE TRILLING SOUNDS CLOSER: NOT LOUDER, MORE INTIMATE.

HE PROWLS ROUND THE MONUMENT, SEEKING THE SOURCE OF THE LIGHT, AND SEES ON A BRIGHT SURFACE WHAT SEEMS THE SHADOW OF A GREAT BIRD, THE BODY STATIC BUT THE WING TIPS TWITCHING. HE GLANCES UP TO SEE WHAT CASTS THE SHADOW.

SOUND: THE TRILLING STOPS. A LOW BELL-CLANG.

THE SHADOW BECOMES A DISTINCT MOUTH.

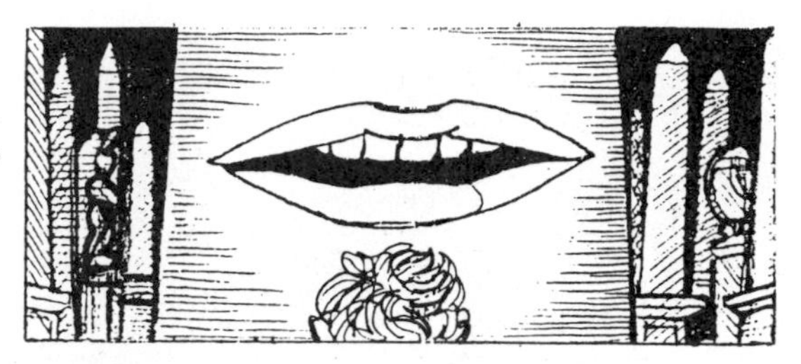

MOUTH: I am the way out.

LANARK: What do you mean?

THE MOUTH CLOSES AND DESCENDS TO THE SNOWY EARTH, PASSING LIKE A COLOURED SHADOW OVER THE PROJECTIONS OF THE MONUMENT BASE. IT STOPS AND OPENS JUST IN FRONT OF LANARK'S FEET, AND OPENS. HE PEERS IN. AN UPDRAUGHT MOVES HIS HAIR.

LANARK: Where will you take me?

THE MOUTH SHUTS AND STARTS FADING.

LANARK: (DESPERATELY) Stop! I'll come.

THE MOUTH GROWS DISTINCT.

LANARK: (HUMBLY) How should I come?

MOUTH: Naked and head first.

LANARK: I'll come how I can.

HE PULLS OFF PULLOVER AND SHIRT, TEARING THEM ON THE SCALES AND SPINES WHICH COVER HIS RIGHT ARM AND SHOULDER.

HE SITS ON THE HARD SNOW, PULLS OFF HIS SHOES, AND DROPS HIS LEGS INTO THE MOUTH OVER THE UNDERLIP.

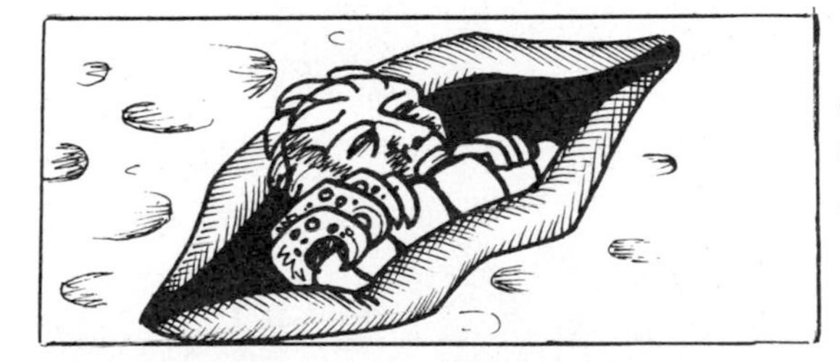

HE LEANS FORWARD, GRIPS THE TEETH OPPOSITE AND SLIDES DOWN TILL HE HANGS FROM THEM. SUDDENLY THE HUMAN HAND LOSES HOLD. IT AND HIS HEAD FALL FROM SIGHT. CUT TO—

GULLET SEQUENCE

AN UPWARD VIEW OF THE OPEN MOUTH FROM FAR BELOW. LANARK'S BODY, LIT BY COLD BLUE LIGHT, DANGLES FROM IT BY THE DRAGON ARM. ALL ELSE IS BLACKNESS.

LANARK: (SHOUTING) Shut! Bite Shut!

THE MOUTH SHUTS.

IN COLD BLUE LIGHT HE FALLS THROUGH BLACKNESS, LEAVING THE SCREEN BOTTOM RIGHT.
CUT TO—

DOWNWARD SHOT OF HIM, LARGE, FALLING INTO THE FRAME FROM THE BOTTOM EDGE AND

DIMINISHING TO NOTHING IN THE CENTRE.
CUT TO—

OBLIQUE UPWARD SHOT OF HIM SOMERSAULTING DOWN INTO CLOSE-UP FROM TOP LEFT. BEFORE LEAVING THE SCREEN BOTTOM RIGHT HE IS SUDDENLY CAUGHT BY A HUGE INVISIBLE HAND, THE LIGHT ON HIM GOES HOT ORANGE RED AND

<u>SOUND</u>: HARSH BUZZING

THE INVISIBLE HAND TIGHTENS, SQUEEZING HIM INTO A PAINFUL KNOT.

HE FIGHTS THE PRESSURE AND MANAGES TO STRAIGHTEN HIS ARMS. LIGHT ON HIM GOES COLD BLUE AND—

SOUND: BUZZING STOPS

HE FALLS AGAIN. CAMERA KEEPS HIM IN FRAME FOR 2½ SECONDS UNTIL—

SOUND: HARSHER BUZZ

IN HOT ORANGE LIGHT THE HAND CATCHES HIM AGAIN AND SQUEEZES TIGHTER. THE SPINES ON ARM AND SHOULDER ARE FLATTENED AND SNAP. WITH HUGE EFFORT HE JERKS ONE LEG STRAIGHT—

SOUND: ¾ SECOND OF SILENCE.

HE FALLS IN BLUE LIGHT TILL CAUGHT AGAIN—

SOUND: STILL HARSHER BUZZ, AS

IN RED LIGHT HE IS SQUEEZ-ED TIGHTER STILL UNTIL—

SUDDEN BLACKOUT. SILENCE.

SOUND: BUZZ.

MEDIUM CLOSEUP. INTENSE PRESSURE IN A DIFFERENT POSITION, IN A DARKER LIGHT, EXCEPT THE DRAGON ARM WHICH GLOWS BRIGHTER.

CUT TO—

BLACKOUT
SILENCE

CUT TO—

SOUND: BUZZ.
CLOSE-UP OF FACE IN DARK CRIMSON LIGHT, DISTORTED BY G-FORCE PRESSURE, THEN SOUND AND IMAGE FADE INTO—

TOTAL BLACKNESS FOR FIVE SECONDS.

SOUND: SCISSORS FAINTLY SNIPPING, THEN SILENCE.

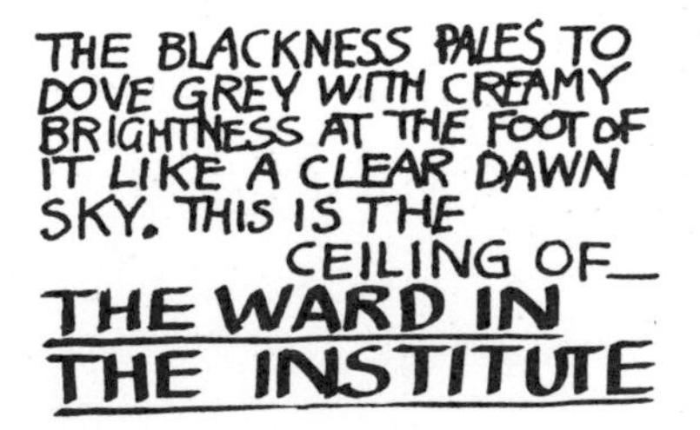

THE BLACKNESS PALES TO DOVE GREY WITH CREAMY BRIGHTNESS AT THE FOOT OF IT LIKE A CLEAR DAWN SKY. THIS IS THE CEILING OF—

THE WARD IN THE INSTITUTE

SOUND: SNIPPING. GIRLISH GIGGLE AND WHISPERS.

TILT DOWN PAST DIAL OF A 25 HOUR CLOCK AND ARCHES. COLOURS ARE ALL WARM WHITES APART THE REVOLVING SCARLET SECOND HAND OF THE CLOCK AND AZURE SKY BEHIND CLOUDS BEYOND THE ARCHES.

P.O.V. SHOT OF LANARK'S LEGS AT THE BOTTOM OF A HOSPITAL BED, NAKED AND APART, YOUNG NURSES CLIPPING HIS TOENAILS AND GOSSIPING.
LANARK'S RIGHT HAND, HUMAN AGAIN, RISES INTO CENTRE OF SCREEN FROM THE BASE OF IT. THE LEFT HAND RISES TO TOUCH IT. THE NURSES NOTICE.

LEFT NURSE: Feeling better, Bushybrows?

LANARK: (AFTER PAUSE) Yes. (OTHER PAUSE) Why do you call me Bushybrows?

THE LEFT NURSE LIFTS AN OCTAGONAL MIRROR AND HOLDS IT CENTRE SCREEN. LANARK'S FACE IN IT IS OLDER AND MOUSTACHED, WITH BUSHY EYEBROWS.

LANARK: I see. (PAUSE) How old do I look?

LEFT NURSE: (REMOVING MIRROR) A bit over thirty.

RIGHT NURSE: No chicken, anyway.

THEY ROLL THE SHEET DOWN FROM HIS STOMACH AND TUCK IT IN. LANARK FOLDS HANDS ON STOMACH.

LANARK: A short while ago I was a bit over twenty.

LEFT NURSE: Well Bushybrows, that's life, isn't it!

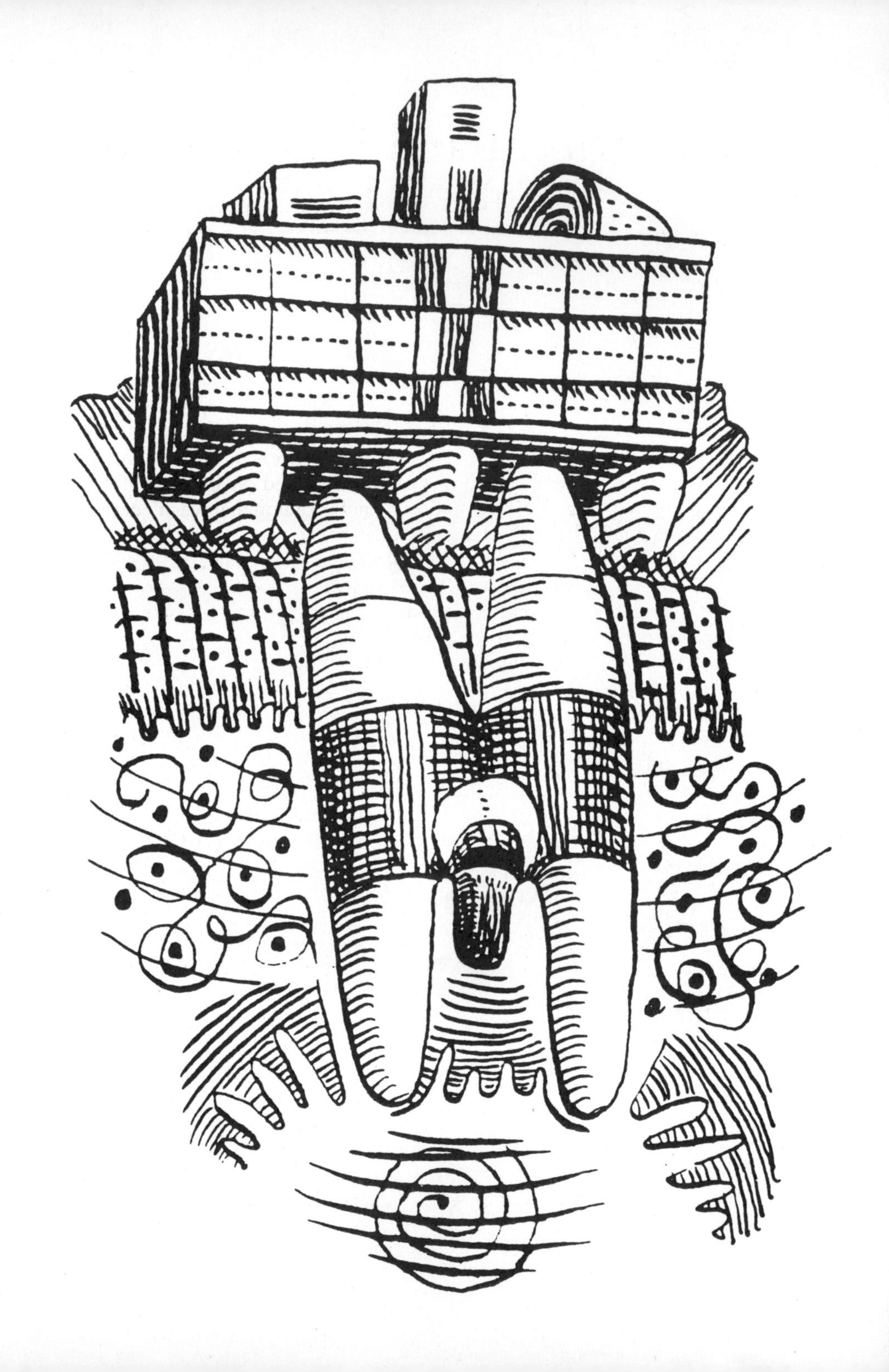

Postmodernism and Friday Night Football

DAVID RIEFF

I wore a nice expression, really I did, and smiled at the swarm of strangers who surrounded me the night of the opening. Not once did I look at my watch.

Well all right, maybe my nice expression isn't all that nice, and maybe, when no one was looking, I did segue into a sly grimace, but I segued out too and nobody noticed, I'm sure of that. Certainly, I didn't offer a single opinion that wasn't cravenly admiring of the paintings and sculpture on display. I didn't say, for example, 'Christ, not this again.' I didn't say, 'Postmodernism makes me want to join the Hezbollah.' None the less, I admit that, as I stood in front of works, most untitled, or ironically titled, or excessively titled, works that made Marcel Duchamp's most casual toss-offs look as pious as Duccios, I was probably less than credible.

It had already been a long evening. I was sure that my friend Dahlia Morgan, who had, as they say in the trade, 'curated' the show, knew me for a fraud. Dahlia's husband Andrew hadn't helped matters any by continually winking at me like a tiqueur in a monkey house. Hypocrite! Although he managed to look the picture of middle-aged innocence in his blue Trippler blazer and his scuffed deck shoes, he wasn't fooling me any more than I was fooling Dahlia. Anyway, he'd already let the cat out of the bag when he told me that he would rather have been at a ballgame, any ballgame, even the Special Olympics, than at one of his wife's openings. He didn't like postmodernism either.

We watched, never focusing on anything for very long. Impatiently, itchily, we watched as Dahlia worked the room, as she greeted the sun-dried patrons of the museum of Florida International University, all the while enveloping the entire gallery with a benevolence only faintly kissed by detachment. Meanwhile, Andrew and I had retreated with as much dignity as we could muster, backing away slowly from the art lovers towards the relative quiet of the gallery office. If the room had only had a door with a lock on it, we would have been home free. There was a cable TV in one corner, with its promise of a hundred and forty broadcast channels, ninety-five of which were sure to be in English. It would have been easy enough for us to clear the brochures and catalogues away, safe in the assumption that there would be a sporting event on at least thirty of the stations, or maybe more. There would be baseball from Minneapolis, Houston and Seattle; jai alai from Connecticut and Mexico City; Canadian football on tape from Edmonton and Calgary; the Mexican league live from the Atlantic coast; Dominican baseball highlights; ethnic soccer – Bhutan versus

Cracow from South San Francisco; professional wrestling, of course; full contact karate from some dojo in Watts; roller derby; even dwarf throwing, which, if I'm not mistaken, has recently been imported from Australia, and enjoys a considerable popularity in the Upper Midwest.

Unfortunately, it would have embarrassed Dahlia had we switched the set on, and so, though both Andrew and I would occasionally turn and stare wistfully at the blank screen, imagining sweating jocks going at it full throttle everywhere from Anchorage to the Yucatan, the continent competed in silence. We stood carefully sipping white jug wine out of plastic cups shaped like champagne flutes and marvelling over the fact of simultaneity.

That being said, we probably had a better idea of what was happening on those thirty-odd sports channels than we did of what the weather was like outside the room in which we were so morosely loitering. Perhaps we should have checked the weather station, a national service on air twenty-four hours a day. But instead, let's say it was an air-conditioned night in South Florida, typical for that time of year. Let's say that everyone was speaking English inside the art gallery, as they were most definitely not in the rest of Dade County, or even, for that matter, on the television itself, where Andrew could easily have flicked the channel selector from that weather station to one broadcasting a Mexican cowboy movie, a Cuban-American fundraiser in aid of some right-wing cause, the Contras perhaps, or a variety show live from Caracas. Let's add that by the true standards of the world as a whole everyone in that room was a rich person, though few of them, as they stood under the bright halogen lights staring at all that postmodernist art, would have admitted to privilege, let alone to wealth.

I was still holding the remote control attachment for the TV as I walked over to the window and looked outside. The view was somewhat obscured by the all too articulated reflections of the lighting fixtures, and by the thickness of the plate glass itself, which was tinted after the manner of a sheikh's sunglasses or some of the quieter buildings of Philip Johnson. Still, I could vaguely make out the crickets that swarmed like cheerleaders at a pep rally, the fireflies as thick as traffic, and a representative sampling of the rest of South Florida's insect population as it swooped, dived and rolled in the manner of Rumanian gymnasts. Across the quad, which had been a parking lot, and, before that, a mangrove swamp, the new brutalist buildings of the campus oozed verdure, and it was impossible to tell for certain whether the cracks in these façades formed part of the architect's conceit, or whether things were just really coming apart. More than normally, I mean. Then, for a second, the doors of the gallery opened, and I watched two students wearing T-shirts reading 'Exotic Miami' arguing fiercely in Spanish about Homecoming Week.

'*Bienvenido a los Estados Unidos, bienvenido a Miami,*' said Andrew, who had followed my glance.

I grinned apologetically, but he knew I had immigration on the brain. Whenever he tried to talk to me about anything, whether it was Degas or sailing in Maine, he was more than likely to hear me respond with some off-centre musing about how the instructions on the coffee maker in his kitchen were printed in both Spanish and English. But this time he had meant only to forestall me. 'It's Friday night,' he said, 'there must be a high-school football game going on somewhere around this place.'

Andrew had been the quarterback for Kenyon College in the late 1930s when John Crowe Ransom had taught there. Robert Lowell had been a classmate and an acquaintance; his muscular feats had put the jocks to shame. Usually, listening to Andrew's stories, all I could think of by way of reply was to say, 'You see, it was another America then,' his line really, but you see how easy it was to set me off. Actually, Andrew was no fonder of reminiscence than he was of gallery openings, preferring either to stay at home and paint his determinedly unfashionable water-colours, or else put on his orange sun-visor and go root for the University of Miami Hurricanes, one of the best college baseball teams in the country.

'*Age quod agis*,' he said.

'What?'

'You're no Latin scholar. It means, roughly speaking, "Do what you do." Lowell used to quote it a lot when he was at Kenyon. It was the motto of his prep school.'

I laughed. This I took to be Andrew's way of saying that we should leave the gallery. But American WASPs have their own peculiar inscrutability, and I was by no means certain that I had understood him correctly. I laughed again, mirthlessly this time, and waited.

'Well come on,' he said. After only a moment, I followed his retreating form out of the small side door.

The initial effect of being outside was intensely confusing. At first, it seemed very hot, and very dark, and very quiet, all in a completely undifferentiated way. I couldn't tell the heat from the dark from the quiet. Andrew must have felt the same, for he stood, a few feet ahead of me, off the concrete path in the thick grass border, frozen like a deer caught in the high beams of an onrushing car. He stared at me, shaking his head as if to clear it. Mine needed urgently to be filled. I realized that neither of us knew what to do or where to go next. In another few seconds, I probably would have suggested some fatuous excursion, downtown perhaps, or maybe out along the Tamiami Trail, away from Miami proper towards the Everglades – a road that leads straight past the Krome Detention Center for Illegal Aliens, the coming attraction for twenty-first-century America. At that moment, fortunately, Andrew began to stumble towards the parking lot, and I went after him, aping his movements from a few paces behind, the way one might do in an aerobics class. As we drew nearer, we could see not only the concrete stanchions of the parking field lamp-posts, with their hazy rectangular lights surrounded by haloes of fluttering insects, but, seemingly only a few hundred yards beyond, several enormous grids of Klieg lighting, powerful enough to pierce the sky. Then we heard the sound of a crowd roaring.

'There *is* a game on,' Andrew whispered.

Do the caribou feel this inexorable pull when they drown themselves, *en masse*, in the rivers of northern Ontario? Do whales feel this way when they rush to beach themselves? Moving with a peculiar, impatient gracelessness, we set out in the direction of the stadium. There was no way we were going to get there, it was simply too dark. After only a few hundred yards, I slipped and fell along the muddy levee and almost fell into the bayou. Bayou? It might as well have been a sewage ditch for all I could tell. After that, even Andrew's enthusiasm began to flag a bit. We tried to move cautiously, but no matter where we tried, we were unable to pick our way through the tangle of giant cypresses, hanging ficus and tree ferns. Every place in Miami that is not overwhelmed by concrete is overwhelmed by the recalcitrant tropical flora. Every so often, we could hear the crowd in the stadium yelling, and we would speed up, the thought of some great pass or ferocious tackle spinning in our heads. 'What do you think the score is?' Andrew asked, just before we stopped and gave up.

In a small clearing, the ground proved, finally, too inviting. We were out of breath, and first only paused, bent over with our hands on our knees. Then Andrew sat down crosslegged, leaned back, and lay full out in the soft, damp grass. A moment later, I toppled down too, stretched, stared up at the sky. We lay there in silence for a long time, just listening to the game.

I'M YOURS
HUG ME
HEART THROB

Sharon Loves Darren

FAY WELDON

'Sharon,' said Nurse Emily Fitt, patiently, 'now, Sharon, if you don't swallow this tube, you will *die*.'

'Want to die,' said Sharon, petulantly. And then she called her lover's name aloud, so that the sound bounced back from pale green walls, up and down the casualty cubicles, softened by stacked cardboard boxes (labelled 'Cardiac Infibulation', or 'Tracheotomy', or 'Paediatric Artery' or whatever), sharpened by racks of stainless steel and instruments for the cutting and closing of human flesh, 'Darren! Oh Darren, save me!'

'Look,' said Nurse Emily Fitt, who wore a badge claiming 'a legend in her time' on her tidy uniform, and whose face was neat and intelligent and composed – she was all of twenty-four – 'look, Sharon, just swallow this tube or you'll go into liver failure and *die*. Do you understand?'

But all Sharon did was shriek for Darren again and then clamp her mouth shut against the intrusive poking pale yellow tube. Sharon was seventeen. She wore laddered black tights and a bra. They'd stripped her of everything else. She'd drunk a bottle of sherry, a bottle of whisky and a bottle of wine during the course of the evening, and taken twenty-five Paracetamol tablets, a whole bottleful, for love of Darren, who had taken Debbie to the cinema instead of her.

Darren was nineteen, and sitting out in the waiting-room, reading the sports page of last Saturday's *Sun*. I'd noticed him earlier. He had acne and cropped pale reddish hair. What he thought it was impossible to tell. If Sharon's voice reached him he was deaf to it. Or perhaps it just bored him. He'd heard it too often.

'Sharon,' said Nurse Emily Fitt, 'we want to help you but if you don't make an effort yourself we can't.'

I lay in the next cubicle, in no particular medical trouble, and listened. Sharon went into fits of bitter weeping. 'Oh, Darren, Darren, my heart is breaking.' I believed her. I'd cried like that myself.

Sister Radice, all bosom and big dark eyes, fetched me a cup of tea. I was privileged. I had responded to medical treatment and could now be sent home. I was waiting to be fetched. 'These girls,' she said, 'they don't know how dangerous Paracetamol is. They take it by the handful. We do our best but sometimes they don't make it. I blame the drug companies.'

'Oh, Darren, Darren,' cried Sharon, lovesick Sharon, and tears came to my own eyes.

'I want to go to the loo,' yelled Sharon, suddenly, furiously, like the spoilt and naughty child she was.

'Not yet, not yet,' said she whose name was a legend in her own time, 'it can wait. Just swallow.'

'It can't wait,' said her patient nastily. 'What am I supposed to do, wet my pants?'

'Better than dying,' said Nurse Emily Fitt, but Sharon didn't agree.

'Leave me alone,' Sharon begged, 'leave me to die.'

'Look,' said Nurse Emily Fitt, who was little more than a child herself, but at least was sensible, 'if you die your parents will go mad.'

'They're mad already,' said Sharon, cunningly. 'They hate Darren anyway.'

'Not surprised,' muttered Nurse Emily Fitt. 'So do I.'

Sharon's sick soaked into a newspaper on the floor. They'd made her vomit when the ambulance came in; given her an emetic before she'd had time to protest. The young doctor (Dr Angus Love, according to his lapel badge, but how could one be sure? Perhaps they made their names up?) had poked through it, fish and chips swirling round in sherry, whisky and wine, but only found four Paracetamol tablets, half disintegrated, which meant there were another twenty-one left inside her. She'd have to be stomach-pumped but a conscious patient, when it comes to it, is more difficult than one in a coma. He'd left the job to Emily. He was busy. Everyone was.

'I say,' said Sharon, plaintively, between shrieks and sobs. 'I feel rather sick.'

'I expect you do,' said Nurse Emily Fitt. 'Sick to death. Swallow the tube!'

'You want to hurt me.'

'We don't want to hurt you. Why should we want to hurt you?'

'Because you don't like me,' said Sharon, acutely. 'Because I love Darren! Darren, save me! Let me see Darren. Please, let me see Darren.'

'No,' said Nurse Emily Fitt, and the department filled again with the sound of Sharon's noisy distress, and Sharon's furious little laddered and holed foot banged against the partition wall and saline drips everywhere trembled and faltered, and heart monitors, over-sensitive, gave perfectly absurd readings.

'I love Darren. I want to die for Darren!' cried Sharon.

'Just shut up, will you,' said Nurse Emily. 'If you think I haven't better things to do than look after you, you're mistaken. There are children in casualty. You're scaring them to death carrying on like this. You don't want to frighten little children, do you?'

'I love Darren,' shrieked Sharon. 'Fetch me Darren, you bitch!'

'Swallow the tube.'

'No. Won't.'

'Die then,' said Nurse Emily Fitt, and went off to attend to a heart attack (or so he feared) and a young woman with an abscess on her Fallopian tube (or so she said, but was certainly grim and white with pain and would swallow anything at all to put a stop to it). I was formally discharged.

'Goodbye,' said Nurse Emily Fitt, cheerfully.

'Look,' I said, 'tell her if she dies Debbie will get Darren.'

'That's an idea,' said Nurse Emily, but I didn't think she was going to go back and say any such thing. I had a feeling that if young Doctor Love didn't return from the broken back (mother of three, drunk, backwards out of a first-floor window: slowly and clearly, 'Mrs Able, do you understand? Try to listen. You are in hospital. You fell out of a window and have broken your back. We are admitting you') quite promptly, and look in upon Sharon, she would simply go into liver failure, and die, and Nurse Emily Fitt would be busy elsewhere, and Sister Radice would break the news to Darren, who would look up from the sports page, and be quite astonished, if so strong an emotion were available to him, which I rather doubted, at what could happen if you took Debbie to the cinema one Sunday night, instead of Sharon.

Good for Sharon, say I. Death before dishonour.

The Equilibrist

KURT TIDMORE

Voices echoed up through the empty air like the calls of some gentle species of herbivore. The modulations and abrupt starts and stops had the diction of bird songs, but also something in common with the songs of whales, mournful and resonant. When the band played the notes crashed together in the rigging, but speech echoed back upon itself until only the overlapping vowels were left. Once, early in the morning when the great tent was empty, a workman removing litter had begun to whistle, and the sound had taken on such a crystalline brilliance that the equilibrist felt his heart pierced. From the high perch where he sat eating he watched the oblivious workman move from ring to ring, and suddenly the isolation of his great height impressed him. He stopped chewing and watched the foreshortened figure slowly clean each ring in order. Walking back across the centre ring the workman halted momentarily directly below his secret observer and turned his head from side to side, taking in the empty bleachers. Then he bent slightly at the waist and gave a little sweeping gesture with his free hand, a gesture of opening; it was only the vaguest hint of a bow, but for that split second the equilibrist felt that he and the workman were brothers. It was only an instant, but for him it was like the tug of a long fragile umbilical pulling him slightly off balance, and suddenly he was aware of the smallness of his perch and the great depth of air separating him from the man below. Then the workman put a few remaining tatters of litter into his bag and walked back along the path of streaming light into the morning. The equilibrist was left alone on his high platform in the twilight of the vacant tent shaking his head as if to rouse himself from a dream.

He had walked the wire since childhood, learning the skill from his parents the way other children learned to do household tasks or ride a bicycle. The wire was his only expertise, but he knew it intimately, the way a blacksmith knows the colours of hot metal. Because he was ignorant of what others knew and ill at ease in situations which made them happy he was virtually friendless. Even his acquaintance with the clown fell short of friendship. Their only common ground was the history they had shared as two workmen might share a box lunch or a six-pack of beer.

When the circus arrived in a new town the equilibrist supervised the erection of his rigging, the hanging of the wire itself, the turnbuckles and tensioning tackle, the stabilizing guys. Then he climbed to the larger of the two platforms and pulled the rope ladder up behind himself. From the platform he would adjust the wire like a violinist tuning for a performance, and, this done, he rarely descended to the ring. He had no conscious belief which kept him so long separated from the ground – he went down for occasional meals and to sleep, although he had been known to go for days on end without leaving the rigging – but he felt most at ease on the high wire. On the ground he was a short, shambling figure with feet and hands too big for his body and a slight cast to one eye; the kind of man who could be a mechanic or a bartender or a bricklayer. When he spoke he sometimes stammered, and his voice was soft and accented; and when someone spoke to him he listened with a faintly distracted air as if half his mind was following another conversation entirely, one no one else could hear. But when he put on his spangled white tights and pulled himself up the swinging rope ladder higher and higher into the darkness beyond the footlights, up to his private world of tensioned cable and thin air, his aspect changed, and those who had seen him below were suddenly struck by their own failure of perception, like people who have watched a swan waddle about the land without ever thinking that it might swim or fly. In the air, pinned against the dark upper reaches of the tent by converging spotlights, the equilibrist would extend his arms out to his sides and step on to a wire so fine that its very existence could be doubted except for his presence on it. A hush would fall; children would stare up in the darkness with owlish eyes, men would hold their breath, women would knot their hands together, and the voice of the ringmaster would announce the wire-walker's act in words which echoed like the beats of a drum. Then, perfectly calm, completely in his own element, he would walk slowly across the open air, executing turns, flips, leaps, in a quiet broken only by gasps from the crowd below and the soft rhythm of his own breath. And when he finally reached the opposite platform, and the audience exploded into applause, and the music of the band crashed around him, he would sweep his arm in broad arcs and bow to those below. Then the spotlights would swing away and pick out some new target – an animal act or a troupe of tumblers – taking the attention of the audience with them, and the equilibrist would sit on his small platform and watch the rest of the show with bored professional attention. Sometimes, later, someone in the audience would look up and see a pale form recrossing the wire in the dark to the greater comfort of the larger platform, walking with the nonchalance of a man coming home from work.

But there was nothing casual about the equilibrist's work. The clown had been there the day he had come into the ring with a knife and slowly cut down the safety net, vowing never to use it again.

'Why are you doing this?' the clown had asked.

'Because the net makes me think of falling,' he had answered, sawing slowly through the last guy.

Then he turned and handed the knife to the clown, and went back up to the wire and performed with more grace than ever, trusting to the air as if the wire were a mere convention like a magician's wand, a convenience which could be dispensed with at any time.

Once he began working without the net, the crowds, which before had been appreciative, became fanatic. Every performance was packed, and in each heart was the secret thought: maybe tonight gravity will prove too slippery for him.

On the ground now he was set apart more than ever. When he approached all conversation died, and eyes followed him like gun turrets. At first the other performers still spoke to him, but they knew he was no longer one of them. Beyond simple formalities – greetings, discussions of the weather or the crowd, complaints about work – there was nothing to say. So eventually only the clown spoke to him, trying to understand what moved him along the tensioned wire. But in spite of their shared history the clown was a different kind of creature, and he could not fathom the responses he drew. One day, seeking some easy commonplace on which to build a conversation, he asked the equilibrist, 'Will you wear your sequined tights tonight?'

The equilibrist looked at him and said, 'The sequins cast stars around the tent but blind the audience. You'll see.'

And that night when he appeared on the wire the clown looked up and saw whole constellations in orbit around the dark canvas as the wire-walker moved in the spotlights. And on the faces of the crowd he saw stars reflecting back from bright eyes and spectacles. And when he looked back up at the equilibrist he found his gaze returned. Never before had the clown realized how far away the man on the wire was from him.

After this the clown could never quite get the equilibrist out of his thoughts. He still took his falls, did his tricks, produced bouquets from his sleeves; he still threw buckets of confetti on to the unsuspecting people in the front rows. But as he worked he felt the gaze from the top of the tent shining down on him like moonlight, so that, although he never looked up during his act, the audience he thought of most was the man in white waiting in the shadows overhead.

One night when he could not sleep the clown rose from his bed and dressed and went out of his trailer into the dark. There was a breeze and the huge tent moved gently, pulling against the ropes and stakes as if it were sleeping uneasily in close captivity. The clown walked towards the entrance with no particular purpose in mind. At the edge of the moon's shadow he stopped. In one direction he could hear the slow shuffling of the elephants tethered on their chains, the horses stamping in the silvery dark. In the other direction was the sleeping town. Ahead was the entrance to the tent, yawning and square. He lit a cigarette and went in. At the edge of the ring he looked up through the darkness towards the equilibrist's perch. The bottom of the perch gave no hint of occupation. Was the wire-walker up there now, curled up like a dog, surrounded by the abyss, a dreamer on his tiny island in the sky; or was he in his trailer, asleep in front of his TV with a beer grown warm on the floor beside his chair? The clown took a final drag on his cigarette, flipped the butt in a comet's arc towards the centre of the ring, and turned back towards his own trailer. Was that a sleeper's sigh he heard? Maybe it was only the breeze, or the elephants blowing through their trunks.

After months of two- and three-day stops the circus finally arrived in a city where it was scheduled for a week. The clown was glad to rest from the strain of travel, and glad of the opportunity for his colleague to rest. The equilibrist had seemed increasingly distracted lately. On the wire he still moved flawlessly, but when he came down his dark eyes looked strained and his thick fingers twitched slowly as if feeling for something.

A reporter from the newspaper requested an interview with the wire-walker, and the circus management granted it. So one morning a woman with a notepad and a man with a big black camera came into the tent and stood below the wire shouting up.

'Heellooooooo. Heeeellooooooooo.'

The equilibrist's head appeared over the edge of his perch. The woman shouted something up at him. He looked down at her, but couldn't make out what she said. Finally she gestured with her arm that he should descend, and then she made a gesture of writing. He shook his head and disappeared back above the perch. The rope ladder unrolled down the column and came to rest, swinging slowly along its length. He reappeared at the edge of his perch and waved an invitation for them to come up. The reporter and photographer looked at each other, then they went to the ladder. The woman put her foot on the first rung and tried to climb, but immediately found herself hanging nearly horizontal four feet in the air. The photographer had to help her regain the ground. The equilibrist watched all this from above. When the two newspaper people had retreated to the centre of the ring they turned their faces upward again.

'Come down! I want to interview you!' she shouted up at him, but it echoed into a wordless bray.

The figure on the perch disappeared from their sight for a moment, then stepped on to the wire and walked out above the ring. They watched in surprise. Then the photographer began to fiddle hurriedly with his camera, groping into the big brown bag that hung from his shoulder, looking for a film holder and flashbulb.

'Hurry. Hurry. Look what he's doing,' the reporter said.

Far above their heads the equilibrist took his pose, steadied, then leapt into the air, executing a backward flip, and landing in a slight crouch with the wire bouncing gently beneath him.

'Hurry, hurry,' the reporter kept saying softly, without taking her eyes off him.

'Ready now,' the photographer said, raising his camera.

The equilibrist crouched, braced himself, and then leapt up high off the wire, extending his legs straight out in splits with his arms parallel above them. The photographer snapped his camera, illuminating the dim tent with a powerful bluish light and projecting the shadow of the equilibrist huge against the canvas roof.

'Got it,' the photographer said.

In mid-leap, the equilibrist was caught by the sudden explosion of light and saw the silhouette of himself on the canvas overhead; a man in flight, no wire, no net, no platform, astride gravity itself. But the sudden flash blinded him so that when he landed the wire shook uncertainly for a moment, and he swung his arms precariously to regain balance. When he had stabilized himself he looked down, but the reporter and photographer were talking to each other. They looked up again only to wave goodbye. The equilibrist stood in the centre of his wire and watched them go.

The next day, when he hauled up his meal, there was a newspaper clipping in the basket. Surprised, he looked over the perch and saw the clown standing below, beside the workman who brought his food.

The clown's mouth moved and some sounds echoed up. The equilibrist smiled and nodded. The photograph in the clipping showed him in mid-air, outlined by the halo of his shadow. He remembered the black silhouette hovering above him and the feeling of uncertainty when he'd regained the wire. He nodded down at the clown again and waved the clipping.

Later, standing between bleachers, the clown listened to the crowd when the equilibrist appeared. 'He hasn't got a net,' he heard someone say. The audience buzzed with speculation. Their faces were upturned and softly lit in the dim light like faces in a religious painting; the expressions were open-mouthed and intense. Perhaps it was only his private anxiety, but still he was uneasy. After the performance this feeling was shouldered aside by the crush of daily considerations; show followed show, make-up went on and came off, crowds changed, the week passed.

On the day of departure the clown woke early and packed his belongings. He was walking among the sideshows, watching their disassembly and passing casual talk with the carnies when he saw a workman hurrying towards him.

'Come with me. Quick,' the workman said, turning back towards the tent.

The clown followed, trotting to catch up.

'He's crazy,' the workman said. 'We don't know what to do.'

The clown felt as if his stomach had been filled with ice.

Inside the tent a small group of workmen had gathered in the centre ring, their faces all turned upward like spotlights. The ringmaster was among them, wearing a long white bathrobe. Above them the equilibrist stood in the centre of his span with his hands on his hips, not looking down, but clearly tense.

'I can't do a thing with him,' the ringmaster said when he saw the clown.

'What's wrong?'

'He won't come down.'

The clown looked up and said, 'Let me talk to him. Everyone else be quiet. Back up.'

The ringmaster nodded. He and the workmen moved away.

'Hello? Hello?' the clown shouted up.

The equilibrist looked down, and after a moment he smiled a little, shyly.

'What's wrong?' the clown asked, holding his hands out.

'Nothing,' the equilibrist said in a soft conversational tone which reached the floor of the tent almost like a whisper.

'Why won't you come down? It's time to strike the tent.'

'I'm not coming down.'

'You have to come down. You can't stay up there for ever.'

'I'm not coming down.'

The clown was wearing no make-up. His expression was concerned, pleading. The equilibrist walked a little on the wire, unhappy but feeling the rightness of the air around him and hoping the clown would see. He walked back and forth, calming himself.

'Come down. Please. Please come down,' the clown said. He could think of nothing else to say. Arguments about the necessity of moving the circus to another town would mean nothing to a man who lived entirely in the unchanging enclosure of the tent. 'We'll talk,' he added hopefully.

The equilibrist felt the atmosphere soft and buoyant around him, the wire less substantial than ever before, only the thinnest crack in the air, hardly more than an idea, a straight line from where he was to anywhere he might want to be. There was no other way to live. He looked down at the clown's face, the mouth moving, the echoing vowels ascending sadly.

The clown could see that he was not listening. There was tiredness in the way he moved; the glittering tights were baggy from days of constant wear. There was nothing to do but plead. Perhaps this would pass; he would grow tired and relent. Then, as the clown looked up, he saw the equilibrist stop pacing and fix his eyes on the entrance.

The morning light shone in the open doorway, sending its broad beam to the edge of the ring. The equilibrist saw something small move there, glowing against the dark background like a spark from a hearth. It traversed the avenue of light and then entered the shadow of the tent, flying with erratic wingbeats. And then it began to sing, high and clear as it rose in the tent, plying the shaded air, floating in open space on its own song.

The clown followed the equilibrist's eyes to the entrance and saw the bird flying in a zig-zag pattern, trapped inside now, climbing towards the top of the tent. Then he looked back up towards his friend and saw one foot step away from the wire.

Airy Hall, First Light

FRED D'AGUIAR

When asleep, my back turned
On Airy Hall's first light,
Every corner faced takes
A mirror's silvered edge
Flashed and flashed at me.

When I fasten my lids,
A thick dark is punctured
By stars; when I surrender
The stars become flowers;
When the flowers are thrown

They sprout doves,
Doves that arc fluently
Back to my clasp:
Star, flower and dove,
Bring me the light I love.

Airy Hall Iconography

The Tamarind hangs its head,
stings the eyes with its breath.

The Mango traps the sun by degrees,
transforms its rays into ambrosia.

The Coconut's perfect seal lets in rain,
bends with solid milk and honey.

The Guava is its own harvest,
each seed bound in fleshy juice.

The Guinep's translucence is all yours
if you skin its lips, chew its seed for the raw.

The Stinking-toe might be lopped off a stale foot,
on the tongue it does an about-turn: myrrh.

The Pawpaw runs a feather along your nose,
you want it to stop, you want more.

The Sour-sop's veneer is the wasp
treading air at the vaulted honeycomb.

The Sapadilla ducks you twice in frankincense,
you are fished out fighting to go down a third time.

The Wine of Scotland

PATRICIA HIGHSMITH

Henry and Sarah Pilsbury lived on a South Pacific island, the only children of two American missionary couples who had come to the islands forty years before. It had been taken for granted by their parents that Henry and Sarah would marry, and they did when they were about thirty. The marriage wrought few changes in their lifestyle. The greatest change came when the medicine men of the island persuaded the natives that a hurricane was coming. Henry's and Sarah's parents, whose preachings had never brought the islanders a jot closer to Christianity, could not even get a hearing for their argument that the hurricane was only superstition. All the natives took off in outriggers for parts unknown.

The hurricane arrived. Henry and Sarah and their parents had just time to bury themselves in the earth below the sturdiest of the wooden houses they had built – the church – before the wind took away the church, the natives' abandoned huts, and much of the animal and bird life. Henry and Sarah and their parents emerged from their burrow and with characteristic perseverance began to rebuild what had been destroyed. But within a year the older generation one by one died of tropical fever. Henry and Sarah were spared, and suffered only temporary enervation.

Alone now, Henry and Sarah made of the island a more orderly and productive place than it had ever been. Where once an untidy cluster of reed huts stood, there was now a soldierly orchard of fruit trees. The orchard was divided by a straight path that went on through trim tura gardens to the hip-roofed house that Henry had built of boards hewn with his own hands. The Bible was their cornerstone and the only reading matter they had ever known, apart from a handful of religious pamphlets mostly concerning sexual abstinence among primitive peoples. The things they did not know – such as what Europe or America or an aeroplane looked like – they did not care to know. Henry did not talk enough to keep Sarah from feeling lonely now and then, and Sarah had a streak of contrariness in her that vexed Henry sometimes, as when she contended that her father had said Massachusetts was on the west coast of America, and that the sun did not move. Henry remembered very well the map that had been lost in the hurricane and, as for the sun's moving, there was the Bible's word.

They abhorred idleness, and from sun-up to sundown could always find something to do. There was endless mending of clothes and ropes and tools and roofs, sweeping of dirt floors, weeding of gardens, storing of produce, and feeding of the gluttonous wild chickens they kept in a henhouse, though the island was so full of wild chickens that one could not walk far in any direction without stepping on eggs which had been laid in the grass. The busier Henry and Sarah were, the happier, and when they felt especially busy and happy the strains of some old New England hymn, distorted by time and the tone-deafness of Henry and Sarah and of their parents, too, would float in the warm sunny air.

It was Henry's habit in the morning to go down to the beach, spear one of the sluggish, white-meated bolas that swam in the shallow water there, and bring it back for Sarah to cook for breakfast. One morning he saw what looked like a lot of floating boxes far out to sea. With a call to Sarah that he would be late with the bola, Henry got into the outrigger and paddled towards the strange object. The boxes had SCOTCH WHISKY PRODUCT OF SCOTLAND lettered on their sides. Henry did not think he knew the meaning of the second word, but the boxes themselves would be useful. Besides, the boat on which they were floating was made of inflated rubber, that wonderful substance of which Henry's father had told him, and that Henry had seen only in the form of a few rotting circles in his father's desk. Henry gathered other objects floating nearby: a section of shiny bevelled wood, and a canvas ring with SS *Arcadia* printed on it.

'There must have been a shipwreck,' Henry remarked to Sarah.

The wooden boxes contained bottles of a brownish liquid, twelve to a box, all labelled Cutty Sark Scotch Whisky.

'Whisky?' Sarah's weathered face assumed an expression of puzzled anxiety. 'Isn't that what your father used to talk against?'

'I think you're right,' Henry said, though he had not thought of it until Sarah reminded him. 'But medicinally he said it was permissible to drink. He had a bottle of whisky when I was a boy. Then it got used up. Anyway, it's useful stuff and it can serve as wine at our sacraments.'

They planned a sacramental ceremony for Sunday morning, but they were too curious about their trove to wait that long. They opened a bottle the first evening and sampled some before supper.

'It's sharp,' said Sarah, wrinkling up her nose.

'But it's got a fine flavour.' Henry had a bit more. A pleasant sense of well-being spread through him as he ate his supper. He smiled at Sarah and she smiled back, which was pleasant, too.

They fell asleep shortly after supper, and Sarah, who awoke first when the moon was high, had to shake Henry to waken him to come to bed.

On Sunday, Henry and Sarah conducted a sacrament using the whisky and a piece of tura cake as wafer. They were pleased that their wine was of such a rich, delicious kind. Luxury was to be shunned, of course, but if the Lord had not wanted them to have the whisky he would not have sent it.

The rains started, and one afternoon when they were working indoors and actually finding little to do Henry proposed they drink a gourd of whisky.

'I think we might,' Sarah said with an excited smile. She had been hoping Henry would propose just that.

They drank two or three gourdfuls apiece in the course of the afternoon. Finally, Henry left off the plaiting of a rush seat and stared thoughtfully at the setting sun that blazed with a vermilion radiance over the horizon.

'The sunset's very pretty tonight,' Henry said. He had a queer feeling that he had never noticed it before.

'Isn't it pretty!' Standing beside Henry with her gourd, Sarah wobbled ever so slightly as she bent to see through the window. There was an expression of wondering pleasure on her face, as if she had never seen a sunset before either.

A swift arrow of dazzling blue crossed their vision – a pupu winging its way home. And the wonder, the beauty was not merely outdoors. When they looked at their simple room, the two rush-bottomed chairs, the plain brown-and-tan blanket Sarah was weaving on the wall loom, the chest of drawers Henry had made, the very tilt of a stick that propped a shutter open – all these commonplaces seemed charged with a new splendour and a kind of rightness.

Later that evening, Henry was inspired to build a bonfire on the beach. It might be a good idea, he thought, to show any possible survivors of the shipwreck where the island was. Sarah, seeing the fire and associating it with cooking, started preparing a supper of roast pig and fried pineapple. Henry asked her what she was about. They had already eaten supper, he said. Sarah insisted they hadn't, and Henry just as firmly that they had.

'Oh, have a bit of whisky,' Sarah said, handing him the bottle she had been carrying under her arm.

'Is that all that's left of that bottle?' Henry asked. It was their second, and she had evidently drunk a third of it in the house. A little piqued that he had not had his share, Henry poured his gourd full and sipped it as he watched Sarah sprinkling the coarse salt over the roasting pig.

'We haven't eaten yet,' Sarah repeated, looking at him provocatively.

Henry burst out laughing. Why should he quarrel with her if she wanted to say they hadn't eaten supper? Then Sarah giggled, too, and in a few moments they were sitting on the sand eating hot roast pig and pineapple, happy as two children on a picnic.

They woke up the next morning with the sun boiling down on their aching heads. The headaches stayed with them until mid-afternoon.

'We must be careful not to fall asleep on the beach any more,' Henry said.

Henry counted the bottles of whisky again – he had never been good at arithmetic unless he used his fingers – and discovered they had thirty-six boxes instead of the twenty-four he had thought. Thirty-six boxes of twelve bottles each summed up to an incalculable number of bottles. They decided they might drink as much as they wished and still have plenty for the two sips that the sacrament demanded. For a fortnight or so, they drank a bottle between them each day. Life had never seemed so sweet before. They had never got on better.

But they noticed that they sometimes had headaches on mornings when they had not fallen asleep on the beach. They remembered that their parents had complained of drowsiness in the first days of their fever, and they certainly noticed a drowsiness in themselves. Occasionally, generally in the evening, one or the other of them would fall asleep in the middle of an action, and in the morning have no memory of the events just before – clearly a sign of delirium. Many a quarrel developed over differing accounts of the evenings. The only reassuring fact was that neither of them seemed to be running a temperature. But when they found that their hands trembled they began to fear that the fever which had carried off their parents had come back to take them.

'There's no doubt we're infected,' Henry said. 'Remember how Papa's hands shook?'

As if to confirm their suspicion, the mornings suddenly became worse, stripping them of fortitude, even of dignity. There was Henry with a crushing headache as like as not, his discomfort aggravated by Sarah's refusing to admit something she had done the night before, such as taking off her clothes and skipping along the beach singing hymns. And there was Sarah, shaking like all the fronds on a medicine man's head-dress, making a mess of breakfast, dropping the eggs, burning the fish – providing Henry was able to catch a fish.

'Your habits are getting pret-ty bad lately,' Sarah sneered.

'What about yours?' Henry fixed her with a bloodshot eye. 'You haven't cooked an edible breakfast in thirty days.'

'You cook it then.' Sarah groped for something stronger, then said in a shrill voice with a crack in it, 'Why don't you sharpen your spear so you'll catch a fish once in a while? Why don't you fix the roof? It leaks like a sieve every afternoon. Why don't you – '

'Why don't you clean out the henhouse?' Henry interrupted.

'Why don't you – '

But Henry shut her up with a slap across the mouth.

Silent the rest of the morning, Sarah retaliated by burning the house down. Henry was asleep in the house at the time, dreaming that he was dying in a holocaust of fever. He staggered down the smoking reed ladder carrying a box of whisky. Remembering that all the whisky was indoors, Sarah ran into the house, too, and helped him carry out the boxes. The whisky, the Bible, and Sarah's wall loom was all they could salvage before the roof fell in with a poof.

'Just as well I never mended the roof after all,' was Henry's only comment, which struck him as brilliantly philosophic.

Their palm-leaf kindling was too damp to use that evening – an afternoon rain had extinguished the last embers of the house – so Henry tore out a few leaves of the Bible.

They made a jolly supper of young chicken which Henry skewered on his spear and roasted over the fire. It was the end of the wooden spear, but Henry only laughed at that. He would make a better one, he said, might even invent a new weapon.

'We've got to build a new house, I suppose,' Sarah remarked, licking chicken grease from her fingers.

Henry was lying on his elbow, picking his teeth with a splinter of reed. 'If we turn the chickens out of the henhouse and fix that up, we can live in there. It's big enough.'

So they moved into the henhouse.

'Stupid of us to have had a henhouse in the first place,' Henry observed. One thing he could say for his fever, it made him think more clearly and practically about almost everything.

Their mornings, however, became blacker. Petulant quarrels undid the mood of felicity and affection in which they always went to sleep. The new spear Henry had made was not so good as the one he had burnt. He had not been able to construct a table whose legs were even. And Sarah was merciless in her taunts.

'How can I spear a fish with you shouting at me every time I start to strike!' Henry said in quivering exasperation one morning when he came back with an empty spear.

'Gabble, gabble, gabble!' said Sarah, reverting to an old phrase her mother had used.

Henry's eyes narrowed with hate. Recently he had seen a great deal in Sarah that reminded him of her mother, a nagging, quarrelsome woman who had been her husband's cross his life long. Henry snatched a fresh bottle of whisky down from a shelf.

'Are you going to drink whisky before breakfast?' Sarah asked with contempt.

'I don't want any breakfast.'

'Neither do I.' Sarah untied her apron and left the house saucily.

The breakfast fire was blazing in front of the door. Henry yanked Sarah's half-finished blanket down from the wall loom, and threw it into the fire. There were a lot of mistakes in the bottom part of it anyway. He rolled the remaining whisky around in his gourd and drank it off. He was feeling better than he had a few minutes ago. He strolled to the window. Look at Sarah down there on the beach, shaking and twitching, wandering around like a chicken! He hoped she stayed away all day! Then, as he reached for the yellow-labelled bottle once more, something made a connection in Henry's mind: it was the gourdful of whisky that had made him feel so much better. It couldn't have been anything else.

'Sarah!' he shouted, forgetting all about their quarrel. He ran to her with a gourdful of whisky. 'Drink this!'

And Sarah did. In a matter of minutes, she stopped shaking. And Henry did catch a bola that morning, and Sarah prepared a delicious breakfast which they ate with their old appetites. Sarah was so glad to be feeling better that she forgave Henry for burning her blanket. She started a new one that afternoon with more exciting colours. And Henry invented a rocking chair. Both were so pleased with their day, they drank a bottle apiece that night to celebrate.

It was easy to banish their tremblings the next morning with a gourdful of whisky. The thirty-six – now twenty-two – boxes of whisky had indeed been a godsend, and the fever would certainly pass before their supply was exhausted. Henry and Sarah adopted the habit of carrying gourds of whisky at their belts as they went about their chores. Unfortunately, Henry was often too tired to do all the repairing and hunting and fishing he should have done, and Sarah had not touched the garden in weeks.

Henry shrugged. 'Matter of habit, that's all, whether we keep every blade of grass out of the garden.'

So they left off tending the garden and the orchard, and found they lived just as well, only more pleasantly.

Then one day the henhouse caught on fire. Seeing the conflagration from the wood, where he was trying to catch a pupu with a string-and-rock device, Henry's first thought was that Sarah had flown into another of her childish tantrums. Then he remembered: Sarah never lost her temper now. And he was right. The henhouse had caught fire when Sarah had been trying to drive out a winged insect with a burning brand, an accident that might have happened to anybody. So Henry only laughed, kissed Sarah's cheek, and told her to forget about the old henhouse. They got the whisky boxes out and what was left of the Bible, and moved into the woodshed, a sturdy, lean-to structure.

Weeks went by, and the fever hung on in its incipient but terrifying form. Now and then, they tried to decrease their consumption of whisky in order to conserve it, but they always felt so much worse that they would end by throwing economy to the winds and drinking what they needed. When their supply stood at eight boxes, though, they decided on a regimen: only half a bottle apiece per day. They adhered to it, but it did not improve their health or their tempers.

'We've only four boxes left now,' Henry said solemnly one morning.

'Have you been looking out for more rafts?' Sarah queried accusingly.

'Have you?'

'I told you, the fever's got my eyes.'

'It's got mine, too,' Henry retorted, suddenly in a pet.

He went back to the woodshed where the whisky boxes were. It was time somebody reckoned how many days they could exist, if each day took one bottle, and Henry had to see the bottles, even feel them, in order to count them. He tripped over something and fell headlong. One of his hands landed in a bowl of something wet – a mess of tura that Sarah had prepared for the chickens. He shook his hand with disgust, got up and groped for the nearest box which he hoped would be two. He saw two, but there was only one.

'My goodness,' he said aloud, 'even if I saw double this morning, there were two boxes – or was that yesterday morning?' Absently he licked the forefinger of his sticky hand. It tasted rather pleasant. He looked at the grey, bubbly mess in the bowl and wondered what Sarah had put in it.

But the missing box. Sarah had probably buried it. With his bare feet – his straw shoes had worn out weeks ago and he had put off making new ones – Henry stamped on the ground around the woodshed, alert for signs of digging and burying. Then he ran back to Sarah.

'Where've you hidden it, Sarah?' he demanded.

'Where've *you* hidden it? You needn't think you can fool me, Henry Pilsbury!' Sarah had his spear in her right hand.

Henry grabbed her and shook her by the shoulders until her teeth rattled. Only Sarah's excruciating grip on his beard made him turn her loose. He ran back towards the woodshed. The long spear whistled past his ear and dived into the sand in front of him. Henry vented his wrath in furious digging with one of his broken wooden shovels. Not to be outdone, Sarah seized another shovel and began to dig too. In the course of the day, a wide area around the woodshed was torn up, every last weedy row of tura was trampled, and no buried box was discovered. Henry sat down heavily, and scooped up some more of the stale mush with his gourd. He was hungry, not having had even breakfast that day, but he was too proud to ask Sarah to cook anything. The mush had some of the pungency of whisky.

'Sarah!' he called with a sudden thought, scowling. 'Why did you put whisky in this, if you were going to let it go to waste?'

'I don't know what you're talking about,' she said prissily, though she weaved as she walked away from him.

Henry didn't know whether to believe her or not. She wouldn't have remembered, probably, if she had put whisky in it. 'Whisky on tura mush!' he sneered. The mush was rather rotten, but the liquid was good. Suddenly he remembered another bowl of the stuff by a tree near the burned-down henhouse. He went to the tree, priding himself that the bowl was really there and he had not imagined it, and tasted the mess in it. The same flavour, stronger if anything. Henry cursed her. Probably she'd poured out bottles and bottles of whisky on mush! And all out of spite, out of petty female malice!

'Sarah!' Henry cried, running to her with the bowl. 'There's whisky in this, too! Don't deny it!'

But Sarah did deny it, told Henry he had lost his mind and that he had probably poured the whisky into the bowls himself. 'It's just gone sour, *I* think. I've seen tura mush look all bubbly like that. You're so full of whisky, you can't taste anything else, that's all.'

The argument went on in circles all night. Henry caught a wild chicken, forced some of the stuff down its throat, and triumphantly pointed out that the chicken began to stagger. But Sarah refused to admit that it was staggering.

'How do you know you didn't catch a chicken that has tropical fever?' was her retort.

Female logic! Useless to tell her that the chicken was drunk because it was so much smaller than he was, it took less to make it drunk. He wasn't drunk, he was down with fever. Finally, frothing with rage, Henry said he was going to prove her deceit by letting a bowl of fresh tura mush stand, under his eye, for a few days.

So he made a bowl of mush from the tura roots that they had dug up in looking for the missing box of whisky. Henry put the bowl beside his straw bed in the woodshed. For several days, nothing happened, Henry could tell, because he tasted the stuff morning and evening. Sarah was quite good about bringing him gourds of whisky, but he suspected that her purpose was to pour a little on the mush when he wasn't looking. He hadn't let that happen. The few times a day that he bestirred himself, he took the bowl of mush with him. But mostly he slept, with his arm across the bowl. One of the times he was out of the woodshed, with the bowl, he came upon Sarah asleep on the beach beside the missing box of whisky which she had clearly just dug up. She had not even bothered to fill in the hole! Henry hid his bowl behind a coconut tree, then took the box away and buried it in the centre of the island, marking its place well by some nearby palm trees.

When Sarah awakened, he could see that she realized what had happened. But both she and he kept a grim silence.

Slowly but surely, Henry's bowl of mush began to taste like whisky. Henry was puzzled. He was pretty sure Sarah had not put any whisky in it. He experimented by drinking off all the liquid from the mush at a time when his hands were shaking with fever. His hands stopped shaking as if he had drunk whisky from a bottle.

'Our tura makes whisky!' Henry announced to Sarah. 'It's a miracle!'

'I told you so,' said Sarah.

Henry loathed her at that moment. 'If not for me – *I* discovered it! *I've* solved the problem of how to get more whisky!'

Sarah refused to show any interest or gratitude. But she did taste the last drops of the mush, and after that set to work as hard as Henry to gather tura roots and to replant the little turas that were not fully grown. By evening, they had ten gourds and fourteen bowls – all the bowls they possessed – standing about the woodshed full of tura and water. They took turns the next day guarding them from the wild chickens, though the greediness of the chickens was a help to their food problem: Henry would let them get very close to a bowl, then quite often he could grab one, if he were quick enough, and wring its neck.

Sarah began to make bowls out of sections of trees, but it was slow work. Henry tried to make a container by caulking an empty whisky box, but he could not stop it from leaking. And the whisky supply was dwindling. Sarah sneered at him about the box he had stolen from her, and said she supposed he had drunk it up.

'No, I haven't,' said Henry, and he went and got it.

But even so – a little more than a box now – how long could that last? They had thought to conserve their whisky by drinking tura mush, but their shaking limbs drove them to the whisky more often than not. They planted more tura. But tura took time to grow. Sarah kept saying it was a losing battle – just as her mother would have said – but Henry did not mean to give up so soon.

'Hope springs eternal in the human breast, as my father used to say,' Henry told her. 'Hew a heaven out of the wilderness! Man is distinguished from the animal by his brain! Where there's a will, there's a way!'

Half a box of whisky was left now. Sarah was praying night and day between rationed gourds of whisky and tura mush. Henry prayed, too, but he remembered another saying of his father's, dimly: God helps those who help themselves. He couldn't remember whether his father had been for it or against it, but *somebody* had said it at some time, and it seemed very sensible to Henry. Yet he did hope for a miracle, a very modest one, just a big container of some sort to come floating in from the sea, something big enough to hold a lot of mush. What a pity that the rubber boat had rotted in the sun!

'We've got to do something in less than a week,' Henry said, his whole body beginning to twitch with fever and panic. 'The thought of facing this fever without any whisky at all – '

'Oh, let's not think about it!' Sarah said. 'You haven't thought of anything with all your God-given intelligence and you never will. The only thing to do is get into the old outrigger and hope we'll find another island where they have whisky.' She pulled him towards the beach where the outrigger, with its tattered sail, lay under some palm trees.

It was sudden, but Henry could think of no alternative either. 'Shouldn't we take some things with us?' he asked.

'What things?'

Henry looked around him. He could not see farther than a few yards, but there seemed indeed to be nothing they should take. Except the rest of the whisky, of course. He started for the woodshed to get the box in which only five bottles remained.

'On second thoughts,' Sarah said, entirely too slyly for Henry not to suspect something, 'let's leave tomorrow morning. Get a nice early start.'

'All right,' said Henry, just as slyly.

So they sat up all night, watching each other to see that he or she did not take a bottle from the box and drink it, or dig up other bottles that they suspected each other of having buried. Henry was the first to fall asleep, but his purpose was accomplished anyway, because Sarah dug up a cache of two bottles, so they now had seven. Henry opened his mouth to give her a piece of his mind, but Sarah poked a full bottle into his hands.

'A present for you. We won't count these two. Drink it!'

So they drank a bottle apiece before they set out.

They started in the direction the natives had taken, with a strong wind at their tail to cheer them, but they lost their sense of direction as soon as the island was out of sight. The island came into view again. They changed their tack, though with no assurance now that they were not sailing away from the opposite side of the island. Happily, Sarah had brought a few pineapples and some dried fish, but the serious problem was the whisky supply. They were down to four and a third bottles.

'We may have to sail all the way to America to get whisky,' Sarah said cheerlessly. 'Or Scotland.'

A few hours later, noticing that the tiller seemed to be hitting against something, Henry investigated and found three bottles of whisky tied by withes to the stern. They had been there all the time! He dragged them up softly, intending to hit Sarah over the head with one, though not hard enough to break the bottle. But Sarah surprised him by pushing him overboard from behind.

When the last bottle gave out one bright morning, Henry and Sarah prepared for a feverish death. They jittered and twitched, unable to sit still or to move about either, and each kept telling the other he was dying, at that very instant. But neither did, so they stopped believing or paying any attention to each other. As far as his poor eyesight permitted, Henry watched for land, land anywhere. He even looked behind the boat for land. Sarah was of no use at all, lying in the bottom of the boat, complaining.

'You're a bad sailor,' Sarah said to him from time to time with a trace of her old maliciousness in her fevered eyes.

'You can burn in hell,' Henry replied. In his delirium, he cursed the fate of men to be burdened with stupid, vicious women in the name of wives. Once he sneered, 'It is not good that the man should be alone. Hah!'

To add to his bitterness, Sarah happened to be at the tiller when they sighted land. Henry was asleep when Sarah cried out in a loud, cracking voice: '*I see land!*'

Henry got up on his elbow. He couldn't see it, but he did not want to accuse Sarah of imagining it and then be proven wrong. 'How big is it?' he asked.

'See for yourself, you fool!' Sarah replied unkindly, knowing he couldn't see the horizon.

'Is it a town? Are there people?'

But evidently Sarah couldn't see too much either, because she didn't say anything more until Henry himself saw the tan hump of land in front of them. 'God has answered us!' Henry said.

'I saw it first,' Sarah said.

'God made it,' Henry replied, scowling. In a crisis, women forgot all the principles on which they had been brought up.

'Looks like our island,' Sarah said listlessly.

'It couldn't be. We've been – ' But then Henry saw the black spot that had been their house, and the smaller black spot that had been the henhouse. It was their island.

'We've got to turn around,' Sarah said with resignation.

'No!' Henry dragged himself to the tiller before Sarah could turn it. 'No, Sarah! God must have willed this! I'll – '

Sarah gave him the tiller with a shrug, and reached for her bottle. The bottle was empty, but holding it gave her comfort.

Henry had no need to steer, because the wind was taking them straight in to their beach. It seemed another sign from God. God was going to show them how to survive on their own island. Henry began to feel happy and hopeful, in spite of his whining shell of a wife at his feet. Hope springs eternal! He would hew a heaven out of the wilderness! He would find a way to grow tura faster, and save both their lives. Where there's a will, there's a way!

Sarah was giving him a contemptuous smile, as if she knew what was going on in his head.

'I invented a moving chair, didn't I?' Henry said. 'I'll invent a better way to make whisky.'

Sarah giggled foolishly, but even as the boat's prow scraped the sands of their shore Henry had his first idea. The outrigger had been hollowed from a tree and its form was that of a great elongated bowl. Now that would hold a lot of mush, Henry was thinking. He continued to stare at the boat's gentle curve as he held to its side and climbed out on to the beach. Sarah had got out too, and with an air of bustling and grimly resigned activity was reaching for empty bottles and the basket that had contained their pineapples and dried fish for the voyage.

'Do something!' she shouted at him, and trudged off.

Henry seized a rope at the prow of the outrigger, and pulled as hard as he could. He would have to roll the vessel up on pieces of wood, he realized, to get it near the tura fields, and under some kind of shelter so rain wouldn't fall in and dilute the mush. 'Sarah!' he called.

When she strolled back finally, he explained his idea, and at once she was enthusiastic. Wood pieces, yes, the roundest kind! They hauled the boat up to their little plantation in hardly more than an hour. As if to bless their labours, clouds gathered, which meant that they could collect much-needed fresh water.

'Next we'll plant tura! We shall win!' Henry cried, exhausted, yet full of plans.

'Look!' Sarah had discovered a dusty whisky bottle somewhere, one-third full, and was waving it at him.

Plainly she meant to share it. Henry smiled, unscrewed the top and gallantly offered Sarah the first quaff. Raindrops began to fall, large and soft. Then Henry drank. 'A heaven out of the wilderness!' said Henry.

'Amen!'

Too Bad

CAROL ANN DUFFY

It was raining. Wilson had just said
we should have one in the Dog. So we did,
running through the blue wet streets
with our heads down, laughing, to get there,
down doubles in front of our drenched reflections.
The barmaid caught my eye in the mirror. Beautiful.

We had a job to do, but not till closing-time,
hard men knocking back the brandy, each of us
wearing revenge like a badge on his heart. Hatred
dresses in cheap, anonymous suits, the kind
with an inside pocket for a small gun. *Good health.*
I smiled at her. Warm rain, like blood, ran down my back.

I remembered my first time, my trembling hand
and Big Frank Connell hissing *Get a grip.*
Tonight, professional, I walked with the boys
along a filthy alley to the other pub, the one
where it happened, the one where the man
was putting on his coat, ready for home.

Home. Two weeks in a safe house and I'd be there,
glad of familiar accents and my dull wife.
He came out of a side door, clutching a carry-out.
Simple. Afterwards, Wilson was singing *lala lu lu*
Tom Someone, hang down your head and cry.
Too bad. I fancied that barmaid all right.

Somewhere Someone's Eyes

What if there had been a painter, he was drunk, *equal*
to Picasso, who filled his canvases for years,
destroyed them all, and died? It was the old one
about the tree, the empty wood, the unheard moan
of a great oak falling unobserved. We thought
we'd humour him. *Or a composer, whose scores*
were never played – who also died – nor ever found?

Because I remember this, a cool room flares
with the heat of a winter's fire, briefly. His face
glowed red-brown when he spoke to the flames.
I recollect it more than well, smell malt. *What*
happens to the lost? The shadow his mind made legless
lurched against the wall, glass raised. He cursed,
demanded an answer from the dog. All night it snowed.

Somewhere . . . he said, but we'd had enough, began
to joke and get half-screwed ourselves. *Somewhere someone's* . . .
Outside, the trees shifted under their soft burdens,
or I imagine so; our footsteps disappeared. It was easy
to laugh in that snug house, talk nonsense
half the night, drink. Across the white fields somewhere
someone's eyes blazed as they burned words in their mouth.

ANWU
nen
tion
oranting
Park
Yong
ngdingmen 102 106
uochezhan 203 14
337
309
Xuanwum
Beixi
wumen St.
W.

An Insular Depression

CHRISTOPHER HITCHENS

Insight Tour Guides are customarily upbeat about the cities and countries they cover. It is their business to boost trade and to make smooth the way of the traveller and the credit-card holder. So I was intrigued to see an entry under 'Walled City' in their Hong Kong handbook. It read:

> Visitors are advised to stay out of the Walled City . . . between shops you'll see dark stairways which lead down into the gloom; these are narrow, filthy 'streets', much like byways in a human-sized rabbit warren, or a confusing obstacle course in a circus house of horrors. There is an invisible boundary here. One step from a sunlit street in the colony and you'll be within a mad maze from which there is *a good chance you may never return* (my italics).

I'm not much of a danger man myself, but there was something enticing in this discouragement. There was something enticing, too, in the reactions of Hong Kong residents to any mention of the place. 'Oh, you don't want to go there – you'll get knifed and buggered.' 'How do you know? Have you been there?' '*Been* there. You must be joking.' This was the month of the Queen's tour of China and Hong Kong; a time for accentuating the positive. Young squirts from the Hong Kong and Shanghai Bank (always known as 'The Bank') were to be found peering at the history of the Long March. The Governor's office was working full time on the allaying of unease. The four figures 1997, for the year that Hong Kong is to revert to its mainland parent, are taking on an almost hieroglyphic significance. It is well understood by the colonial authorities that nothing must be done to mar or impede an orderly transition. Orderly transition – that's the ticket.

Our largest and most exciting remaining colony consists of Hong Kong island and adjacent islets, the urban district of Kowloon and the so-called New Territories, of which the last pushes out to meet the Cantonese border. The Walled City is in Kowloon, and was a Chinese garrison at the time when the lease was extracted from China in July 1898. Though it was exempted from the terms of the lease, its mandarin and guards were roughly turfed out the following year, and the Chinese view is that the British writ has never run there. As a result, it has been a hole in the map and a rent in protocol. Over the years, it has evolved into a sort of enclaved Casablanca; a haven for dope-pushers, hookers, fugitives from justice and – a fetching touch – unlicensed doctors and dentists. The British let it rot, and the Communist authorities consider it undignified for them to insist on a clean-up, lest they appear to recognize unlawful

British authority. Thousands of people live in the inch of difference that is created by this century of anomaly. It did seem like the place to go.

If the British residents had been discouraging about a visit, the well-to-do Hong Kong Chinese were positively annihilating in their non-cooperation. Rupert Winchester, a young English teacher, had (rather to my relief) offered to come with me. He had been in Hong Kong too long, he said, not to feel bound to go to the Walled City. Trouble was, it didn't seem to be on any map. (It doesn't feature, for example, on the detailed endpaper in David Bonavia's standard *Hong Kong 1997*.) Rather like Soweto, or Granny's fanny, people know it's there but don't know how to get there.

We began by asking directions from the suave Chinese concierge at the suave Regent Hotel. Walled City? What Walled City? Further enquiries drew us up the echelon of management as far as an ultra-suave *fonctionnaire* who said, 'Gentlemen, I have lived here all my life. Let me assure you that there is no such place as the Walled City.' Rupert produced the *Insight* guide for his inspection. Was it likely that it would warn us off a non-existent quarter? Cogitation and scrutiny, and much to-ing and fro-ing in Cantonese, followed this. 'Look,' I said, 'just write a few directions in Chinese and we'll show them to a taxi-driver. Surely you can do that?' After measurable hesitation, the manager inscribed some characters on a card and passed it over. Feeling as if initiated into some recondite brotherhood, we dashed out and hailed a cab, showed the driver the card, and watched his tyres burn as he drove away from us without a word. This seemed promising. The next cabbie just took the card and nodded, which was disappointing by contrast but at least meant that we were off.

Some time later, he announced, 'Here you are.' 'Here' was Kowloon City, a big and crowded township built around Hong Kong International Airport. 'Where is the Walled City?' 'Walled City?' An exchange followed. We made the driver ask other drivers and several policemen – all of them Chinese. We made him show them the card. Nothing. Repressed clichés about inscrutability began to flicker in my mind. At last we told the man to drive back to the Regent.

There, I became colonial. I had the characters on the card translated for us by an impartial witness. They said 'Kowloon City', which is like giving a stranger in London a card saying 'South of the River'. I banged the reception desk. 'You have wasted our time and our money. *Where* is the Walled City?' At length, a manager who was less ultra-suave than post-suave took charge. 'I must emphasize, sir, that you go at your own risk.' 'Oh, so you *do* know where it is.' 'Yes, but you go at your own risk.' 'Who else's risk could we possibly go at?' (A slight wince here at my want of finesse.)

All this had been reminding me of something, and I suddenly realized what it was. In 1972 I had been in Northern Ireland with James Fenton. It was a period of very intense, localized sectarian violence, and we heard that there had been a mini-pogrom against the Catholics of the town of Antrim. Nothing of this had so far appeared in the press, so we decided to set off and have a squint at the situation. (We put up, I remember, at an inn, since levelled by bombers, on the fringes of the Clotworthy

Skeffington estate.) Our reception by the burghers was akin to the opening of a Maigret novel, where the torpid hamlet guards its secrets from the outsider. 'Everything is fine here,' said the police chief, the Catholic priest, the local Rotarians, the man who kept the pub and the man who edited the local sheet. 'Everyone gets along just fine. There's nothing to interest you, welcome as you are. Now please *go away*.' There *had* been a pogrom a few nights earlier, complete with cross-burning, but it took an awfully long time to find out and we might have given up if it hadn't been for the continual assurance that everything was okay, there was nothing to see, and that the relevant housing estate was too difficult to get to anyway. This sort of thing stiffens the resolve even as it slightly increases the apprehension.

It was too late to try again that day, and overnight I found a knowledgeable Chinese who agreed to make sure that we got there. She wouldn't come with us, but would and did arrange to have us dropped within strolling distance. As the car passed through narrower and darker streets, I prepared myself for some scene from a pestilence. 'A cesspool of crime and filth,' the *Insight* guide had said. Then, 'There you are. This is as far as I go.'

Well, I'm as inured to anticlimax as the next bloke. But what was this? Across a bleak expanse of mud and garbage, traversed by duck-boards and littered with old oil drums, there loomed an enormous, scarred, grimy tenement block. It wasn't walled, for a start (I later found that the Japanese occupiers had torn down the walls in the war and used the stone to make an airport runway). But it was *wired* in. Three concentric zarebas of fencing surrounded it; the outer one strung through military-looking concrete posts of the kind that demarcate prison-camps and airfields, and the inner ones more haphazard and Beirut-like. It was as if the inhabitants had thrown up one quarantine and the authorities, not to be mocked, had trumped them by erecting an even more thorough one.

Rupert and I squelched across the no man's land, feeling very exposed. We had been warned that people would enquire our business, suspect that we were policemen, and stick to us like plaster. It's always essential in places like this to look as if you know what you are doing and where you are going, so I had procured an introduction to Jackie Pullinger, a sort of Mother Teresa only useful, who runs a mission to the Walled City's numberless drug-addicts. But nobody evinced a twitch of curiosity about our presence or our business, and no one with an atom of street cred could have mistaken either of us for cops.

A blind man could have found his way by the stench, which was a rich combo of chemicals, drains, ordure and *ad hoc* cuisine. The Walled City is famed for the size and daring of its rats, but they weren't in evidence. Great smears of rat poison, sometimes marked with warning signs, were. Perfect for the children, I thought, as we arrived at the outer glacis. Here was yet another fence, enclosing the walkway that skirted the tenement. It was not quite possible to walk abreast, and open sewer runnels kept criss-crossing the path. To the right – a mesh fence and the mud beyond. To the left – the unlicensed dentists! There they were; little holes in the wall with sinister-looking chairs and gaping, candid plastic mouths full of false teeth. Spare rows of gnashers beamed foolishly from trays next to these silent screams. I would, as Vladimir Nabokov once said in another connection, as soon try a sardine can with my penis as submit to open my mouth in such a chair. Occasionally, little Hogarthian tussles could be observed going on inside. It didn't seem prudent or polite to stop and gape.

Until now, we realized, we had been walking intrepidly along the outside of the wall. We were still in the sunlight. There had been narrow, crepuscular openings to the left, marking the start of alleyways. They were about the width of a fattish man. It was these alleys which the guide had said marked the point of no return. We looked at each other. 'Okay, the next one?' 'Okay.' The expression 'like a rat up a drain' came to me irrelevantly as we dived into the crevice.

The first impression was of slime. Everything was oozing. Underfoot was slippery with water and (I think) fish scales. The walls were suppurating and crumbling. Overhead was a dank tangle of naked electric wiring, festooned and encrusted with great tendrils of rubbish and vegetation from the upper storeys. Like a jungle roof, these lianas had grown and entwined to blot out the sky. I wondered how much protection they would afford if a piss-pot was to come whistling down from an ill-wishing roof-dweller. Meanwhile the din was enormous. Everyone seemed to be hammering something or trying to make themselves heard through the walls. Obviously, the perfect place for an opium den or a thieves' kitchen. As in Ali la Pointe's Casbah, the advantages would all be with the locals. They seemed to sense this, continuing to react to us with unaffected indifference.

After a while I started to notice what nervousness had prevented me from seeing. Everybody seemed to have something to do, and to be doing it. Radios were being repaired, food was being cut up for the pot, corrugated iron was being hammered into shape, children were being dressed, laundry was being carried to and fro. There were no beggars or hustlers, no pimps or idlers. I had been seeing the place through the lurid Fu Manchu stories that are peddled in the expensive high-rises on the other side of the harbour. The Walled City was pretty noisome, but it seemed to suffer unfairly from its reputation as (the guidebook again) 'a historical and geographical embarrassment'. Existing in a political limbo, these people seemed to make reasonable shift for themselves. What's so great about a dentist's licence anyway? I asked myself generously as we threaded our way out and back to the relative hedonism of Kowloon proper.

Nobody knows how many Chinese live in the Walled City, though the official minimum estimate is 40,000. This is undoubtedly swelled by the hundreds of illegal immigrants (known casually to the Brits as 'Eye Eyes') who nightly risk drowning and deportation in order to splash across Deep Bay at the entrance to the Pearl River. It must be a comedown for the successful ones to find themselves immured in this giant block, half slum and half time-warp, still under the nominal tutelage of Beijing and scheduled in any case to return to its rule in 1997. Meanwhile, to live right under the flight path of Kai Tak airport, with its screaming jets bearing the legal and the well-heeled day and night through your airspace, could be irksome.

From a Chinese journalist I later heard a fascinating explanation for the general denial of the Walled City's existence. It was an aspect, she said, of the widespread Hong Kong practice of cognitive dissonance. The mainland, in this scheme, is both there and not there. One Hong Kong hand trades and deals with it, but the other hand affects not to know. And one of Hong Kong's key exports to China is night soil. Every evening after dark, the shit of the plumbing-free Walled City is collected by wretched labourers with buckets slung on poles across their shoulders. The resulting tubs are taken to a vat near the airport and poured in. The associated stench and miasma, she told me, have caused complaints of corrosion to come from nearby aircraft repair workshops! The stuff then sells to China, at twenty Hong Kong dollars the ton, for the ostensible purpose of fertilizing the fields. But it is, in brute fact, used in its untreated form as fish meal in the *poisson* farms of Canton. The fish is then sold back to Hong Kong. This is a telling sign of under-development, but it is also the means by which most of the fish eaten in the colony is fattened for the skillet. A television programme some years ago, describing the *sub fusc* trade in Walled City excrement and its link to the staple diet, was 'discouraged' by the authorities and never made it on to the air.

The Walled City is only one of the metaphors for the unspoken collusion between the Hong Kong élite and the Chinese Communists. Take, for instance, the case of Daya Bay. In this part of Guangdong Province, about thirty miles from the centre of Hong Kong, the Chinese government proposes to build a nuclear power plant. A Chernobyl in Guangdong would have consequences many times as dire as anything the Walled City's latrines could come up with, and you might think that the British governor would express and convey some of the concern felt by his subjects. One million signatures were gathered in an exceptional display of political activism in the colony, and polls suggested a 70 per cent majority against the Daya Bay reactor. But the response of the 'Legislative Council' (then headed by the late Sir Edward 'Youde the Obscure' Youde) was to refuse to discuss the matter until all material contracts for the plant had been signed. This was because both British and Hong Kong contractors hope to supply the turbines, and much else, to Daya Bay. It's a safe bet that these will be among the numerous contractors who move their assets and their offices to Panama or the Cayman Islands by 1997.

Hong Kong is living out its remaining days as a British possession, apparently determined to end as it began – as a sort of showcase of opportunism. Even though the Beijing government solemnly signed a 1984 agreement for an elected legislature and an accountable executive, the colonial establishment has been too timorous to take them up on it. Only in September 1985 was any move made to elect any members of the governor's rubber stamp council. And even then, care was taken to keep the elected members a permanent minority. If the mainland breaks the agreement after 1997, and represses an independent Hong Kong, nobody will be able to say that it supplanted a thriving democracy.

A small but suggestive little sign, these days, is the increase, in Hong Kong, in the display of the Kuomintang flag. Nobody has a clear explanation for this resurgence of Chiang Kai Shek's emblem, because for years Taiwan was the bolt-hole for corrupt Hong Kong policemen and other colonial riff-raff on the run. It still shelters many fugitives from local justice. And since the reconquest of the mainland by the KMT is now more than ever a fantasy, abandoned even by its former American patrons, there seems to be something atavistic in this reversion to visceral anti-Communism. Perhaps it is the assertion of something unambiguously nationalist and distinctively Chinese, in the face of a smooth collaboration between British expatriates and Beijing bureaucrats. The people of the Walled City can watch this process with the millennial cynicism that tells them they are due for the room at the bottom no matter what.

On 14 January 1987, a simultaneous announcement was made by Her Majesty's Government and the authorities in Beijing. By March 1990, they jointly affirmed, the so-called 'Walled City' would be 'cleared'. This would, said the Chinese, conduce greatly to the 'hygiene' of the new Hong Kong. Consideration would naturally be given to resettlement of the inhabitants, but meanwhile a park (a luxury hitherto unknown to the Colony) would be created in place of the only home they knew.

Then she said she had to go

MARK FORD

The drawing-room was full.   The commuters half-turned
At last the angry hostess   to wave goodbye to
approached and   their friends. About their
whispered   feet fell the
black words
into my   of their
unsuspecting ear.   evening newspapers.

My new cow   Lunch is a strange experience here.
is loose in the field.   The big hall is
With her tail she   full of birds
swishes   swooping around –
away flies
and wanders   a carrot I
off happily to the fence.   was about to eat.

A large sea swell   The desk was littered
swamped the bay;   with books. She banged
the streets were   the front door, and I tried
drenched, and   to imagine
salt water
was found as   flowing
far inland as Newton.   from her lovely eyes.

THE CHAMPION

Smorgasbord

TOBIAS WOLFF

'A prep school in March is like a ship in the doldrums.' Our history master said this, as if to himself, while we were waiting for the bell to ring after class. He stood by the window and tapped the glass with his ring in a dreamy, abstracted way meant to make us think he'd forgotten we were there. We were supposed to get the impression that when we weren't around he turned into someone interesting, someone witty and profound, who uttered impromptu *bons mots* and had a poetic vision of life.

The bell rang.

I went to lunch. The dining hall was almost empty, because it was a free weekend and most of the boys in school had gone to New York, or home, or to their friends' homes, as soon as their last class let out. About the only ones left were foreigners and scholarship students like me and a few other untouchables of various stripes. The school had laid on a nice lunch for us, cheese soufflé, but the portions were small and I went back to my room still hungry. I was always hungry.

Snow and rain fell past my window. The snow on the quad looked grimy; it had melted above the underground heating pipes, exposing long brown lines of mud.

I couldn't get to work. On the next floor down someone kept playing 'Mack the Knife'. That one song incessantly repeating itself made the dorm seem not just empty but abandoned, as if those who had left were never coming back. I cleaned my room. I tried to read. I looked out the window. I sat down at my desk and studied the new picture my girlfriend had sent me, unable to imagine her from it; I had to close my eyes to do that, and then I could see her, see her solemn eyes and the heavy white breasts she would gravely let me hold sometimes, but not kiss . . . not yet, anyway. But I had a promise. That summer, as soon as I got home, we were going to become lovers. 'Become lovers.' That was how she'd said it, very deliberately, listening to the words as she spoke them. All year I had repeated them to myself to take the edge off my loneliness and the fits of lust that made me want to scream and drive my fists through walls. We were going to become lovers that summer, and we were going to be lovers all through college, true to each other even if we ended up thousands of miles apart again, and after college we were going to marry and join the Peace Corps and then do something together that would help people. This was our plan. Back in September, the night before I left for school, we wrote it all down along with a lot of other specifics concerning our future: number of children (six), their names, the kinds of dogs we would own, a sketch of our perfect house. We sealed the paper in a bottle and buried it in her backyard. On our golden anniversary we were going to dig it up again and show it to our children and grandchildren to prove that dreams can come true.

I was writing her a letter when Crosley came to my room. Crosley was a science whiz. He won the science prize every year and spent his summers working as an intern in different laboratories. He was also a fanatical weight lifter. His arms were so knotty that he had to hold them out from his sides as he walked, as if he were carrying buckets. Even his features seemed muscular. His face was red. Crosley lived down the hall by himself in one of the only singles in the school. He was said to be a thief; that supposedly was the reason he'd ended up without a room-mate. I didn't know if it was true, and I tried to avoid forming an opinion on the matter, but whenever we passed each other I felt embarrassed and dropped my eyes.

Crosley leaned in the doorway and asked me how things were.

I said okay.

He stepped inside and looked around the room, tilting his head to read my room-mate's pennants and the titles of our books. I was uneasy. I said, 'So what can I do for you,' not meaning to sound as cold as I did but not exactly regretting it either.

He caught my tone and smiled. It was the kind of smile you put on when you pass a group of people you suspect are talking about you. It was his usual expression.

He said, 'You know Garcia, right?'

'Garcia? Sure. I think so.'

'You know him,' Crosley said. 'He runs around with Hidalgo and those guys. He's the tall one.'

'Sure,' I said. 'I know who Garcia is.'

'Well, his stepmother is in New York for a fashion show or something, and she's going to drive up and take him out to dinner tonight. She told him to bring along some friends. You want to come?'

'What about Hidalgo and the rest of them?'

'They're at some kind of polo deal in Maryland. Buying horses. Or ponies, I guess it would be.'

The notion of someone my age buying ponies to play a game with was so unexpected that I couldn't quite take it in. 'Jesus,' I said.

Crosley said, 'How about it. You want to come?'

I'd never even spoken to Garcia. He was the nephew of a famous dictator, and all his friends were nephews and cousins of other dictators. They lived as they pleased here. Most of them kept cars a few blocks from the campus, though that was completely against the rules, and I'd heard that some of them kept women as well. They were cocky and prankish and charming. They moved everywhere in a body with sunglasses pushed up on their heads and jackets slung over their shoulders, twittering all at once like birds, *chinga* this and *chinga* that. The headmaster was completely buffaloed. After Christmas vacation a bunch of them came down with gonorrhoea, and all he did was call them in and advise them that they should not be in too great a hurry to lose their innocence. It became a school joke. All you had to do was say the word *innocence* and everyone would crack up.

'I don't know,' I said.

'Come on,' Crosley said.

'But I don't even know the guy.'

'So what? I don't either.'

'Then why did he ask you?'

'I was sitting next to him at lunch.'

'Terrific,' I said. 'That explains you. What about me? How come he asked me?'

'He didn't. He told me to bring someone else.'

'What, just anybody? Just whoever happened to present himself to your attention?'

Crosley shrugged.

I laughed. Crosley gave me a look to make sure I wasn't laughing at him, then he laughed, too. 'Sounds great,' I said. 'Sounds like a recipe for a really memorable evening.'

'You got something better to do?' Crosley asked.

'No,' I said.

The limousine picked us up under the awning of the headmaster's house. The driver, an old man, got out slowly and then slowly adjusted his cap before opening the door for us. Garcia slid in beside the woman in the back. Crosley and I sat across from them on seats that pulled down. I caught her scent immediately. For some years afterwards I bought perfume for women, and I was never able to find that one.

Garcia erupted into Spanish as soon as the driver closed the door behind me. He sounded angry, spitting words at the woman and gesticulating violently. She rocked back a little, then let loose a burst of her own. I stared openly at her. Her skin was very white. She wore a black cape over a black dress cut just low enough to show her pale throat and the bones at the base of her throat. Her mouth was red. There was a spot of rouge high on each cheek, not rubbed in to look like real colour but left there carelessly, or carefully, to make you think again how white her skin was. Her teeth were small and sharp-looking, and she bared them in concert with certain gestures and inflections. As she talked, her little pointed tongue flicked in and out.

She wasn't a lot older than we were. Twenty-five at the most. Maybe younger.

She said something definitive and cut her hand through the air. Garcia began to answer her, but she said 'No!' and chopped the air again. Then she turned and smiled at Crosley and me. It was a completely false smile. She said, 'Where would you fellows like to eat?' Her voice sounded lower in English, even a little harsh, though the harshness could have come from her accent. She called us *fallows*.

'Anywhere is fine with me,' I said.

'Anywhere,' she repeated. She narrowed her big black eyes and pushed her lips together. I could see that my answer disappointed her. She looked at Crosley.

'There's supposed to be a good French restaurant in Newbury,' Crosley said. 'Also an Italian place. It depends on what you want.'

'No,' she said. 'It depends on what you want. I am not so hungry.'

If Garcia had a preference, he kept it to himself. He sulked in the corner, his round shoulders slumped and his hands between his knees. He seemed to be trying to make a point of some kind.

'There's also a smorgasbord,' Crosley said. 'If you like smorgasbords.'

'Smorgasbord,' she said. She repeated the word to Garcia. He frowned, then answered her in a sullen monotone.

I couldn't believe Crosley had suggested the smorgasbord. It was an egregiously uncouth suggestion. The smorgasbord was where the local fatties went to binge. Football coaches brought whole teams there to bulk up. The food was good enough, and God knows there was plenty of it, all you could eat, actually, but the atmosphere was brutally matter-of-fact. The food was good, though. Big platters of shrimp on crushed ice. Barons of beef. Smoked turkey. No end of food, really.

She was smiling. Obviously the concept was new to her. 'You – do you like smorgasbords?' she asked Crosley.

'Yes,' he said.

'And you?' she said to me.

I nodded. Then, not to seem wishy-washy, I said, 'You bet.'

'Smorgasbord,' she said. She laughed and clapped her hands. 'Smorgasbord!'

Crosley gave directions to the driver, and we drove slowly away from the school. She said something to Garcia. He nodded at each of us in turn and gave our names, then looked away again, out the window, where the snowy fields were turning dark. His face was long, his eyes sorrowful as a hound's. He had barely talked to us while we were waiting for the limousine. I didn't know why he was mad at his stepmother, or why he wouldn't talk to us, or why he'd even asked us along, but by now I didn't really care. By now my sentiments were, basically, fuck him.

She studied us and repeated our names sceptically. 'No,' she said. She pointed at Crosley and said, 'El Blanco.' She pointed at me and said, 'El Negro.' Then she pointed at herself and said, 'I am Linda.'

'Leen-da,' Crosley said. He really overdid it, but she showed her sharp little teeth and said, '*Exactamente*.'

Then she settled back against the seat and pulled her cape close around her shoulders. It soon fell open again. She was restless. She sat forward and leaned back, crossed and recrossed her legs, swung her feet impatiently. She had on black high heels fastened by a thin strap; I could see almost her entire foot. I heard the silky rub of her stockings against each other, and breathed in a fresh breath of her perfume every time she moved. That perfume had a certain effect on me. It didn't reach me as just a smell; it was personal, it seemed to issue from her very privacy. It made the hair bristle on my arms. It entered my veins like fine tingling wires, widening my eyes, tightening my spine, sending faint chills across my shoulders and the backs of my knees. Every time she moved I felt a little tug, and followed her motion with some slight motion of my own.

When we arrived at the smorgasbord – Swenson's, I believe it was, or maybe Hansen's, some such honest Swede of a name – Garcia refused to get out of the limousine. Linda tried to persuade him, but he shrank back into his corner and would not answer or even look at her. She threw up her hands. 'Ah!' she said, and turned away. Crosley and I followed her across the parking lot towards the big red barn. Her dress rustled as she walked. Her heels clicked on the cement.

You could say one thing for the smorgasbord; it wasn't pretentious. It was in a real barn, not some quaint fantasy of a barn with butter-churn lamps and little brass ornaments nailed to the walls on strips of leather. At one end of the barn was the kitchen. The rest of it had been left open and filled with picnic tables. Blazing light bulbs hung from the rafters. In the middle of the barn stood what my English master would have called the 'groaning board' – a great table heaped with food, every kind of food you could think of, and more. I had been there several times and it always gave me a small, pleasant shock to see how much food there was.

Girls wearing dirndls hustled around the barn, cleaning up messes, changing tablecloths, bringing fresh platters of food from the kitchen.

We stood blinking in the sudden light. Linda paid up, then we followed one of the waitresses across the floor. Linda walked slowly, gazing around like a tourist. Several men looked up from their food as she passed. I was behind her, and I looked forbiddingly back at them so they would think she was my wife.

We were lucky; we got a table to ourselves. On crowded nights they usually doubled you up with another party, and that could be an extremely unromantic experience. Linda shrugged off her cape and waved us towards the food. 'Go on,' she said. She sat down and opened her purse. When I looked back she was lighting a cigarette.

'You're pretty quiet tonight,' Crosley said as we filled our plates. 'You pissed off about something?'

I shook my head. 'Maybe I'm just quiet, Crosley, you know?'

He speared a slice of meat and said, 'When she called you El Negro, that didn't mean she thought you were a Negro. She just said that because your hair is dark. Mine is light, that's how come she called me El Blanco.'

'I know that, Crosley. Jesus. You think I couldn't figure that out? Give me some credit, okay?' Then, as we moved around the table, I said, 'You speak Spanish?'

'*Un poco*. Actually more like *un poquito*.'

'What's Garcia mad about?'

'Money. Something about money.'

'Like what?'

He shook his head. 'That's all I could get. But it's definitely about money.'

I'd meant to start off slow but by the time I reached the end of the table my plate was full. Potato salad, ham, jumbo shrimp, toast, barbecued beef, Eggs Benny.

Crosley's was full, too. We walked back towards Linda, who was leaning forward on her elbows and looking around the barn. She took a long drag on her cigarette, lifted her chin, and blew a stream of smoke up towards the rafters. I sat down across from her. 'Scoot down,' Crosley said, and settled in beside me.

She watched us eat for a while.

'So,' she said, 'El Blanco. Are you from New York?'

Crosley looked up in surprise. 'No, ma'am,' he said. 'I'm from Virginia.'

Linda stabbed out her cigarette. She had long fingernails painted the same deep red as the lipstick smears on her cigarette butt. She said, 'I just came from New York, and I can tell you that is one crazy place. Just incredible. Listen to this. I am in a taxicab, you know, and we are stopping in this traffic jam for a long time and there is a taxicab next to us with this fellow in it who stares at me. Like this, you know.' She made her eyes go round. 'Of course I ignore him. So guess what, my door opens and he gets into my cab. "Excuse me," he says, "I want to marry you." "That's nice," I say. "Ask my husband." "I don't care about your husband," he says. "Your husband is history. So is my wife." Of course I had to laugh. "Okay," he says. "You think that's funny? How about this." Then he says – ' Linda looked sharply at each of us. She sniffed and made a face. 'He says things you would never believe. Never. He wants to do this and he wants to do that. Well, I act like I am about to scream. I open my mouth like this. "Hey," he says, "okay, okay. Relax." Then he gets out and goes back to his taxicab. We are still sitting there for a long time again, and you know what he is doing? He is reading the newspaper. With his hat on. Go ahead, eat,' she said to us, and nodded towards the food.

A tall, blonde girl was carving slices of roast beef on to a platter. She smiled at us. She was hale and bosomy – I could see the laces on her bodice straining. Her cheeks glowed. Her bare arms and shoulders were ruddy with exertion. Crosley raised his eyebrows at me. I raised mine back but my heart wasn't in it. She was a Viking dream, pure *gemütlichkeit*, but I was drunk on Garcia's stepmother and in that condition you don't want a glass of milk, you want more of what's making you stumble and fall.

Crosley and I filled our plates again and headed back.

'I'm always hungry,' he said.

'I know what you mean,' I told him.

Linda smoked another cigarette while we ate. She watched the other tables as if she were at a movie. I tried to eat with a little finesse and so did Crosley, dabbing his lips with a napkin between every bulging mouthful, but some of the people around us had completely slipped their moorings. They ducked their heads low to receive their food, and while they chewed it up they looked around suspiciously and kept their forearms close to their plates. A big family to our left were the worst. There was something competitive and desperate about them; they seemed to be eating their way towards a condition where they would never have to eat again. You would have thought that they were refugees from a great hunger, that outside these walls the land was afflicted with drought and barrenness. I felt a kind of desperation myself; I felt as if I were growing emptier with every bite I took.

There was a din in the air, a steady roar like that of a waterfall.

Linda looked around her with a pleased expression. She bore no likeness to anyone here but she seemed completely at home. She sent us back for another plate, then dessert and coffee, and while we were finishing up she asked El Blanco if he had a girlfriend.

'No, ma'am,' Crosley said. 'We broke up,' he added, and his red face turned purple. It was clear that he was lying.

'You. How about you?'

I nodded.

'Ha!' she said. 'El Negro is the one! So. What's her name?'

'Jane.'

'Jaaane,' Linda drawled. 'Okay, let's hear about Jaaane.'

'Jane,' I said again.

Linda smiled.

I told her everything. I told her how my girlfriend and I had met and what she looked like and what our plans were. I told her more than everything, because I gave certain coy but definite suggestions about the extremes to which our passion had already driven us. I meant to impress her with my potency, to inflame her, to wipe that smile off her face, but the more I told her the more wolfishly she smiled and the more her eyes laughed at me.

Laughing eyes – now there's a cliché my English master would have eaten me alive for. 'How exactly did these eyes laugh?' he would have asked, looking up from my paper while my classmates snorted around me. 'Did they titter, or did they merely chortle? Did they give a great guffaw? Did they, perhaps, *scream* with laughter?'

I am here to tell you that eyes can scream with laughter. Linda's did. As I played big hombre for her I could see exactly how complete my failure was, I could hear her saying, *Okay, El Negro, go on, talk about your little gorlfren, how pretty she is and so on, but we know what you want, don't we? – You want to suck on my tongue and slobber on my titties and lick my belly and bury your face in me. That's what you want.*

Crosley interrupted me. 'Ma'am . . . ' he said, and nodded towards the door. Garcia was leaning there with his arms crossed and an expression of fury on his face. When she looked at him he turned and walked out the door.

Her eyes went flat. She sat there for a moment. She began to take a cigarette from her case, then put it back and stood up. 'Let's go,' she said.

Garcia was waiting in the car, rigid and silent. He said nothing on the drive back. Linda swung her foot and stared out the window at the passing houses and bright, moonlit fields. Just before we reached the school Garcia leaned forward and began speaking to her in a low voice. She listened impassively and did not answer. He was still talking when the limousine stopped in front of the headmaster's house. The driver opened the door. Garcia fixed his eyes on her. Still impassive, she took her pocketbook out of her purse. She opened it and looked inside. She meditated over the contents, then withdrew a bill and offered it to Garcia. It was a one-hundred-dollar bill. 'Boolshit!' he said, and sat back angrily. With no change of expression she turned and held the bill out to me. I didn't know what else to do but take it. She got another one from her pocketbook and presented it to Crosley, who hesitated even less than I did. Then she gave us the same false smile she had greeted us with, and said, 'Goodnight, it was a pleasure to meet you. Goodnight, goodnight,' she said to Garcia.

The three of us got out of the limousine. I went a few steps and then slowed down, and began to look back.

'Keep walking!' Crosley hissed.

Garcia let off a string of words as the driver closed the door. I faced around again and walked with Crosley across the quad. As we approached our dorm he quickened his pace. 'I don't believe it,' he whispered. 'A hundred bucks.' When we were inside the door he stopped and shouted, 'A hundred bucks! A hundred fucking dollars!'

'Pipe down,' someone called.

'All right, all right. Fuck you!' he added.

We went up the stairs to our floor, laughing and banging into each other. 'Do you fucking believe it?' he said.

I shook my head. We were standing outside my door.

'No, really now, listen.' He put his hands on my shoulders and looked into my eyes. He said, 'Do you fucking *believe* it?'

I told him I didn't.

'Well, neither do I. I don't fucking believe it.'

There didn't seem to be much to say after that. I would have invited Crosley in, but to tell the truth I still thought of him as a thief. We laughed a few more times and said goodnight.

My room was cold. I took the bill out of my pocket and looked at it. It was new and stiff, the kind of bill you associate with kidnappings. The picture of Franklin was surprisingly lifelike. I looked at it for a while. A hundred dollars was a lot of money then. I had never had a hundred dollars before, not in one chunk like this. To be on the safe side I taped it to a page in *Profiles in Courage* – page 100, so I wouldn't forget where it was.

I had trouble getting to sleep. The food I had eaten sat like a stone in me, and I was miserable about the things I had said. I understood that I had been a liar and a fool. I kept shifting under the covers, then I sat up and turned on my reading lamp. I picked up the new picture my girlfriend had sent me, and closed my eyes, and when I had some peace of mind I renewed my promises to her.

We broke up a month after I got home. Her parents were away one night, and we seized the opportunity to make love in their canopied bed. This was the fifth time that we had made love. She got up immediately afterwards and started putting her clothes on. When I asked her what the problem was, she wouldn't answer me. I thought, *oh Christ, what now.* 'Come on,' I said. 'What's the problem?'

She was tying her shoes. She looked up and said, 'You don't love me.'

It surprised me to hear this, not because she said it but because it was true. Before this moment I hadn't known it was true, but it was – I didn't love her.

For a long time afterwards I told myself that I had never really loved her, but this was a lie.

We're supposed to smile at the passions of the young, and at what we recall of our own passions, as if they were no more than a series of sweet frauds we had fooled ourselves with and then wised up to. Not only the passion of boys and girls for each other but the others, too – passion for justice, for doing right, for turning the world around – all these come in their time under our wintry smiles. But there was nothing foolish about what we felt. Nothing merely young. I just wasn't up to it. I let the light go out.

Some time later I heard a soft knock at my door. I was still wide awake. 'Yeah,' I said.

Crosley stepped inside. He was wearing a blue dressing-gown of some silky material that shimmered in the dim light of the hallway. He said, 'Have you got any Tums or anything?'

'No. I wish I did.'

'You too, huh?' He closed the door and sat on my room-mate's bunk. 'Do you feel as bad as I do?'

'How bad do you feel?'

'Like I'm dying. I think there was something wrong with the shrimp.'

'Come on, Crosley. You ate everything but the barn.'

'So did you.'

'That's right. That's why I'm not complaining.'

He moaned and rocked back and forth on the bed. I could hear real pain in his voice. I sat up. 'Crosley, are you okay?'

'I guess,' he said.

'You want me to call the nurse?'

'God,' he said. 'No. That's all right.' He kept rocking. Then, in a carefully offhand way, he said, 'Look, is it okay if I just stay here for a while?'

I almost said no, then I caught myself. 'Sure,' I told him. 'Make yourself at home.'

He must have heard my hesitation. 'Forget it,' he said bitterly. 'Sorry I asked.' But he made no move to go.

I felt confused, tender towards Crosley because he was in pain, repelled because of what I had heard about him. But maybe what I had heard about him wasn't true. I wanted to be fair, so I said, 'Hey Crosley, do you mind if I ask you a question?'

'That depends.'

I sat up. Crosley was watching me. In the moonlight his dressing-gown was iridescent as oil. He had his arms crossed over his stomach. 'Is it true that you got caught stealing?'

'You fucker,' he said. He looked down at the floor.

I waited.

He said, 'You want to hear about it, just ask someone. Everybody knows all about it, right?'

'I don't.'

'That's right, you don't.' He raised his head. 'You don't know shit about it and neither does anyone else.' He tried to smile. His teeth appeared almost luminous in the cold silver light. 'The really hilarious part is, I didn't actually get caught stealing it, I got caught putting it back. Not to make excuses. I stole the fucker, all right.'

'Stole what?'

'The coat,' he said. 'Robinson's overcoat. Don't tell me you didn't know that.'

I shook my head.

'Then you must have been living in a cave or something. You know Robinson, right? Robinson was my room-mate. He had this camel's hair overcoat, this really just beautiful overcoat. I kind of got obsessed with it. I thought about it all the time. Whenever he went somewhere without it I would put it on and stand in front of the mirror. Then one day I just took the fucker. I stuck it in my locker over at the gym. Robinson was really upset. He'd go to his closet ten, twenty times a day, like he thought the coat had just gone for a walk or something. So anyway, I brought it back. He came into the room while I was hanging it up.' Crosley bent forward suddenly, then leaned back.

'You're lucky they didn't kick you out.'

'I wish they had,' he said. 'The dean wanted to play Jesus. He got all choked up over the fact that I had brought it back.' Crosley rubbed his arms. 'Man, did I want that coat. It was ridiculous how much I wanted that coat. You know?' He looked right at me. 'Do you know what I'm talking about?'

I nodded.

'Really?'

'Yes.'

'Good.' Crosley lay back against the pillow, then lifted his feet on to the bed. 'Say,' he said, 'I think I figured out how come Garcia invited me.'

'Yeah? How come?'

'He was mad at his stepmother, right? He wanted to punish her.'

'So?'

'So I'm the punishment. He probably heard I was the biggest asshole in the school, and figured whoever came with me would have to be an asshole too. That's my theory, anyway.'

I started laughing. It hurt my stomach, but I couldn't stop. Crosley said, 'Come on, man, don't make me laugh,' then he started laughing and moaning at the same time.

We lay without talking for a time. Crosley said, 'El Negro.'

'Yeah.'

'What are you going to do with your C-note?'

'I don't know. What are you going to do?'

'Buy a woman.'

'Buy a woman?'

'I haven't gotten laid in a really long time. In fact,' he said, 'I've never gotten laid.'

'Me neither.'

I thought about his words. *Buy a woman.* He could actually do it. I could do it myself. I didn't have to wait, I didn't have to burn like this for month after month until Jane decided she was ready to give me relief. Three months was a long time to wait. It was an unreasonable time to wait for anything if you had no good reason to wait, if you could just buy what you needed. And to think that you could buy this – buy a mouth for your mouth, and arms and legs to wrap you tight. I had never considered this before. I thought of the money in my book. I could almost feel it there. Pure possibility.

Jane would never know. It wouldn't hurt her at all, and in a certain way it might help, because it was going to be very awkward at first if neither of us had any experience. As a man, I should know what I was doing. It would be a lot better that way.

I told Crosley that I liked his idea. 'The time has come to lose our innocence,' I said.

'*Exactamente*,' he said.

And so we sat up and took counsel, leaning towards each other from the beds, holding our swollen bellies, whispering back and forth about how this thing might be done, and where, and when.

Desk Duty

HUGO WILLIAMS

If I were Lord of Tartary,
Myself and me alone,
My bed should be of ivory
Of beaten gold my throne.
Walter de la Mare

My desk has brought me
all my worst fears on a big tray
and left it across my lap.
I'm not allowed to move
Till I've eaten everything up.
I push things around on my plate.
I kick the heating pipes.

A piece of worn carpet on the floor
proves how long I've been sitting here
shuffling my feet,
opening and closing drawers,
looking for something I've lost
under piles of official papers and threats,
roofing grants and housing benefits.

Am I married or single?
Employed or self-employed?
What sort of work do I do?
Is my house being used for business
or entertainment purposes? (See Note 3)
If I am resident at my place of work,
who supplies the furniture?

I suspect myself
of deliberately wasting time
writing my name and place of birth
under 'Who else lives with you?'
It has taken me all day
to find something true to write
under 'Personal Allowances' – or not untrue.

I know all about my little game
of declaring more than I earn
to the Inland Revenue – or was it less?
I'm guilty as hell,
or I wouldn't be sitting here like this
playing footy-footy with my desk.
I'd be upstairs in bed with my bed.

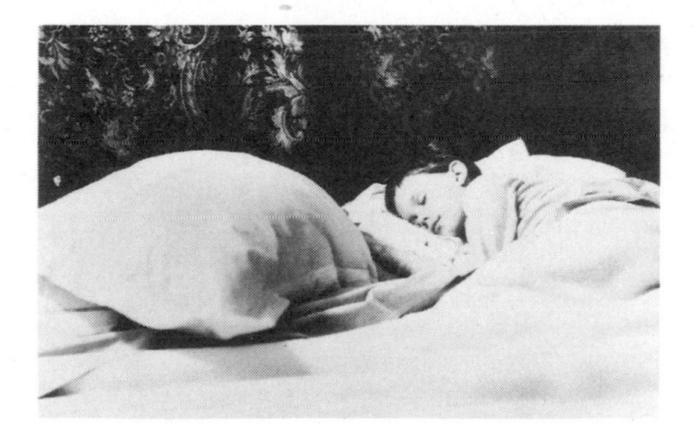

WITH DEADLY ACCURACY, ROBIN'S FLASHLIGHT PICKED OUT THE HIDDEN GOURDS

Through the Telescope

BARRY YOURGRAU

I lean forward in the chair again and peer back into the telescope. I give the focus knob the slightest of turns. The moon shimmers at me, brilliant and spectacular: pale bright silver with grey blotches. A tubby, spectral figure rests on his forearm along the top edge, like a swimmer pausing at the side of a pool. With his free hand he waves deliberately, staring not quite in the telescope's direction. There's a big, friendly grin on his face. I give a wave back, even though I know he can't see me.

I get out of the chair, very carefully, so as not to change its position. I go down to my mother's room. I knock and open the door. 'I've got Dad on the telescope,' I tell her. She looks up at me from her book in bed. She has on her reading glasses; she peers over them. 'What, *tonight*?' she says. 'Yes,' I tell her. 'The weather's very clear, he must want to take advantage of it.' 'Boy, I'll hurt my eyes looking through that thing now,' she says, putting her glasses on the night table and climbing out of bed. She shuffles along stiffly beside me down the hall in her nightgown, her grey hairs gathered in a loose, wispy ponytail. She looks sleepy. 'Now careful not to bump anything, it's all set up,' I tell her. I steady the back of the chair for her. She screws up an eye and puts the other to the eyepiece. 'I don't see a thing,' she says. 'Oh yes I do!' she cries. She gives a yelp of happiness and waves her arms. 'I love you, I love you!' she cries, and she blows kisses up along the telescope. 'All right, all right, take it easy,' I tell her. 'He can't see us, you know.' She sits back finally, her hand to her chest. 'That was lovely,' she says, panting. 'But now I must get back to my bed.' I walk her slowly along to her room. 'But tell me,' she wonders quietly, 'how does he manage to have the entire moon to himself?' Then she snorts, in response to her own question. 'Naturally,' she says. 'He always had to have special accommodations, when he was alive. So why should it be any different, now that he's departed?'

Grapes

'The rain left these marks on the table,' says the girl. She rubs a finger thoughtfully into one of the pitted ruts. 'I don't mind the occasional, small disaster,' I tell her. 'It alleviates the tedium of daily life. Smoke?' The girl shakes her head. 'The wind blew in five directions all at once,' she says. 'Or maybe six or seven. The papers reported it. What do you think of our brand new grapes?' 'I've been noticing them,' I tell her. 'I've never seen grapes that exact colour before. Most unusual.' The girl shrugs. 'They're father's hobby,' she says. 'You can ask him all about it. He's around here somewhere.' She turns her head and listens attentively to something. 'Was that the telephone?' she says. 'Excuse me,' she murmurs. She goes back into the house.

I amble about the patio, smoking. Because of the grape arbour, the light is slightly dim and noticeably red. I reach up into the beams overhead and snap off a pair of the small scarlet fruits. I look at them in the palm of my hand. I sniff them and grimace and fling them over the railing into the greenery and wipe my hand on my trousers. I sniff the palm, to check it, and grimace again, and wipe my hand forcefully, irritated. I sniff again, and grimace in alarm now, and wipe, and sniff and grimace and wipe and sniff and grimace and wipe. I am caught up in a seemingly interminable repetition of this sequence when I hear the girl coming back. I shove my hand into a trouser pocket. 'Have you met Fuzzy?' asks the girl. She cradles a fuzzy stuffed animal to her breast. 'Fuzzy is my pet,' she says. 'Hello there!' I address the animal, tickling it under an ear with my unpocketed hand. 'He's tame, isn't he,' I tell her. 'Unlike that bathing suit you have on.' The girl giggles. 'Father stole this colour for the grapes,' she says, bending her head to rub noses with the animal. 'Fuzzy and I are going swimming later. The rain pulverized a big patch of ferns, and now it's oozy and muddy and clingy, a real swamp.' She lifts her head and sniffs. 'Something smells wonderful around here,' she says. I blush prodigiously. The girl squeezes the animal close and slowly swivels back and forth. 'I love this crinkly little fellow,' she murmurs. Her slightly parted lips by the animal's ears are vivid and glossy, and she has on white vinyl teardrop sunglasses with pitch-black lenses. She presents a garish figure in the reddish light under the arbour. 'You look *sordid*,' I tell her urgently. She smiles, as if in secret. 'You can come watch me swim, if you'd like,' she says softly.

There is a sudden clattering noise behind us, like a pile of aluminium pots and pans tumbling off a shelf. The girl peers around past my shoulder. 'Oh, father!' she cries. She turns and starts to run off, but then swings about and lunges and pushes the animal into my chest, and then goes hurrying away towards the patio steps. I sniff the animal quickly before dropping it into a chair. Furtively I hunch over and take my hand out of my pocket and sniff it. I gnash my teeth and rub the palm along my pants leg. I sniff again, and groan savagely, and immediately become entangled once more in the frenzied, potentially endless cycle. I wrench myself away and go to the railing, my hand crammed back into its pocket.

Below the patio, the girl is retrieving a pair of spectacles for an old man who sits awkwardly in the weeds and wild grass. He suggests a load of laundry blown off a line: he is dressed in fact solely in a large sheet, Hindu-style. A wicker basket which he had obviously been carrying lies on its side nearby, its contents of long-stalked, large- and purple-blossomed hydrangeas spilled in a wide area. 'Is he all right?' I call down to the girl, reaching across myself to a side jacket pocket for my cigarettes. '*Comment ça va, mon vieux?*' I address him. I contort myself violently to reach the cigarettes, which are lodged in a far, almost inaccessible corner of the pocket. 'He only speaks English,' says the girl, helping the old man to his feet. '*Bene, bene,*' he says, nodding and waving weakly to me. '*Grazie, prego, prego!*' 'Oh, stop it, father,' the girl mutters. On his feet the old man sways infirmly, righting the sheet about him. The girl stoops and begins gathering hydrangeas, which make a tinny clanking and tinkling as she loads them into her arms. 'I want to congratulate you on your wonderful grapes!' I tell the old man, my cigarettes finally in hand. I lean over the railing. '*Ich gratuliere Sie, ihre Trauben sind ausgezeichnet!*' The old man beams up at me. '*Grazie, grazie!*' he wheezes, raising both arms aloft and bowing repeatedly. I realize he is drooling. 'Father is addicted to flattery,' the girl says, dropping a noisy bundle of flowers into the basket. 'It does something strange to him. That's what this mania for botanical experiments is *for* – to elicit praise.' The old man stands beaming and nodding at me fixedly, his eyes glazed and dilated behind their spectacles, a long ribbon of spittle wavering from his chin.

A gust of wind buffets the patio. The girl drops the new bundle she has started. She points dramatically up at the trees. 'Here we go again!' she cries. The leaves on the branches stream upwards, wildly agitated. Suddenly, as we watch, they jerk to the left, then to the right, then straight down. 'Quick, father, we have to take shelter!' the girl shouts, and she hurriedly steps over and reaches for his arm. But he squeals and wrenches away and starts stooping desperately to collect the loose flowers around him. I watch a grotesque, nightmarish slapstick unfold: the girl tugging with all her might at the old man's sheet, the old man bent over at the waist, flapping and pawing at the products of his invention just beyond his reach because of the girl's constraints. '*Mais non, non, mon vieux!*' I shout down at him. '*Pourquoi ce clameur? C'est un folie, certainement!*' The wind shoves the girl's sunglasses up into her hair. The hydrangeas lift in the grass. I hurry over to the patio steps as the girl manages finally to half-drag, half-batter the old man to the border of the house. I reach down with my free hand and grip a handful of sheet to help bring him up the steps. He burbles and protests, frantically trying to set his heels, clutching the few hydrangeas he's rescued in an arthritic, claw-like hand. Behind his head the air goes crazy. Something hits like a solid blow on the planking beside us. 'For God's sake, we'll all be killed!' the girl mutters. I let go of the grip I have and seize the folds of sheet at the old man's neck and twist savagely so his tongue sticks out. I wrench one-armed with all my might and in this fashion we drag him up the steps and into the house.

The old man lies curled in a ball on a soiled mat in a corner. He snuffles wretchedly, his treasured metal flowers pressed against his withered cheek. I stand beside the girl at the glass doors. 'Nice, comforting patter,' I observe drolly. The raindrops hammer down through the arbour as if fired from guns. Grape fragments flurry slowly through the air, covering the patio and its furniture with a red litter that constantly shivers at the impact of the raindrops. 'More work for father,' the girl sighs. She has removed her sunglasses and put on huge cheap green earrings. She still wears her bathing suit. It blazes sleazily beside me. I feel the warmth of her body, and I tremble. She glances at me, noticing, and smiles. 'Perhaps I will have one cigarette,' she says. As I hold up the lighter flame to it, I tell her: 'I'm on fire!' She acknowledges this *bon mot* with a giggle behind the fingers of her cigarette-supporting hand – then she jerks back, as if stung. 'Fuzzy!' she gasps. She twists around towards the panes of glass. 'Where's my darling Fuzzy!' she cries. 'He's out there, I'm afraid,' I confess, trying to sound legitimately sad. 'What's left of him,' I add. The girl whimpers, staring into the catastrophic rain. I edge closer to her. 'I want to console you,' I tell her, my voice dropping to an urgent, tropical whisper. 'I want you to forget Fuzzy. I want you to have this.' And, with an almost unbearably exquisite confusion of foreboding and release, I draw my hand out of my pocket. I lift it breathlessly up to her face, and open it.

Executrix

My hands are suddenly ice-cold. To thaw them, I stuff them inside my mouth. The freezing flesh adheres to my tongue, to the tissue of my cheeks. I can't get my hands out. I manage to turn on the oven with my feet, and I kneel and stick my head assemblage into its warmth.

Footsteps come up behind me. My girlfriend's voice announces that killing myself that way is no solution to anything. I try to explain my situation, but my hands gag me. She starts tying my feet up behind me. She learned this in class, she explains, they have more successful deaths than I would believe because the professor is so good, he really knows about these things. I pull my head out finally, to try to get across what I'm really doing before she tries anything irrevocable. I twist around and am confronted by the sight of her in scuba gear and feather head-dress. I garble a scream into my hands and throw myself to the floor as a harpoon crashes into the oven, missing me by a hair's breadth. 'You little faker!' she shrieks, flinging down the harpoon gun and stamping off to the doorway. 'I can't believe you did that, I can't *believe* you'd pull a stunt like that! I thought you were serious!'

I cower on the floor, blubbering and shaking my head and pulling helplessly at my hands. She's still hot as hell. 'Shit!' she cries, banging her fist against the door-jamb. '*Shit!*' But then she stops. She squints down at me near-sightedly. 'What is that you're doing?' She bends closer. 'Oh wow, I didn't notice that! Oh wow! That's really amazing, *eating yourself up*!'

Prelude

'This is not a joke,' says my mother. 'Your father is furious. Your elder brother says he didn't take it and your younger brother says he didn't take it, so that only leaves you.' I don't answer. I can hear my father clumsily slamming drawers in the bedroom. My heart pounds. I spring past my mother and bolt out of the room. 'Bring it straight back!' she shouts after me down the stairs.

I rush through the backyard, through the gate, across the lane and into the woods. I come to the trickling creek and I run in it, splashing, so no tracks will show. Around the bend I clamber up on to the bank. Above me, the trunks of two dead trees have fallen against the rising ground. I squeeze in between them. A cave of sorts has been dug into the earth behind the trees. At the back of the cave sits a mass shrouded in newspaper, on a platform of stones. I crouch in front of this and snatch the newspaper away and huddle against the clammy wall. Upside down my old man's head gapes with unfocused astonishment. The corners of his pale lips are bruised dark, from hour-long manipulations to shape his open-mouthed surprise into an affable grin or a clownish grimace. His low, broad forehead is scratched from its passage through brush and bush.

I gape back at him in wild, feverish distraction. My arms are lashed about my chest, squeezing. A dark bug buzzes in the hot, dim air. Suddenly a great decision strikes through my tumult, like a wedge driven into wood – a single stroke that will spread with time into a great angle far from its point of impact.

I seize my father's head. I squirm out again between the dead trunks. I swarm, slithering, down to the edge of the bank and jump in. With my father's head tucked under my arm I set off splashing up the creek, away from our house, towards the deeper, sun-crowned woods and the great unknown world beyond them.

THERE WERE TIMES WHEN I BEGAN TO TIRE OF POLISHING MR. THRONGUE

AS COLLECTIONS OF TEETH GO, IT WAS CERTAINLY IMPRESSIVE

IT WAS NOT TOO LONG
BEFORE WE BEGAN TO
ORGANIZE REGULAR MEETINGS

Somebody's Wife

ANDREW MOTION

1 You were Caesar's wife before you were mine,
and that's how I saw you first: a silky hawk
borne in on a ripple of light when the curtain rose,
and dangling in heavy shadow behind the throne.
Now that you're somebody's wife again

your naked wings, your white contemptuous face
half-lost in its velvet hood of hair,
come back like the first frames of a film
of our life together: unbidden, unchangeable,
triggered by anything under the sun:

my short-cut to work, for instance, which day
after day means I slip through behind the Dominion
and see, by the door where the stars come out,
the tracks of stilettos pricked in the tarmac –
claw-marks in snow, after the birds have flown.

2 When first we were married,
and I was Edward Thomas,
and you were no more Helen
than bloody Marie of Rumania,

we rented an attic flat
like a boat (hunched ceilings
and lop-sided walls)
on course for the open country.

Our view from the sitting-room prow
was a green drop through sky
and a crinkled bow-wave of elms
to fields where a herd of friesians

drifted like wind-scattered shadows –
fields dotted and dashed with nettle,
dreamily rolling and lifting
as if they were canvas flapped out

then billowing up to the Chilterns.
And that was the map of the walk

we took whenever we could –
hands clammily sticking to hands,

Adam and Eve in love
on a wandering contour of mud
which began at the elms, trickled
any old how through gappy hedges,

swerved down a tunnel of beech,
and emerged in the end on the hills.
It was there that our choices began:
on to the clouds, then home? Or what?

I've forgotten the ways we went,
but never the trampled patch
where the path split up like veins
wriggling away from a heart

and we would decide to go forwards,
or sideways, or back,
and maybe lean for a breath
on a mangled crab-apple stump

collapsed there years before,
or gingerly stoop and peer
over the tottering walls
of a pen someone had built

which never held hide nor hair
of any creature we'd seen,
though one (we supposed) had littered there,
then been drummed back to its yard.

3 As if it were happening now
I see us kneel at the kerb
in a parched puddle of grit.

It is after the witching hour
and this is Longwall Street:
not a sound from Magdalen's trees,

no late-night walkers' voices
drowning the faint click-blink
of traffic lights marking time

although no traffic draws up.
It's like the still seconds to come
just after a droning siren

has driven the world to hide,
and the air goes deaf with screaming.
But the seconds pass and it's not

screams I hear but a sigh.
I am cradling the head of a girl
we've come across – simple as that –

trounced into rags in the gutter,
her bike like a broken puzzle
flung down in the curving road.

On my hand, on the hard tarmac,
blood is slipping – not much,
but more than enough to explain

why her eyes should swivel
and angrily glare into mine
as if I were all she loved,

and why they should lose their light
like stones picked out of water
and left to dry in the sun.

Then the police appear
and carefully shoosh us away –
arms out as though we were sheep

to be squeezed through a narrow gate –
and we're back in the darkened home
we are trying to make together,

undressing for bed like strangers
who haven't a clue what to say
but already imagine a morning

when they will awake alone,
with sunlight splitting the curtains
and pouring its fatuous heat

in the vacant space beside them:
the perfect undimpled pillow;
the blank sheet.

The Kiss

Hauntings

JOHN FULLER

This is the greatest sadness, like Handel
Ascending a staircase to loud tribute
That is already worms although
We have to pretend that it is music.
And other sadnesses: that she
Whose whole existence is an answer
Has questions of her own that strike
Us dumb. Only our smile survives,
To haunt our quiet retreat from life,
And that abundant love bred out
Of loneliness which only puzzles
Its busy, sensual, happy victims.

Inside a piano in a cottage
A mile out of the nearest village
A spirit in the jangling strings
Practises ascending thirds in
Moments of calculated stillness:
Not Peter Lorre's scampering hand,
Nor the ghost-print of Cage prepared
For his strange business, nor even Handel
Reduced to such vague finger-stirrings
As an ecto-presence might manifest,
Like picking the nose, but a ditsy shrew
To whom is allowed its privacy.

Do all such hauntings have precise
Explanations? Only the failure
That makes us feel pursued is never
Exorcized, for we ourselves
Become the terrible excuse
That it projects, our shadow-play,
Our mirror, our familiar.
Out there, though, every kind of music
Is ready to re-create the worldly
Heartache or triumph it once became,
And having once become it, will
Again do so, and yet again.

Look, The Monkey's Laughing

RUPERT THOMSON

There's a sort of peace about the rubbish-dump. It's nicely placed, for one thing. The outskirts of Athens. Just off a road that winds up through pines to a monastery.

I built a hut here out of sheets of corrugated iron and beer crates and bits of old machinery. I built a wall too, all the way round, and a gate that opens and shuts. I even improvised a bell: two olive-oil cans and a toilet-chain. That way I know if someone's coming. You get some pretty unsavoury types in the rubbish-dump.

I make my living from cardboard. I push a barrow up and down Syngrou, the avenue that runs from the city centre to the sea. I collect my cardboard from dustbins, car-parks, the backs of shops, and sell it to the paper factory.

On days when the light's too harsh for my eyes I stay at home. I walk out through my gate and sit under the nearby eucalyptus tree and let its shade into my head. There are no memories then. I sit under my tree and know I belong. No looking forwards, no going back. Stasis. A good Greek word, that.

I was born Michaelis, but, fifteen years ago, I was given a new name. It was Constantine, my closest friend, who thought of it. He was sitting outside the Café Diana with the morning paper and, even from a distance, I could tell that he was scanning the obituaries. He used to say that there's nothing like obituaries to make you feel alive. You begin to see why I liked him so much.

I walked over and stood at his shoulder. He blinked as my shadow fell across the page.

'You know, Michaelis,' he said, 'you're like the sky. Every time I look up, there you are.'

Someone at the next table chuckled.

After that I was never Michaelis again. Everybody called me Sky.

That same year my eyesight started going. The doctor had a fancy name for it: photophobia. Pretty soon it was all I could do to keep my eyes open when I walked round the city during the day. He prescribed a pair of special glasses. Even so, I found myself staring at the ground. Out of necessity at first, but then with growing interest. I got to know kerbstones and manholes the way other people know trees and buildings. I could recognize streets by their surfaces, friends by their shoes (Constantine, for instance, wore tan leather sandals). I became an expert on the world at ground level.

And still everybody called me Sky.

Everybody except my wife, Adriana. She didn't believe I had trouble with my eyes. She thought I was making it up, fishing for something – sympathy, I suppose, or attention. And the fact that my glasses were tinted, well, that confirmed it. I tried to show her a letter from my doctor once as proof. She tossed it aside without even glancing at it. 'Anyone can fake a letter,' she said.

Our marriage had been arranged as marriages in those days often were. Adriana's parents gave her a two-storey house in Kolonaki with a lemon tree in the courtyard. It was a generous wedding present. We could never have afforded to live in an area like that on my salary. I worked for the Aliens' Bureau, a minor branch of the civil service. I had what's known as a future, I suppose. I had no assets, though. All I owned of any value was a silk shirt that I'd inherited from my father.

I didn't expect love to come immediately. I was prepared to work at it, to watch it emerge from the ore of our marriage like gold.

But Adriana –

When I wanted to make love to her, she recoiled as if from an obscenity. Sometimes she submitted, but then I saw a fierce silver light in her eyes that said, Why are you degrading me like this? Afterwards she'd lock the bathroom door, scrub herself until she bled, remove every last trace of me. I seemed to be dealing with her across some great physical distance. Touching her only widened it. This distance soon became definable, took shape: two separate rooms with a good solid wall between.

I went out to the Café Diana most evenings and played backgammon with Constantine, often until one or two in the morning. We always sat at the same table. Tucked away in one corner, it was. Under a poster of the Acropolis. We threw each other shrewd glances, we slapped our counters down theatrically on the scratched marble, we cheated whenever we got the chance.

Constantine was a bit of a showman. He used to balance all his counters on the side of his hand at the beginning of each game. I was always waiting for them to topple, but they never did. Leaning Tower of Pisa, I called it. He liked that. He liked being one of the seven wonders of the world.

'Ah, it's good sitting here, just the two of us, isn't it?' he'd say every few weeks. 'It's enough, isn't it?' he'd say.

And I'd say, 'Yes, it's enough.'

I'd glance round at the old men in the café, their hands bunched on the bar like boxing-gloves that had seen too many fights. I often noticed their eyes pin women to the corner of the street, but their desire, I suspected, had long since lost its edge. It was bravado, nothing more. We Greeks are famous for it.

Looking down, I'd pinch the skin on the back of my hand and it would stay pinched. My father had told me once that that was how you could tell you were getting old.

No matter how hard I tried, I just couldn't get through to Adriana. I often wondered who exactly I'd married. I sometimes thought that maybe she'd come from another planet.

I remember her saying once, 'Don't think you have any power over me.' She was drawing the curtains at the time. Two brisk strokes and the darkness was nowhere.

That was like her. She dismissed things with such coolness, such precision. What had existed a moment before no longer did. The darkness. Me.

Then, in her own time, she explained. 'You're not what I want,' she said, 'you never were, you never will be,' her chin nearer to me than her eyes, as if she was daring me to hit her.

I wish I could've said, 'If that's what you think, then you're not what I want either,' something like that, anyway, but I couldn't. It would've been untrue. I did want her.

Oh, you can laugh.

I'd watched the gold emerge, but there was no richness in it, no value. Without Adriana watching too, it was worth precisely nothing.

Me and Constantine, we never talked about things like that.

Talking to Constantine was like swimming in the Dead Sea. There was none of the normal problem of staying afloat.

Once I arrived back early from the office. Adriana was in the kitchen stirring some soup. She had muscular white calves that tightened as she reached up for the salt.

When she saw me standing in the doorway she laughed. The way you might laugh if someone's just insulted you.

'Do you have to stare at me like that?' she said.

I said, 'Can't I look at my own wife?'

'You're always creeping up on me, staring at me,' she said. 'Why can't you behave like anyone else?'

'I'm not anyone else, Adriana. I'm married to you.'

'Stop being childish. You know perfectly well what I mean.'

'I'm not being childish. I – '

'Sometimes I think you do this deliberately. Come in here and make a scene.'

That was another thing. She was always accusing me of *doing* things to her. Marriage was something I'd *done* to her. Sex was something I'd *tried* to do to her.

'Make a scene?' I said. 'I suppose if I was the electrician everything would be all right.'

Now perhaps that was childish, but I was thinking of the way she'd behaved when the electrician called round the previous night to repair the fusebox. All charm and smiles suddenly, she'd taken him by the arm (yes, actually *touched* him!), ushered him into the lounge and offered him a whisky. Why? I wanted to ask her. Why do you treat total strangers like that and me like this? but before I could go on she turned to face me and I saw outrage cool in her as white-hot metal cools in water. I watched it harden into contempt.

'Can you mend them?' she said.

'What?' I said.

'Fuses.'

'You know I – ' Can't see well enough, I was going to say, but she cut me off.

'Well then,' she said. She was almost smiling. She might've been trying on an expensive evening gown and admiring the effect in a full-length mirror.

It's funny. Sometimes I try to see her now. I try to remember habits, moods, exclamations. The way she laughed. What colour her toothbrush was. How she answered the phone.

But it's the same every time. All I see is that expensive evening gown.

At midday she usually went out. She had friends in Kolonaki who thought siestas were old-fashioned. They were unctuous women, these so-called friends of hers, with hair piled high on their heads and bangles jangling on their fat wrists and little fingers that stuck out when they drank coffee.

Me, I used to like coming home and closing the shutters and lying down for an hour or so. I'd watch the sunlight swimming in fluid gold bars on the ceiling. I'd count them, I'd imagine they were three-dimensional and estimate their weight, then I'd work out their value according to the price of gold in the morning paper. Later I'd close my eyes and wonder what to do with all my money. Most of my lunchtimes were like that. I'd come home, lie down and be a millionaire for a while.

It was during one of these siestas that the phone rang. I stared at it with irritation from my bed. I'd invested in property that day. I'd spent a small fortune on a mansion in Delphi and I was about to inspect its ancient tiled floors and I didn't want to be disturbed. I heaved a sigh, picked up the receiver.

'Yes?'

'She wants you out of there, Michaelis.'

Out of where? I thought. My mansion in Delphi? But I've only just –

Then I realized what they were talking about.

I couldn't identify the voice, but I could've sworn I heard laughter in the background. The laughter of women with hair piled high on their heads. And, ever so faintly, the jangle of heavy bangles.

It couldn't have been more than a couple of weeks after the phone-call that the director of the Aliens' Bureau summoned me to his office. He toyed with his gold cufflinks, lips pursed, eyebrows raised, then he leaned forwards, forearms resting on his desk, fingers interlocked. There was an expensive pause.

'Michaelis,' he said finally.

Well, well. First-name terms. This was new.

'We've been rather worried about you,' he went on. 'In fact, we've been worried about you for some time.'

I began to see how Mr Kyriakos had come to be director of the Aliens' Bureau.

'You see, we know about your eyesight,' he said. 'We understand how difficult it must be for you. The forms and so on. The small print. That's why we think it's time you were given some, well, some less *demanding* work – '

The sentence hung on in the silence for a while.

'Unfortunately,' he went on, 'we just don't seem to have a suitable position at the moment – ' He spread his arms out sideways like some kind of Jesus, suffering on my behalf.

I walked towards the door, a plump brown envelope in my breast pocket. Beautifully handled, I thought. Magnificent cufflinks.

I couldn't wait to tell Adriana. Travelling home by tram that afternoon, I ran through the story in my head. The whole thing was ludicrous, hilarious. Had there really been tears of compassion in the director's eyes? What a buffoon the man was. A real buffoon.

But Adriana didn't laugh. She didn't even smile.

'Don't tell me,' she said. 'I don't want to know.'

'But it was *funny*.' God, how feeble I sounded.

'There's nothing funny about losing a job,' she said. 'Though I can't say I'm particularly surprised.'

I stared at her in disbelief. I'd really thought that the events of that afternoon could put drinks in our hands, could bring us magically together through the bedroom wall, but she just saw it as another of my perverse attacks on her. All I'd done was find a new way of humbling her in front of her pretentious friends.

I left the house that same week. I packed up my belongings and stored them in the cellar. All I took with me was one suitcase. A change of clothes and – a last-minute decision, this – my father's silk shirt.

'I'm leaving for good,' I said. 'Mine,' I said, 'not yours.'
I think it was the first time that I'd ever silenced her.

It was early May. I could tell the greenness of the trees by the density of shade on the pavement and the smell of sap in the air. I remember standing at the top of that decaying flight of steps that runs down the side of the old stadium and breathing to the bottom of my lungs that peculiar mixture of blossom and urine. Some strange expansion of the present then, as if I'd found my way into one moment of exhilaration that would last for ever.

Once I saw Kyriakos drive past in a chauffeured car. He raised his hand, a gesture that struck me as having as much to do with self-defence as with greeting. I looked at him for a second, then I looked away. My hands stayed clasped behind my back. A rich man, I thought. A rich man, but a poor liar.

I could've afforded a hotel off Omonia Square on the proceeds of the brown envelope, but I chose to sleep rough instead. I'd slip into the Royal Gardens just before they closed and hide in the shrubbery until the park-keepers locked the gates and went home. I used to spend the night in a tiny arbour near the memorial to Caesar. It had a wide wooden bench, surrounded on three sides by a wild canopy of vines and creepers. I found evidence to suggest that the place was often used by courting couples, but it suited my purpose just as well. I used to wake at dawn and walk to the public baths for a shower and a shave. The only people up and about that early were the President's bodyguards on duty outside his apartment. If they'd looked up they might've seen me squeezing through a gap in the park railings, but they were too busy checking their chunky Swiss watches and drawing brutally on American cigarettes.

One afternoon I caught a bus to the sea-front. The sun, still fierce at five o'clock, sheeted the surface of Syngrou in thin gold foil. A hot wind reeking of diesel came streaming through the open windows.

I waited until we passed the racetrack with its screen of dry grey trees, then I stood up and moved down the aisle. Some sudden reflection from outside blinded me for a moment. I fell against a young man who was standing by the door.

He took one look at me. 'Keep your fucking hands to yourself,' he said in a loud voice.

There were murmurs. Heads turned.

I climbed down on to the street. The bus thrust past me with a clashing of gears, flung my shirt against my back. I waited until it had vanished round the curve, then I began to walk.

I thought of the last time I'd seen Constantine. Between the games, he mentioned that he'd been down to the market at Monasteraki the previous Sunday.

'What did you go there for?' I said. 'That place is always swarming with tourists.'

He narrowed his eyes as the smoke from his cigarette lunged and gusted in the draught from the doorway as somebody walked in.

'Exactly,' he said.

I smiled, which was an invitation to continue.

'Of course, it's not really all that unusual, I suppose – '

My smile probably widened. It was typical Constantine. He was always devaluing things in advance in case they turned out disappointing.

'It was in that square, the one where they lay out knives and forks on bits of cloth. There was a boy there, must've been about eight, real crafty little face, though. He was trying to sell this mirror to a foreign woman. Anyway, the mirror was cracked and she wasn't really interested. I mean, you don't come to Athens to buy a mirror, do you? "I'm sorry," she told the boy, "I haven't got any money on me at the moment." You know, like you do to beggars. But as she turned away, the sleeve of her dress caught the edge of the mirror and, quick as a flash, the boy gave the mirror a push and it fell off the table and smashed into pieces on the ground. Everyone turned round, of course. The boy ran up to the woman and tugged on her arm and pointed at the mirror. "You break my mirror," he said. "You break my beautiful mirror." I think there were even tears in his eyes. Well, the woman went bright red and started fumbling in her handbag. She got her wallet out and offered him a couple of notes. "Not enough," the boy said. "Not enough." She kept giving him more. In the end she must've forked out ten thousand drachmas for that broken mirror.'

Constantine leaned forwards and crushed his cigarette out.

I thought I understood as I considered my next move. There was no bias in the way he'd told the story. No judgement of any kind.

No, Constantine always gave people rope.

Then you know what happens.

I sat on a stone parapet and closed my eyes. When I opened them again, the sea had turned the colour of fire burning copper. The tankers anchored off Piraeus were vague mauve blocks suspended in the haze. A little girl was hitting a rock with a red spade.

Now I knew what had happened on the bus.

It was my glasses. Their tinted lenses, their metal frames. You see them in the papers sometimes. The headline says, SEX PERVERT KILLS GIRL, 9. And in the picture the murderer's always wearing these weird glasses. I'd brushed against that young man and he'd turned and seen my glasses and he'd thought *sex pervert*.

The sun was setting now and it would soon be dark. I was looking forward to that. I'd be able to take my glasses off.

I walked past the fashionable shops and cafés of Phaleron and turned left into the shadow of a side-street. Looking up, I saw a crowd of people standing by the bus-stop.

They seemed to have gathered round a boy of about fifteen. He had a wet mouth and wore a dirty white T-shirt.

When I reached the fringes of the crowd I realized that it wasn't the boy they were staring at, it was his pet monkey. I watched him unwind a long metal chain from around his hand. He laid out plenty of slack which the monkey used to climb high into a nearby plane tree. Then, just as the monkey was about to spring across to the roof of a house, he jerked on the chain. The monkey swung down through the leaves, dropped like a gymnast to the pavement. Once, though, the boy jerked the chain too hard. The monkey, caught off balance, fell awkwardly, landing on its shoulder. A murmur of

disapproval washed through the crowd, merged with the sound of the sea at the end of the street. Then the monkey picked itself up, shook itself, and stared into the crowd, its mouth wide open.

'Look,' cried a girl with a pigtail, 'the monkey's laughing.'

The boy nodded, grinned. The crowd relaxed. Nobody seemed to have noticed that the chain ended in a leather strap that fastened round the monkey's genitals.

I slept fitfully that night, an east wind running cold blades through the undergrowth. I woke suddenly and the sky was light. Someone had me by the ankles. Grey uniform. The park-keeper.

'Your move,' he said.

I stared at him over my chest. 'Pawn to Queen 3,' I said.

'Not funny. What're you doing here?'

'I would've thought that's obvious.'

'It's illegal, sleeping in the gardens.'

'How did you find me?'

'You were snoring. That's pretty bloody stupid, isn't it, giving yourself away like that?'

'Was I?' I was genuinely surprised. 'I didn't know I snored. All those years and my wife never told me.'

'Yeah, well. She must've had her reasons.'

I didn't follow. 'Reasons?'

The park-keeper leered. 'For throwing you out,' he said.

The lousy bastard.

'And that,' he went on, 'is exactly what *I'm* going to do. Go on. Piss off.'

I walked towards the main gates with my suitcase. No brown envelope this time.

The air glittered, stank of petrol. Everything was happening very fast around me. Rush-hour.

I felt exhausted suddenly. My eyes stung from the glare. I stopped to rest in the shade of a tree. As I stood there I began to scratch myself. Insults are like lice. Your skin crawls.

I suppose I went to Kallithea that night because I'd grown up there. I knew the area better than any other area in Athens. With its smashed kerbs and its wasteground, it had an air of impermanence that had lodged in my bones, that gave me, paradoxically, some feeling of security.

The bus dropped me outside the Tropical cinema. They showed all-night movies on Saturdays so I'd planned on buying a ticket and sleeping in the back row. It seemed as good a place as any.

But when I glanced at the poster on the wall I saw a blonde girl sprawling on a heart-shaped double bed. She had nothing on except a black négligé. She was talking into a telephone. A man in a dark lounge suit watched her from the shadows by the door. Something in the picture disturbed me. I turned away. It looked as if I was going to be spending another night in the open.

I chose a patch of scrubland that had been scrubland for as long as I could remember. I unrolled my sheet of plastic, then I removed my jacket and lay down. After my nights in the Royal Gardens I felt exposed. Blocks of flats on three sides. Hundreds of lit windows. Hundreds of eyes. I was afraid someone would see me from their balcony and call the police.

I lay there sweating, motionless.

Some time later two trucks pulled on to the gravel at the edge of the road. Doors slammed. I listened to the drivers spitting, swapping jokes, scraping at the gravel with their boots.

Then only whispers from bedrooms and the wind moving through dry grass. I was just shifting on to my side when I heard the words I'd been dreading.

'What are you doing here?'

Visions of grey uniforms and leaves stuck on the spikes of rakes and hands like adjustable spanners. The sweat chilled on my back.

'Nothing,' I said.

'You must be doing *something*.' It was a woman's voice. Were they employing women now? I sat up, looked round. But it wasn't a woman, it was a young girl. And she wasn't wearing a uniform.

'You're right,' I said. 'I *am* doing something. I'm trying to get some sleep, that's what I'm doing.'

She stared down at me with a serious face, her arms linked behind her back. 'Funny place to sleep,' she said.

I nodded. What must she be thinking? An old man lying on a patch of wasteground in the middle of the night.

'You live round here or what?' she said.

'Tonight I do,' I said. 'Normally I live in the Royal Gardens. You know. By the palace.'

'How come you live there? Are you important or something?'

I seized on that. 'Yes, I am quite important, really. I'm a sort of royal astronomer. I come out here and lie on my back and look at the stars. Then I report back to the palace and tell the king what's happening. He calls me Sky.' I smiled up at her.

She smiled back. 'There's no such thing as a royal astronomer,' she said. But she wanted there to be.

'All right, I'll tell you the truth,' I said. 'I got kicked out of the house I was living in. I haven't really got a home at the moment. All I've got is that old suitcase over there.

And there's nothing much inside that. The only thing I've got that's worth anything any more is my father's shirt.'

The girl didn't say anything.

'It's silk, the shirt,' I went on. 'It's a kind of family heirloom. I think my father wore it for his wedding.'

The sounds surrounding us – the late TV shows, the arguments, the cars – fell away like scaffolding no longer needed. As the girl sank down on to my sheet of plastic, I looked at her carefully for the first time. Dark eyes, sloping nose, wide mouth. A sphinx of a face. And certainly there was the riddle of her presence.

I was still talking. I told her all the happy things I could never tell my wife. I told her all the sad things I could never tell Constantine. I told her how I sometimes felt my life was a story everyone had read. Everyone except me, that is. How they knew all its twists and turns, all its ungainliness, all its cowardice. How they even knew its ending.

She undid the buttons on her dress and drew it over her head. Her hair landed on her shoulders as softly as parachute silk. She seemed to be holding her breath then. Not nervousness but expectation. Her breasts the sharpest registers of that. Later she bled a little. I know because I put my lips to the glistening and tasted rust. 'I bet they didn't know about this bit,' she said.

When I woke, she wasn't there. My suitcase lay in the grass, its lid thrown back. It looked like someone laughing. The joke was, the silk shirt had gone.

That evening the weather broke. Bright strips of rain hung in open doorways. A wind ran down the streets carrying the smell of wet cement. I hurried through puddles to the Café Diana. I felt hollowed out, divorced from things. As if I was staring, without pain, at the chaos of my own intestines.

Constantine was late for once.

I paced up and down inside the café, watching my feet overtake each other on the lino floor.

'Sky?'

There he was at last in his tan leather sandals, toes blackened by the rain.

'Our table,' he said. 'Look.'

It had been taken. I hadn't even noticed.

I heard someone suffocate a laugh.

There were other tables, of course, but it wasn't the same. They stood at harsher angles to the light. I couldn't settle.

Constantine produced a box of dominoes and laid it carefully on the table. 'Something strange,' he said. 'It's probably nothing.'

I smiled.

'It's just my daughter,' he said. 'She didn't come home last night. And she turned up this morning with a silk shirt.'

Kurt Schwitters in Lakeland

MICHAEL HOFMANN

'Like nothing else in Tennessee'
Wallace Stevens

It was between greens (bowling, cricket),
but the graveyard had stayed immune, half-cut, and smelling
the yellow, abandoned smell of hay. A couple were casting
dead flowers into a wire trash-coop.

Kurt Schwitters's tombstone was hewn in straight lines,
klipp und klar, in the shape of a hat, brim – crown.
Unseasonable, but undeniably local,
someone had left a dozen daffodils.

The man had flown: a refugee,
then interned on the Isle of Man;
released, dead, exhumed, and returned to Germany,
to vote with his feet for the 1950s.

*

His *Merz* was nothing to do with pain or March:
it had been withdrawn from the *Kommerz- und Privatbank*.
Each day he caught the early bus to work,
climbed up to his barn through a jungle of rhododendrons,

and built on to his *Merzwall*. – It too was moved,
cased in a steel frame, and keelhauled down the hill.
The one thing still there that his hands had touched
was a stone on the sill

of the picture-window that had been put in
in place of the wall. It had an air
of having been given a spin –
a duck, a drakkar, a curling-stone.

Max Beckmann: 1915

Nurse, aesthetician and war-artist:
not unpatriotic, not unfeeling.
Calm – excitable. Noted yellow shellholes,
the pink bones of a village steeple, a heated purple sky.
Bombardments. Tricks of the light. Graphic wounds.

An aviator overflew him in the rose night,
buzzed him, performed for him. Friend or foe? *Libellule!*
A room of his own in a villa. *Kriegsblick.*
Medics intellectually stimulating,
one, from Hamburg, familiar with his work.

A commission to decorate the baths
– an Oriental scene, how asinine! –
deserts, palmettos, oases, dead Anzacs, Dardanelles.
A second fresco, of the bath-house personnel.
One thousand male nudes per diem.

A prey to faces. Went for a squinting Cranach.
A man with half a head laughed at his sketches,
recognizing his companions. ('He died today.')
'Several hours' tigerish combat, then gave up
the assault': his description of a sitting.

Some *esprit de corps.* Marching songs,
weirdly soothing, took him out of himself.
Ha, the amusing pretensions of a civilian
trying to commandeer a hotel room!
English prisoners, thirsty mudlarks, plucky, droll.

In the trenches the men had kissed their lives goodbye.
A ricochet, a sniper. In the midst of life.
Crosses plugging foxholes, stabbed into sandbags.
A man with a pistol, head down, intent, hunting rats.
Another, frying spuds on a buddy's grave.

The Flemish clocks told German time.
Sekt and Mosel to wash down the yellow *vin de pays.*
Dr Bonenfant, with his boozy babyface.
'We poor children.' A commission
to illustrate the army songbook. Invalided out.

Totem and Taboo

PHILIP ROTH

I still don't think it was innocent of me to have been as astonished as I was at twenty-six when I found myself up against the most antagonistic social opposition of my life, and not from gentiles at one or the other end of the class spectrum but from angry middle-class and establishment Jews, and a number of eminent rabbis, accusing me of being anti-Semitic and self-hating. I hadn't begun to foresee this as a part of the struggle to write, and yet it was to be central to it.

As intellectually sophisticated as I was, 'self-hatred' was still a new idea to me then; if the phenomenon had ever been present in my world, I had certainly never perceived it as a problem. Growing up in Newark, I hadn't known anyone to whose conduct self-hatred was anything like the key, and, as for college, the Bucknell chapter of Sigma Alpha Mu, whatever its shortcomings, never seemed to chafe under its distinctive identity or noticeably to apologize for itself. When Moe Finkelstein, one of the Sammies' two varsity football players, entered the game for Bucknell, his fraternity brothers invariably sent up a whoop signalling their proud affiliation, a demonstration of feeling that would have driven a self-hating Jew into paroxysms of shame. In fact, what was most admirable about the Sammies was the easygoing way in which they synthesized themselves into a manifestly gentile environment without denying their difference or combatively insisting on it. Theirs seemed to me, even then, a graceful response to a social situation that did not always bring out the best in people, particularly in that conformist era.

And virtually from the day that I arrived in Hyde Park as a graduate student and rented a tiny room in International House, the University of Chicago looked to me like some highly evolved, utopian extension of the Jewish world of my origins, as though the solidarity and intimate intensity of my old neighbourhood life had been infused with a lifesaving appetite for intellectual amusement and experimentation. When I began graduate school in September 1954, the university seemed to me full of unmistakably Jewish Jews far *less* self-conscious and uncertain about themselves, really, than the Irish Catholics from Minnesota and the Baptists from Kansas – Jews wholly secularized but hardly chagrined by a pedigree from which they seemed to derive their undisguised contentiousness, their excitability, and a gift for satiric irony whose flavour I recognized immediately: our family friend Mickey Pasteelnik, Newark's Apple King, had he enjoyed a literary education would surely have talked about *The Wings of the Dove* very much like my ebullient fellow student from Brooklyn, Arthur Geffin. Ted Solotaroff – with whom I profitably debated for years after I returned from the Army in 1956 and entered the Chicago Ph.D. programme –

remembers us referring to Isabel Archer as a 'shiksa'. I recall another conversation, over beer at the University Tavern, where Geffin tended bar at night, in which much scrupulosity was expended determining if Osmond wasn't really a Jew.

This was of course so much off-hours kibitzing, but the pleasure that we took in bringing to *The Portrait of a Lady* what we'd imbibed eavesdropping on our fathers' pinochle games does suggest something about the playful confidence we had in our Jewishness as an intellectual resource. It was also a defence against over-refinement, a counterweight to the intimidating power of Henry James and literary good taste generally, whose 'civilizing' function was variously tempting to clever, ambitious city boys who knew just how casually coarse they could become on a street corner or at a poker game or in the upper deck at Ebbets Field. It seemed less advisable to treat this strain of vulgarity – which we had come to by being both our fathers' sons and our neighbourhoods' creatures – as an impurity to be purged from our speech than to own up to it matter-of-factly, ironically, unashamedly, and to take a real, pleasurable satisfaction in what more than likely would have seemed to Henry James to be our unadventitious origins.

What ignited the Jewish charges against me was the publication in the *New Yorker*, in April 1959, of 'Defender of the Faith', a story about some Jewish recruits in the wartime Army trying to extract favours from their reluctant Jewish sergeant. It was my second piece of fiction to appear in a large commercial magazine. With the $800 I'd earned from the first story, in *Esquire*, and an advance from Houghton Mifflin, I'd quit my instructorship at Chicago – and stepped for good (I thought) out of my wife Josie's life. Intending to live only as a writer, I had moved to Manhattan's Lower East Side, to a two-room basement apartment that was placed perfectly – given my taste then for urban colour – between the bums panhandling on the Bowery and the baskets of bialys on the tables at Ratners. The other stories about Jews that were to be published in the Houghton Mifflin collection, *Goodbye, Columbus*, though they may have attracted a little more than ordinary reader interest, had caused no furor among Jews, appearing as they did in the *Paris Review*, a young literary quarterly then with only a tiny circulation, and in *Commentary*, the monthly edited for years by Elliot Cohen and published by the American Jewish Committee. Had I submitted 'Defender of the Faith' to *Commentary* – whose co-editor at that time, Martin Greenberg, was an early supporter and sympathetic friend – I suspect that the magazine would have published it and that the criticism the story aroused there would have been relatively unspectacular. It's even possible that the ferment inspired a month later by the publication of *Goodbye, Columbus* – the pulpit sermons, the household arguments, the discussions within Jewish organizations gauging my danger, all of which unexpectedly dramatized to people who were essentially non-readers what was, after all, only a first book of short stories – might never have reached troublesome proportions had 'Defender of the Faith' been certified as permissible Jewish discourse by appearing in *Commentary*. And had that happened – had there not been the inflammatory fanfare of the *New Yorker* exposure, had

Goodbye, Columbus had the innocuous cultural fate of a minor critical success – it's likely that my alleged anti-Semitism might never have come to pervade the discussion of my work, stimulating me to defend myself in essays and public addresses and, when I decided to take things more aggressively in hand, to strike back at accusations that I had divulged Jewish secrets and vulgarly falsified Jewish lives by upping the ante in *Portnoy's Complaint. That* was not mistaken for a conciliatory act, and the ramifications of the uproar it fomented eventually inspired me to crystallize the public feud into the drama of internal family dissension that's the backbone of the Zuckerman series, which began to take shape some eight years later.

That the *New Yorker*, like *Partisan Review* and *Commentary*, had a Jewish editor, William Shawn, Jewish contributors – like S. J. Perelman, Irwin Shaw, Arthur Kober, and J. D. Salinger – and a sizeable Jewish readership would only have suggested, to those I'd incensed, that identifying with the *New Yorker*'s privileged, unequivocally non-Jewish aura furnished these Jews (as undoubtedly it did Roth himself) with far more sustenance than they derived from their Jewish status. I soon understood self-hatred to mean an internalized, though not necessarily conscious, loathing of one's recognizable group markings that culminates either in quasi-pathological efforts to expunge them or in the vicious disparagement of those who don't even know enough to try.

Because I didn't have the patience to wait for the author's copies to reach me by mail, the day that the *New Yorker* was scheduled to appear I made three trips to Fourteenth Street, to the news-stand across from Klein's, to see if the issue was in yet. When the magazine finally appeared that afternoon, I bought a copy for myself and another to send off to my parents. While I was at college, they had moved from the Weequahic neighbourhood to a small garden apartment in a pleasant little complex in nearby Elizabeth, on the very street where they had been married in 1926 and where nearly every Sunday of my childhood, after visiting my widowed paternal grandmother in one of Newark's oldest immigrant neighbourhoods, we would drive over to see my widowed maternal grandmother, who shared a small apartment there with my maiden aunt. The *New Yorker* was really no more familiar to my parents than were the other magazines in which my first stories had begun to appear. *Hygeia* had sometimes come to the house, sporadically we had received *Collier's*, *Liberty*, and the *Saturday Evening Post*, but the magazines to which my mother was most faithful were *Ladies' Home Journal*, *Redbook* and *Woman's Home Companion*. In their pages she confirmed her sense of how to dress and to furnish a house, found the recipes that she clipped and filed in her recipe box, and received instruction in the current conventions of child rearing and marriage. Decorum and courtesy meant no less to her than they did to the heroines of the fiction she read in those magazines, and through her genteel example my brother and I became well-mannered boys, always a source of pride to her, she said, on special Sunday outings to the Tavern, a family restaurant favoured by Newark's Jewish bourgeoisie (a class in which we, who had neither money, property, nor very much social self-assurance, had really only half a foothold).

My mother read five or six books a year borrowed from the lending library, not junk but popular novels that had acquired moral prestige, like the works of Pearl Buck, her favourite author, whom she admired personally for the sorts of reasons that she admired Sister Elizabeth Kenny, the esteemed Australian nurse who'd brought to America in the forties her therapeutic techniques for treating polio victims. She responded very strongly to their womanly brand of militant and challenging compassion. Her heroine of heroines was Eleanor Roosevelt, whose column, 'My Day', she followed in the newspaper when she could. After her 1922 graduation from Battin High in Elizabeth, my mother, then Bess Finkel, had worked successfully for several years as an office secretary, a very dutiful daughter, living of course at home, who adored her mother and her elder sister, feared her father, helped raise two younger sisters, and dearly loved her only brother, Emanuel – known as Mickey – an art student, a musician, and eventually a quiet, unassuming bachelor, soft-spoken and witty, and something of a traveller. Artistic ambition moved him to paint portraits and landscapes but he kept himself alive doing professional photography; whenever he could afford to, he shut his tiny Philadelphia studio and sailed to Europe to tour the museums and look at the paintings he loved. My brother Sandy and I were believed by my mother to derive our artistic proclivities through the genetic strain that had determined my Uncle Mickey's lonely career, and for all I know she was right. A woman of deep domestic expertise and benign unworldliness, reassuringly confident right up to the outermost boundaries of our social world though progressively, if respectably, uncertain anywhere beyond it, my mother was unambiguously proud of my first published stories. She had no idea that there could be anything seriously offensive about them and, when she came upon articles in the Jewish press intimating that I was a traitor, couldn't understand what my detractors were talking about. When she was once in doubt – having been shaken by a derogatory remark she'd overheard at a Hadassah meeting – she asked me if it could possibly be true that I was anti-Semitic, and when I smiled and shook my head no, she was entirely satisfied.

The issues of *Commentary* and the *Paris Review* that I'd sent in the mail or brought over with me to Elizabeth when I visited – containing my stories 'Epstein', 'Conversion of the Jews' and 'You Can't Tell a Man by the Song He Sings' – my mother displayed, between bookends, on a sidetable in the living-room. My father, who mainly read newspapers, was more aggressively exhibitionistic about my published works, showing the strange magazines to anyone who came to visit and even reading aloud to his friends lines in which he thought he recognized a detail of description, a name, a line of dialogue that I'd appropriated from a familiar source. After the publication of 'Defender of the Faith', when I told him on the phone that the Anti-Defamation League of B'nai Brith had requested I meet with their representatives to discuss the outcry over my story, he was incredulous. 'What outcry? Everybody loved it. What is the outcry? I don't get it.'

Perhaps if it had been somebody else's son against whom these accusations had been levelled by our Jewish betters, neither he nor my mother would have been quite so sure of the writer's probity, but for them to be wounded as Jews by *me* – whom they'd seen circumcised and bar mitzvahed, whom they had sent for three years to one of our neighbourhood's humble Hebrew schools, whose closest friends were all Jewish boys, who had always, unfailingly, been a source of pride – didn't occur to either of them and never would. My father could become as belligerent about the charges against my Jewish loyalty as he would be in later years when anyone dared to be dubious about a single aspect of Israeli policy.

I should add that not even he would have rushed to defend my achievements as a student of Judaism or my record of religious observance: at age thirteen I had not come away from three years of Hebrew School especially enlightened, nor had my sense of the sacred been much enriched. Though I hadn't been a total failure either, and had learned enough Hebrew to read at breakneck speed (if not with full comprehension) from the Torah at my bar mitzvah, the side of my Jewish education that had made that after-school hour, three days a week, at all endurable had largely to do with the hypnotic appeal, in those environs, of the unimpeachably profane. I am thinking of the witless persecution of poor Mr Rosenblum, our refugee teacher, an escapee from Nazism, a man lucky (he had thought) just to be alive, whom the older boys more than once hung in effigy on the lamp-post just outside the window where he was teaching our 'four-to-five' class. I'm remembering the alarming decrepitude of the old-country *shammes*, our herring-eater, Mr Fox, whom we drove crazy playing a kind of sidewalk handball called 'Aces Up' against the rear wall of his synagogue – Mr Fox, who used to raid the local candy store and pull teenagers at the pinball machine out by the neck in order to scare up enough souls for a *minyan*. And, of course, I'm remembering the mishap of a nine-year-old classmate, a boy of excruciating timidity, who on our very first day of Hebrew School in 1943 – when the rabbi who was religious leader of the synagogue and director of the school began, a bit orotundly, to address us new students in our cubbyhole classroom directly upstairs from the Ark of the Covenant – involuntarily beshat himself, a pathetic disaster that struck the nervous class as blasphemously hilarious.

In those after-school hours at the dingy Hebrew School – when I would have given anything to have been outdoors playing ball until suppertime – I sensed underlying everything a turbulence that I didn't at all associate with the airy, orderly public school where I was a bright American boy from nine to three, a bubbling, energetic unruliness that conflicted head-on with all the exacting ritual laws that I was now being asked to obey devoutly. In the clash between the anguished solemnity communicated to us by the mysterious bee-buzz of synagogue prayer and the irreverence implicit in the spirit of animated mischievousness that manifested itself almost daily in the little upstairs classrooms of the *shul*, I recognized something far more 'Jewish' than I ever did in the never-never-land stories of Jewish tents in Jewish deserts inhabited by Jews conspicuously lacking local last names like Ginsky, Nusbaum, and Strulowitz. Despite everything that we Jews couldn't eat – except at the Chinese restaurant, where the pork came stowed away in the egg roll, and at the Jersey shore, where the clams skulked unseen in the depths of the chowder – despite all our taboos and prohibitions and our vaunted self-denial, a nervous forcefulness decidedly *irrepressible* pulsated through our daily life, converting even the agonizing annoyance of having to go to Hebrew School, when you could have been 'up the field' playing left end or first base, into unpredictably paradoxical theatre.

What I remember from my Hebrew School education is that whatever else it may have been for my generation to grow up Jewish in America, it was usually entertaining. I don't think that an English Jewish child would necessarily have felt that way and, of course, for millions of Jewish children east of England, to grow up Jewish was tragic. And that we seemed to understand without even needing to be told.

Not only did growing up Jewish in Newark in the thirties and forties, Hebrew School and all, feel like a perfectly legitimate way of growing up American but, what's more, growing up Jewish as I did and growing up American seemed to me indistinguishable. Remember that in those days there was not a new Jewish country, a 'homeland', to foster the range of attachments – the pride, the love, the anxiety, the chauvinism, the philanthropy, the chagrin, the shame – that has, for many American Jews now over forty, complicated anew the issue of Jewish self-definition. Nor was there quite the nostalgia for the old Jewish country that Broadway later began to merchandise with the sentimentalizing of Sholom Aleichem. We knew very well that our grandparents had not torn themselves away from their shtetl families, had not left behind parents whom they would never see again, because back home everybody had gone around the village singing show tunes that would have brought tears to your eyes. They'd left because life was awful; so awful, in fact, so menacing or impoverished or hopelessly obstructed, that it was best forgotten. The wilful amnesia that I generally came up against whenever I tried as a child to establish the details of our clan's pre-American existence was not unique to our family.

I would think that much of the exuberance with which I and others of my generation of Jewish children seized our opportunities after the war – that wonderful feeling that one was entitled to no less than anyone else, that one could do anything and could be excluded from nothing – came from our belief in the boundlessness of the democracy in which we lived and to which we belonged. It's hard to imagine that anyone of intelligence growing up in America since the Vietnam War can have had our unambiguous sense, as young adolescents immediately after the victory over Nazi fascism and Japanese militarism, of belonging to the greatest nation on earth.

At my lunch meeting about 'Defender of the Faith' with two representatives from the Anti-Defamation League, I said that being interviewed by them as an alleged purveyor of material harmful and defamatory to the Jews was particularly disorienting since, as a high-school senior thinking about studying law, I had sometimes imagined working on their staff, defending the civil and legal rights of Jews. In response, there was neither chastisement nor accusation and nothing resembling a warning about what I should write or where I should publish. They told me that they had wanted to meet me only to let me know about the complaints they had received and to answer any questions *I* might have. I figured, however, that a part of their mission was also to see whether I was a nut, and in the atmosphere of easygoing civility that had been established among us over lunch, I said as much, and we all laughed. I asked who exactly they thought the people were who'd called in and written, and the three of us speculated as to what in the story had been most provocative and why. We parted as amicably as we'd met, and I only heard from the ADL again a couple of years later, when I was invited by their Chicago branch to participate in an interfaith symposium, co-sponsored by Loyola University, on the 'image' of Catholics and Jews in American literature.

After *Goodbye, Columbus* won the 1960 National Book Award for Fiction and the Daroff Award of the Jewish Book Council of America, I was asked to speak on similar themes before college Hillel groups, Jewish community centres, and temples all over the country. (I was on a Guggenheim in Rome in 1960 and unable to be present for the Daroff Award ceremony in New York. My strongest supporter on the prize jury, the late critic and teacher David Boroff, confirmed the report I got from my friend Bob Silvers – who had been there to accept the award on my behalf – which was that my book had been an unpopular choice, with the sponsors as well as with many gathered together for the ceremony; the year before, another set of judges had given the prize to Leon Uris for *Exodus*.) When I could get away from university teaching, I took up these invitations and appeared before Jewish audiences to talk and to answer questions. The audiences were respectfully polite, if at times aloof, and the hostile members generally held their fire until the question period had begun. I was up to the give-and-take of these exchanges though I never looked forward to them. I'd had no intention as a writer of coming to be known as 'controversial' and, in the beginning, had no idea that my stories would prove repugnant to ordinary Jews. I had thought of myself as something of an authority on ordinary Jewish life, with its penchant for self-satire and hyperbolic comedy, and for a long time continued to be as bemused privately as I was unyielding publicly when confronted by Jewish challengers.

In 1962, I accepted an invitation to appear on a panel at Yeshiva University in New York. I felt it a duty to respond to the pronounced Jewish interest my book continued to evoke and I particularly didn't want to shy away from such an obvious Jewish stronghold; as one of the panel participants would be Ralph Ellison, I was also flattered to have been asked to speak from the same platform. The third panellist was Pietro di Donato, a relatively obscure writer since the success in the thirties of his proletariat novel *Christ in Concrete*.

From the start I was suspicious of the flat-out assertiveness of the Yeshiva symposium title – 'The Crisis of Conscience in Minority Writers of Fiction' – and its presumption, as I interpreted it, that the chief cause of dissension over 'minority' literature lay not in the social uncertainties of a minority audience but in a profound disturbance in the moral faculties of minority writers. Though I had no real understanding of seriously observant Jews – a group nearly as foreign to me as the devoutest Catholics – I knew enough not to expect such people, who would comprise most of the Yeshiva faculty and student body, to be supporters of my cause. But since the discussion would be held in a university auditorium – and I was very much at home in such places – and inasmuch as I had been invited not to address a narrowly Jewish subject on my own but to investigate the general situation of the minority writer in America with an Italian-American writer whom I was curious to meet and a highly esteemed black writer of whom I was in awe, I didn't foresee just how demoralizing the confrontation could be.

I came East from Iowa with Josie, and on the evening of the symposium the two of us took a taxi out to Yeshiva with my new Random House editor, Joe Fox, who was eager to hear the discussion. Random House was publishing *Letting Go*, my second book, later in the year, but as *Goodbye, Columbus* had been published by Houghton Mifflin, Joe had had no direct involvement with those inflammatory stories and, as a gentile, was removed from the controversy and perplexed by its origins. Josie was, of course, gentile also, but after our marriage, on her own steam – and against my better judgement, not to mention my secular convictions – she had taken religious instruction from Rabbi Jack Cohen at the Reconstructionist Synagogue in Manhattan and been converted by him to Judaism. We were first married in a civil ceremony – with only two friends for witnesses – by a justice of the peace in Yonkers; several months later Jack Cohen married us again, at his synagogue, in a religious ceremony attended by my parents. The second ceremony struck me – and perhaps struck my parents, who were too bewildered, however, to be anything but polite – as not only unnecessary but, in the circumstances, vulgar and ludicrous. I participated so that her pointless conversion might at least appear to have some utilitarian value, though my consent didn't mean that it wasn't distressingly clear to me that this was one more misguided attempt to manufacture a marital bond where the mismatch was blatant and already catastrophic. To me, being a Jew had to do with a real historical predicament into which you were born and not with some identity you chose to don after reading a dozen books. I could as easily have turned into a subject of the Crown by presenting my master's degree in English literature to Winston Churchill as my new wife could become a Jew by studying with Jack Cohen, sensible and dedicated as he was, for the rest of her life.

I saw in her desire to be some sort of simulated Jew yet another distressing collapse of integrity; something very like the self-hatred with which I had been stigmatized seemed to impel her drive to camouflage the markings of her own small-town, Middle Western past by falsifying again her affiliation with me and my background. I introduce this story not to have a go at Josie but to reveal a bizarre irony of which I was not unconscious while the spanking-new Jew of unmistakable Nordic appearance sat in the Yeshiva audience looking on at the 'excommunication' of the Semitic-featured young writer whose seventeen years as his parents' child in the Weequahic neighbourhood of Newark couldn't have left him more inextinguishably Jewish.

The trial (in every sense) began after di Donato, Ellison and I had each delivered twenty-minute introductory statements. Ellison rambled on easily and intelligently from a few notes, di Donato winged it not very logically, and I read from some prepared pages, thus allowing me to speak confidently while guarding, I thought, against an interrogator's altering the context in which my argument was being made; I was determined to take every precaution against being misunderstood. When the moderator began the second stage of the symposium by questioning us about our opening statements, the only panellist he seemed truly interested in was me. His first question, following di Donato's monologue – which would have seemed, had I been moderating, to require rigorous clarification – was this: 'Mr Roth, would you write the same stories you've written if you were living in Nazi Germany?' – a question that was to turn up some twenty years later in *The Ghost Writer*, asked of Nathan Zuckerman by Judge Leopold Wapter.

Thirty minutes later, I was still being grilled. No response I gave was satisfactory and, when the audience was allowed to take up the challenge, I realized that I was not just opposed but hated. I've never forgotten my addled reaction: an undertow of bodily fatigue took hold and began sweeping me away from that auditorium even as I tried to reply coherently to one denunciation after another (for we had by then proceeded beyond interrogation to anathema). My combative instinct, which was not undeveloped, simply withered away and I had actually to suppress a desire to close my eyes and, in my chair at the panellists' table, with an open microphone only inches from my perspiring face, drift into unconsciousness. Ralph Ellison must have noticed my tenacity fading because all at once I heard him defending me with an eloquent authority that I could never have hoped to muster from halfway out to oblivion. His intellectual position was virtually identical to mine, but he was presenting it as a black American, instructing through examples drawn from *Invisible Man* and the ambiguous relationship that novel had established with some vocal members of his own race. His remarks seemed to appear to the audience far more creditable than mine or perhaps situated the audience so far from its real mission as to deflate or deflect the inquisitorial pressure that I had envisioned mounting towards a finale that would find me either stoned to death or fast asleep.

With me relegated pretty much to the sidelines, the evening shortly came to an end. From the moderator there were genial good wishes for the panellists, from the spectators there was some scattered applause, and then we all started down off the stage by the side stairs leading into the house. I was immediately surrounded by the element in the audience most antagonistic to my work, whom Ellison's intercession had clearly curtailed only temporarily. The climax of the tribunal was upon me, and though I was now wide-awake, I still couldn't extricate myself that easily from their midst. Standing in the well between the hall and the stage, with Joe and Josie visible beyond the faces of my jury – though in no conceivable way my Jewry – I listened to the final verdict against me, as harsh a judgement as I ever hope to hear in this or any other world. I only began to shout 'Clear away, step back – I'm getting out of here' after somebody, shaking a fist in my face, began to holler, 'You were brought up on anti-Semitic literature!' 'Yes,' I hollered back, 'and what is that?' – curious really to know what he meant. 'English literature!' he cried. 'English literature is anti-Semitic literature!'

In midtown Manhattan later, Josie, Joe and I went to have something to eat at the Stage Delicatessen, down the street from the hotel where we were staying. I was angry at what I had stupidly let myself in for, I was wretchedly ashamed of my performance, and I was infuriated still by the accusations from the floor. Over my pastrami sandwich no less, I said, 'I'll never write about Jews again.' Equally ridiculously, I thought that I meant it, or at least that I should. I couldn't see then, fresh from the event, that the most bruising public exchange of my life constituted not the end of my imagination's involvement with the Jews, let alone an excommunication, but the real beginning of my thralldom. I had assumed – mostly from the evidence of *Letting Go* – that I had passed beyond the concerns of my collection of apprentice stories and the subjects that had fallen so naturally to me as a beginning writer. *Letting Go*, about the unanticipated responsibilities of young adulthood far from Jewish New Jersey, seemed to foreshadow the direction in which new preoccupations would now guide me. But the Yeshiva battle, instead of putting me off Jewish fictional subjects, exemplified as nothing had before the full force of aggressive rage that made the issue of Jewish self-definition and Jewish allegiance so inflammatory. This group whose embrace once had offered me so much security was itself fanatically insecure. How could I conclude otherwise when I was told that every word I wrote was a disgrace, potentially endangering every Jew? Fanatical security, fanatical insecurity: nothing in my entire background could exemplify better than that night did how deeply rooted the Jewish drama was in this duality.

After an experience like mine at Yeshiva, a writer would have had to be no writer at all to go looking elsewhere for something to write about. My humiliation before the Yeshiva belligerents – indeed, the angry Jewish resistance that I aroused virtually from the start – was the luckiest break I could have had. I was branded.

Killing an Elephant

MURRAY BAIL

Glass is precious in Tanzania. Cars and taxis rattle about with cracked windscreens and side-windows, and the shells of cars abandoned in the streets, missing some vital part, are stripped of glass. Wherever the eye rests in Dar es Salaam it settles on a crack in a piece of glass: the windows of shops, offices and small factories, such as the Tanganyika Tyre Retreading Company. Broken pieces are left in place. Sometimes, as in the windows of the courthouse facing the harbour, where pedestrians can simply stop and look in from the footpath, nothing remains of the windows but a small triangle curving out from a corner. Mirrors are cracked too, in lifts and in hotel bathrooms, glass-top desks, and even the framed photographs of leopards reclining in trees, which are screwed on the walls of the unpunctual Air Tanzania planes, have multiple fractures. In poor, hot countries there are more urgent priorities for replacement than glass.

I was idly thinking this while sauntering along Kalute Street, the Indian quarter behind me. On the footpath young men squatted over displays of secondhand textbooks on accounting and chemistry, and it crossed my mind that it was time the history of the world was rewritten, concentrating on the effects of climate – debilitating heat, in the case of Equatorial Africa.

Dar es Salaam has its beginnings in 1857 when the Sultan of Zanzibar decided to turn a creek into a safe port and trading centre. Dar es Salaam – Dar, as the locals call it – means 'haven of peace'.

The streets were pot-holed, the buildings dusty, mostly grey.

In front of me on a corner was a white mosque. As I approached there was a sudden commotion. People were running towards it, and others running away from it. Their eyes and mouths were opened wide and there was shouting. Near me an Indian woman with a child fell on to her hands. Others from across the street and on balconies had stopped and stared.

I turned the corner. A car parked against the wall of the mosque had caught fire. It was an old cream Volkswagen – a Beetle. Around it, a group of young Africans were darting about, pointing and shouting. Nobody seemed to own the car; and nobody seemed to know what to do.

The fire was in the back, in the engine. Already the asphalt underneath was alight. There was certainly something unpleasant about the lick and flow of the flames.

The young men were making brief skipping movements, forward and back, shouting and yelling, trying to push the car out of its spot. One of them would press on a mudguard, then leap back as if it were hot. A tall thin one lifted the lid of the engine. The flames shot higher. He slammed it shut.

By now the fire was into the back seat. The shouting rose into short shrill notes, a kind of hectic jabbering which followed the general darting motions, and always there was that wide-apart expression in their eyes and mouths, in the helpless spacing of elbows and hands, which multiplied like a secondary fire through the crowd, now blocking the street.

Experiences are compressed during travel, I said to myself, especially in strange, slightly uncomfortable places. Pushing forward I noticed the rear window was cracked and, painted on the glass, the hopeful phrase: 'Love and Joy Driving Cabs'.

At that point a young Goan in tight trousers and cream shirt sprinted across in front of everybody, pushing people aside, to reach his red pick-up, a new Datsun, parked behind the burning car. He had a desperate look on his face. Grating the gears he reversed, stalled, reversed again, almost running people over to get it to safety and banged into the corner of the wall. More broken glass. People turned back to the car.

The Beetle was now rolling across the street, its doors open. Briefly, I recalled an item in the *Tanzanian Daily News* that morning inviting tenders for two cars: 'All in good working order', the notice explained, 'except no tyres and engine not working.'

The car stopped and was simply burning. Then a strange thing happened. Out in the open the car seemed defenceless. People broke away from the main crowd and rushed at it, banging the roof with their fists. A man kicked the mudguard. Someone else joined him. A large African woman ran forward and swung her handbag at the headlight. Why? This wasn't putting out the fire. Squashed in the middle I couldn't have left if I wanted to. The crowd tilted as in a wind, and there was an approving murmur. I remembered in a bar the night before, an enormous Idi Amin lookalike, bloodshot and perspiring, who happened to be a Superintendent of Police, telling me that if a thief is caught in the street in Dar es Salaam the crowd will beat him to death. He had seen it several times.

They were throwing things now, anything they could find. The lid of the engine was up. Handfuls of dirt were chucked at the engine, and gravel. Lumps of cardboard were hurled in. A middle-aged man waved a stick. Someone found a piece of tin. It fell back on to the street. Another man threw it back in. A general dancing motion shifted the crowd about in waves. An Arab came forward with a large rock. He hit the flaming engine several times, then left it there. And still people were kicking the body and tyres. They were shouting, leaping about, as others watched.

Finally they killed it. There was a bit of black smoke, then nothing. There was a slight hissing sound.

The crowd relaxed. That wide-open, irrational expression subsided. Everyone looked satisfied.

People stepped forward to inspect the smouldering corpse. I noticed some would look at the wreck, then turn and smile at me. Naturally, I smiled too. Their mouths were so large they appeared to be on the verge of laughter.

Of course, virtually none of them would ever be able to afford a car in their lifetime, not even a Beetle on its last legs. People walk long distances in Africa. Patient lines can be seen, beginning at first light. To see men, women and children fighting to climb on to a windowless bus is horrible. And now, for a moment, before everybody moved on, it seemed as if something of the original order of things had been restored: a familiar, yet out-of-reach example of European progress, and all that it stood for, had been rendered useless.

Otherwise, I don't have an explanation for the incident, which lasted less than five minutes.

Contributors' Notes

Murray Bail is the author of *The Drover's Wife*, *Homesickness*, which won the 1980 Australian National Book Award, and *Holden's Performance*. He edited *The Faber Book of Contemporary Australian Short Stories*.

Glen Baxter's drawings appear in his books *Atlas*, *The Impending Gleam* and *Jodhpurs in the Quantocks* (all Cape), among others. The Colonel lives in London.

Eavan Boland has published four collections of poetry, the most recent of which, *The Journey and Other Poems*, was published by Arlen House/Carcanet earlier this year. She lives in Dublin. Carcanet plans to publish her selected poems in 1989.

Joseph Brodsky has been living in New York since he was exiled from the Soviet Union in 1972. A collection of his essays, *Less Than One*, was published by Viking in 1986 and his most recent collection of poems, *To Urania*, came out earlier this year. He was awarded the 1987 Nobel Prize for Literature.

The Irish journalist **Alexander Cockburn** has since 1972 been living in the United States where he is a regular contributor to, among many other publications, the *Wall Street Journal* and the *Nation*. His collected writings, *Corruptions of Empire: Life Studies and the Reagan Era*, were published in 1987 (Verso).

Fred D'Aguiar grew up in Guyana in a town called Airy Hall. The subject of the poems included in this anthology, *Airy Hall* is also the title of his second book of poems, which will be published by Chatto in 1989.

Carol Ann Duffy was born in Glasgow and now lives in London. She is the author of two collections of poems, *Standing Female Nude* and *Selling Manhattan* (both Anvil Press), the latter of which won the Somerset Maugham Award for 1988.

The German poet and critic **Hans Magnus Enzensberger**'s books include *Poems for People Who Don't Read Poems* and *Sinking the Titanic*. A collection of Enzensberger's essays, *Dreams of the Absolute: Essays on Ecology, Media and Power*, was published this year (Radius). This piece was originally given as a lecture at New York University's Center for the Humanities.

CONTRIBUTORS' NOTES

Mary Flanagan was born in New Hampshire and has lived in England for most of her adult life. Her first book was a collection of short stories, *Bad Girls* (Cape/Futura), and *Trust* (Bloomsbury/Penguin) was her first novel.

Bruno Fonseca is a painter living in Barcelona.

Mark Ford teaches English and American literature at University College London, and his poems will be included in *Chatto New Poets II*.

John Fuller's eleventh collection of poems, *The Grey Among the Green*, was published in the spring by Chatto. He is also the author of a book of short stories and two novels, the first of which, *Flying to Nowhere*, was shortlisted for the Booker Prize and won the Whitbread First Novel Award for 1983. His second novel, *Tell It Me Again*, was published earlier this year (Chatto). He is a Fellow of Magdalen College, Oxford.

David Gilmour is the author of books about the Middle East and about the transformation of Spain since Franco. His biography of Lampedusa, *The Last Leopard*, is published by Quartet. He lives near Edinburgh.

The Scottish painter and novelist **Alasdair Gray** has transformed his novel *Lanark* into a film, which is being made by Midnight Films. This piece is excerpted from his storyboard. His other books include *Unlikely Stories, Mostly* and *1982, Janine* (both Cape).

Nan Green's lifelong commitment to Communism led her, after the Spanish Civil War, to Mao's China, where she worked for many years as a translator. In Britain she worked for the Communist Party publishers and for the International Brigade Association where she organized peace conferences and translated the speeches of Fidel Castro. 'A Chronicle of Small Beer' is an excerpt from her unpublished autobiography which she completed just before her death in 1984. She was eighty years old.

Born in Texas, **Patricia Highsmith** has spent much of her life in England, France and Switzerland. Her most recent book is a collection of short stories, *Tales of Natural and Unnatural Catastrophes* (Bloomsbury/Methuen).

The British journalist **Christopher Hitchens** lives in Washington where he contributes regularly to, among many publications, the *Nation*, the *New Statesman* and the *Times Literary Supplement*. His selected essays, *Prepared for the Worst*, are published this year by Farrar, Straus and Giroux.

Michael Hofmann is the author of two collections of poetry, *Nights in the Iron Hotel* and *Acrimony* (both Faber), and is the winner of the 1987 Geoffrey Faber Memorial Prize. He lives in London.

Mick Imlah was born in Aberdeen and now lives in London. His first full-length collection of poems, *Birthmarks*, is published this autumn (Chatto).

Doug James is a designer living in London.

Alan Jenkins's first collection of poems, *In the Hot-house*, was published by Chatto earlier this year. He is the Fiction and Poetry Editor of the *Times Literary Supplement*.

R. M. Lamming is the author of two novels, *The Notebook of Gismondo Cavalletti*, winner of the 1984 David Higham Prize for Fiction, and *In the Dark* (both Cape). She lives in London.

David Leavitt's first book was a collection of short stories, *Family Dancing* (Heinemann), which was followed by a novel, *The Lost Language of Cranes* (Viking/Penguin). This story is part of a new collection coming from Viking/Penguin in 1989. He lives in New York State.

Michael Leunig contributes cartoons and drawings to the Melbourne *Age* and is responsible for a number of books, including *The Penguin Leunig*, *The Second Leunig*, *A Bag of Roosters* and *Ramming the Shears*.

Lachlan Mackinnon's first full-length collection of poems, *Monterey Cypress*, and a biography, *The Lives of Elsa Triolet*, were published this year (Chatto). He lives in Winchester.

Grant Manheim is a photographer who runs the Warwick Square Press in London.

Daniel Miller is a painter living in London.

Deborah Moffatt was born in Vermont and now lives in Scotland. Her stories have been published in Faber's *First Fictions* and the *Listener*.

Blake Morrison is the author of two collections of poems, *Dark Glasses* and *The Ballad of the Yorkshire Ripper* (both Chatto). He is the Literary Editor of the *Observer*.

The poet and biographer **Andrew Motion**'s most recent collection of poems, *Natural Causes* (Chatto), won the 1987 Dylan Thomas Memorial Award. An Editor at

Chatto & Windus, he is at work on a biography of Philip Larkin as well as a series of novels.

The Irish poet **Paul Muldoon** is the author of five collections, the most recent of which, *Meeting the British*, was published by Faber in 1987. He lives in New York.

José Guadalupe Posada (1851–1913) was a prolific Mexican engraver who exerted a profound influence on, among others, Diego Rivera and José Clemente Orozco. The Redstone Press has initiated a major reappraisal of this surprisingly little-known artist with the publication of two books, *Mexican Popular Prints* and *J. G. Posada: Messages of Morality*. There will be a retrospective exhibition at Oxford's Museum of Modern Art in May 1989.

David Rieff is the author of *Going to Miami* (Bloomsbury). He is a Senior Editor at Farrar, Straus and Giroux in New York, and is currently researching a book on the great immigrant city of Los Angeles.

Philip Roth is the author of seventeen books. This extract is taken from his autobiography *The Facts* (Cape), which will be published later this year.

Carol Rumens has published numerous collections of poetry, the most recent of which are *Direct Dialling* and *Selected Poems* (both Chatto). Her first novel, *Plato Park*, was published by Chatto in 1988. She lives in London.

Helen Simpson worked at *Vogue* for five years, but left to devote herself to writing. She is the author of two cookery books and a thesis on 'Unreasonable Laughter in Restoration Comedy' and has published stories in several publications, including the *Listener* and the *Literary Review*.

Rupert Smith is a peripatetic Englishman who has worked as a professional photographer, and a teacher of Greek and Latin. He is currently the foreman of a mushroom farm in Southwark.

Ahdaf Soueif was born in Cairo and gained a Ph.D. in Linguistics at Lancaster University. She is the author of *Aisha*, published in 1983 by Cape.

Rupert Thomson's first novel was *Dreams of Leaving* (Bloomsbury/Corgi). He is currently in the Far East writing another.

Kurt Tidmore was born in Lubbock, Texas. He worked as a professional photographer for twenty-five years and now lives in Würzburg. 'The Equilibrist' is his first published story.

Augusto Torres was born near Barcelona in 1913. As a young man he worked as an apprentice to Julio Gonzalez and studied with Amedée Ozenfant, but his overwhelming influence was that of his father, the Uruguayan Constructivist Joaquin Torres García. Last year saw the commemoration of seventy-five years of Torres's work: two major retrospectives – in California and New York – and the publication of a book (Scala).

Born in New Zealand, but for many years resident in the UK, **Fay Weldon** is the author of twelve novels, the latest of which is *The Leader of the Band* (Hodder). She has also written the libretto of an opera, which will be performed by the English National Opera in 1989, and numerous television plays.

Hugo Williams's most recent collection of poems, *Writing Home* (Oxford University Press), will be followed by *Selected Poems* (Oxford University Press) next year. He is the Poetry Editor of the *New Statesman* and a columnist for the *Times Literary Supplement*.

Tobias Wolff was born in Alabama and grew up in Washington State. He has twice been awarded the O. Henry Award for short fiction. His collected short stories have been published by Picador.

Barry Yourgrau has published three collections of short stories, including *A Man Jumps Out of an Airplane* and *Wearing Dad's Head* (Paladin). Yourgrau is a performance artist and collaborated on a screenplay with David Byrne. He lives in New York.

Isabel Fonseca was a reader at Bloomsbury when this anthology began to take shape. She is now an Assistant Editor at the *Times Literary Supplement*.